GREAT EARTHQUAKES

GREAT EARTHQUAKES

BY

CHARLES DAVISON, Sc.D., F.G.S.

Author of
A History of British Earthquakes
The Japanese Earthquake, 1923. etc.

With 122 *Illustrations*

LONDON :
THOMAS MURBY & CO., 1, FLEET LANE, E.C.4
1936

37-x112

PRINTED IN GREAT BRITAIN
BY
THE WOODBRIDGE PRESS, LTD., GUILDFORD.

PREFACE

The following pages contain descriptions of some of the greatest earthquakes of the last two centuries. These eighteen earthquakes have been chosen not only for their magnitude and destructive power, but chiefly for the light that they throw on the nature and origin of great earthquakes, and because, in every case, very careful studies have been made of the phenomena that accompanied and followed them.

Of one earthquake that would naturally have found a place in the series—the great Kwanto earthquake of 1923, by which Tokyo and Yokohama were almost destroyed—I have given a full account in a volume, *The Japanese Earthquake of 1923*, issued in 1931 by the publishers of the present work, of which, indeed, it may be regarded as a second volume.

CHARLES DAVISON.

Cambridge.

September, 1936.

TABLE OF CONTENTS

LIST OF PLATES

LIST OF FIGURES IN THE TEXT

CHAPTER I

LISBON EARTHQUAKE: 1755 Nov. 1

1. INTRODUCTION

1. The Lisbon earthquake of 1755 has long held a place among the great earthquakes of the world. This it owes not only to the destruction of a well-known city or to the area disturbed by it, though the loss of life probably amounted to fifty or sixty thousand, and the region over which it was felt must have contained more than a million sq. miles. It would seem rather to be due to a feature that has not, in any other earthquake, been so widely and notably observed—the remarkable seiches or oscillations of the water in lakes far beyond the limits of the disturbed area, in countries so distant as the north of Scotland and the centre of Sweden.

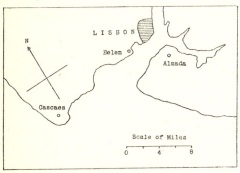

FIG. 1.—Map of the Tagus estuary (*Gentleman's Mag.* 1756).

2. The city of Lisbon lies on the north side of the river Tagus, about 6 miles from its mouth. Built on the slopes of a low range of hills, its length along the river in 1755 was at least 4 miles and its width about 1½ miles. Its situation is shown in *Fig.* 1, reproduced from a map published in the *Gentleman's Magazine* for 1756. Some twenty years before this, it was computed that the city contained 20,000 houses and that the population was not less than 235,000. The houses were usually built of stone, four or five storeys in height, and many of the streets were narrow and inclined. The lower or western part of the city, that suffered most from the earthquake, was built on tertiary strata; the upper or eastern part, erected on limestone of secondary age, was practically unharmed, and now forms the oldest quarter of the city.

II. Seismic History of the District

3. The earthquake history of the Lisbon district is an interesting one. Milne, in his valuable catalogue of destructive earthquakes, records four such earthquakes before 1755 and ten afterwards, the majority of the latter being probably after-shocks of the great earthquake. Of the earlier earthquakes, only one was of the highest degree of the Milne scale*, and none of the later earthquakes, with the possible exception of that on 1761 Mar. 31, attained this strength.

Besides the four early destructive earthquakes, many others of less violence are recorded in the catalogues of Mallet and Perrey.

The following is a list of the more important earthquakes known to us:

1009, at Lisbon and in the country to the south, great earthquakes.

1017, at Lisbon, a considerable earthquake.

1117 and 1146, at Lisbon.

1344, at Lisbon and along the coast, a disastrous earthquake.

1350, at Lisbon.

1356 Aug. 24, at Lisbon. The shocks lasted a quarter of an hour. Many buildings were thrown down.

1531 Jan. 26, at Lisbon and in the rest of Portugal, in Spain and on the opposite coast of Africa. In Lisbon, the shocks were extremely violent (int. 3), 1500 houses and all the churches were thrown down. The sea was greatly agitated and several vessels were wrecked. The waters of the Tagus were driven up its banks by the rush of the waves.

1532, at Lisbon, another violent earthquake.

1551 Jan. 28, at Lisbon, 200 houses were thrown down and more than 2,000 persons killed.

1575 July 27, at Lisbon, a strong earthquake, but without damage to buildings.

1597 July 28, at Lisbon, the houses of three whole streets thrown down.

1598 July 22, at Lisbon, an earthquake not less destructive than the last.

1699 Oct. 27, at Lisbon, strong shocks.

1724 Oct. 12, at Lisbon, two violent earthquakes, many walls cracked.

1750, at Lisbon, a strong shock.

---

*The essential features of the Milne scale are: 1, Strong enough to crack walls, break chimneys or shatter old buildings; 2, to unroof or shatter buildings and to throw down some; 3, to destroy towns and devastate districts. Of the four early earthquakes, that of 1531 reached int. 3, those of 1356 and 1597 int. 2, and that of 1724 int. 1 (*Brit. Ass. Rep.*, 1911, pp. 649-740).

Thus, so far as we know, for five years before the great earthquake, Lisbon was free from noticeable shocks*.

III. INVESTIGATIONS OF THE EARTHQUAKE

4. In addition to its great strength and its varied phenomena, the Lisbon earthquake is remarkable as the first to be investigated on modern scientific lines. By order of the Marquez de Pombal, a list of questions was sent to every parish in the country. If it had been drawn up at the present day, it could hardly have been more complete. The questions refer to the time at which the earthquake began and the duration of the shock, its direction, the effects of the earthquake on the sea, on springs and rivers, the height of the sea-waves and the time for which they lasted, fissures in the ground, and even the times and intensities of the after-shocks. They also ask for the population of each parish, the number of persons killed, the number of houses ruined, the outbreaks of fires, their duration and the damage caused by them. At the time, no detailed report seems to have been written, but the replies were fortunately preserved in the National Archives.

5. The particulars contained in these accounts relate to the kingdom of Portugal only. As regards other countries, as well as Portugal, an important series of papers or letters was read before the Royal Society, and a number of accounts written by residents in Lisbon and elsewhere were published in the *Gentleman's Magazine* and other works. Many of these notices were collected by John Bevis in " The History and Philosophy of Earthquakes," a series of memoirs edited by him in 1757. The last chapter of this work is entitled " Phaenomena of the great earthquake of November 1, 1755, in various parts of the globe " (pp. 280-334). In this, the accounts from each country are arranged alphabetically according to the places of observation. In the same year (1757) was published E. Bertrand's " Mémoires Historiques et Physiques sur les Tremblemens de Terre." The title of the third memoir is " Relation de ce qui a été observé en Suisse le premier de Novembre 1755, etc." (pp. 103-116). Three years later, in 1760, John Michell read before the Royal Society his well-known memoir : " Conjectures concerning the cause and observations upon the phenomena of earthquakes, etc." In several of his papers on earthquakes, Alexis Perrey has inserted accounts of the earthquake, while Sir Charles Lyell has devoted to it several pages in his *Principles of Geology*.

During the present century, F. L. Pereira de Sousa discovered the mine of information collected in reply to the questions issued by the Marquez de Pombal, and, in addition to several short papers,

---

*Mallet, **20**; Perrey, **33**.

has published an extremely valuable memoir of 471 pages under the title " O teremoto do 1°. novembro de 1755 em Portugal, etc."

IV. Loss of Life and Property

6.   No trustworthy estimate has ever been made of the total loss of life in Lisbon and elsewhere.   None, indeed, was possible, for the bodies were removed from the city without being counted. The earthquake occurred on All Saints' Day, at the time of the first mass, and thousands were collected in the churches.   Most of these were killed, for very few of the churches and convents escaped destruction.   The number of killed in Lisbon alone is usually placed at about 30,000, but some estimates rise as high as 50, 60 and even 70, thousand.   These figures, it should be noted, take no account of the losses in other places such as Faro, where 3,000 persons are said to have been killed, or Fez, Mequinez, Morocco and other towns in North Africa, in or near which many thousands of lives were lost.

7.   In the lower part of the city, the destruction of property in the narrow streets was almost universal.   Less than three weeks after the earthquake, one writer went over the ruined city. " There are ", he says, " no signs of streets, lanes, squares, etc., but hills and mountains of rubbish still smoking ".   Out of about 20,000 houses in Lisbon, there remained hardly 3,000 that were habitable with safety.   Among those lost or seriously damaged, must be reckoned 32 churches, more than 60 small chapels, 31 monasteries, 15 nunneries and 53 palaces.

8.   The damage wrought by the earthquake was completed by the fires that broke out some minutes later in six or seven different places, and soon spread over the ruined city.   The outbreak of fire was due mainly to the fall of curtains and woodwork on kitchen fires and on the candles and lamps that illuminated the altars in every church and chapel in the city, and, to a slight extent, on the work of incendiaries bent on plundering the ruins.   The fires, aided by a violent wind, continued burning for six days, without any attempt being made to stop their progress, until most of what the earthquake had spared was consumed*.

V. Summary of the Earthquake Phenomena

9.   *The Principal Phenomena.*—During the morning of Nov. 1, there were three great earthquakes in Lisbon, at about 9.40, 10.0 and noon (Lisbon time).   By the first of these, the greater part of the city was overthrown and many thousands of lives were lost.

---

*Anon, **1**, p. 24; Anon, **7**, p. 199; Davy, **13**, pp. 42-45; *Gent. Mag.*, **17**, vol. 25, pp. 560, 591-592.

Soon after it was over, fires broke out and destroyed most of what the earthquake spared. The first great shock was felt over an area of between 1,200,000 and 1,400,000 sq. miles. One of the most unusual phenomena of this earthquake was the oscillation produced in the water of pools, lakes, rivers and canals near to, and far beyond, the limits of the disturbed area.

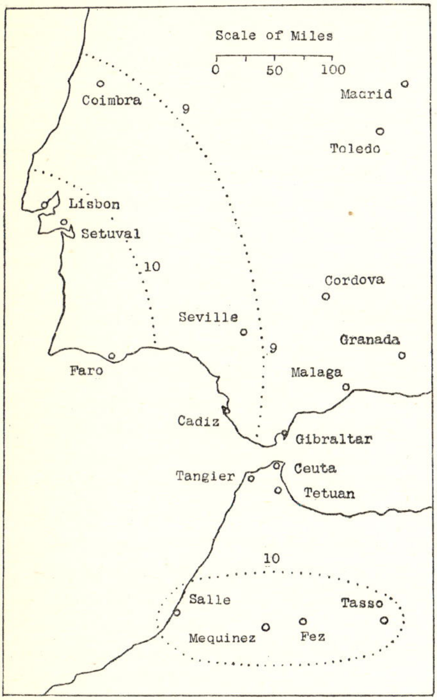

FIG. 2.—Isoseismal lines of the Lisbon earthquake.

Many survivors in Lisbon fled to a quay, newly and strongly built. With, or about the time of, the second great earthquake, this quay sank, with all the people on it, into a fissure, and no trace of quay or people was seen again.

With the first great earthquake, the sea rose and after the lapse of about twenty minutes flooded the coast of Portugal. The waves swept over the Atlantic Ocean, reaching the shores of the British Isles between 2 and 3 p.m. and the coasts of Antigua and Barbadoes shortly after 6 p.m.

10. *Complexity of the Lisbon Earthquake.* — In the chapters that follow, accounts will be given of earthquakes possessing epicentral areas of vast dimensions, such as the Assam earthquake of 1897. Such areas, no doubt, represent foci of extraordinary size and complexity, and are due to deep-seated movements of which we have as yet but a faint conception.

Far more complicated, probably, is the phenomenon known as the Lisbon earthquake of 1755. How complicated is shown at once by the glance at the Map in *Fig. 2*. The main epicentre was not very distant from Lisbon. But only less destructive was the shock at Mequinez, Fez and other places in North Africa. Algiers, again, was injured, though not so seriously as Lisbon and Mequinez. Lastly, in Spain, there was some, perhaps slight, damage to houses at places like Seville, Cordova and Granada. In the Assam earthquake, the epicentral area was 200 miles in length. In the Lisbon earthquake, the area was far greater. The distance that separates Lisbon from Mequinez is 400 miles, Mequinez from Algiers 690 miles, and Lisbon from Granada 317 miles.

Over this vast area, there was no gradual decline in the intensity of the shock from some central point. There seems rather to have been a succession of earthquakes, in what order they occurred we cannot now say, the principal earthquake no doubt in the Lisbon centre, another of less, but still great, strength near Mequinez, and perhaps a third near Algiers. All of these suggested centres, it is important to notice, are occasionally, indeed usually, in action independently of the others. After the earthquake of 1755, the Lisbon and Mequinez centres had their own series of after-shocks, while the centre near Algiers has, for more than a century, been the seat of strong or violent earthquakes.

VI. INTENSITY OF THE EARTHQUAKE

11. *Observations in Portugal and Spain.*—With the data at our disposal, isoseismal lines cannot be drawn with any approach to accuracy. In *Fig.* 2, I have traced, though roughly, the isoseismals of intensity 10 and 8 (Rossi-Forel scale), in Portugal and Spain. The former includes the places at which great damage to buildings occurred, such as Lisbon, Cascaes and Setuval to the north, and along the south coast of Portugal. The latter bounds the area in which there was some, though not considerable, injury to property. Within both curves, there were zones of distinctly less intensity, and beyond the outer curve there are several places, islands, as it were, in which some or many buildings were damaged, as, for instance, at Cordova, Malaga, Granada, and other places in Spain. Even at Madrid, the walls of several churches are said to have been fractured.

The earthquake was felt throughout Portugal, and probably all over Spain, though records seem to be wanting from the north-eastern provinces of Catalonia and Aragon*.

12. *Reported Observations in other Countries.*—At the present time, it is difficult to estimate the trustworthiness of reported observations of the earthquake at distant places. In many accounts, it is merely stated that a shock was felt, without any record of the time. In some, it is clear that the disturbances observed had no connexion with the Lisbon earthquake or that the shock itself was not felt. For instance, (i) shocks felt at Basel between 3 and 4 p.m. or at Locle during the night of Nov. 1-2 cannot have been due

---

*Bevis, 11, pp. 311-325; *Gent. Mag.*, 17, vol. 25, pp. 562-564, 587; Pereira, 24, p. 8; *Roy. Soc.*, 38, p. 403.

to the Lisbon earthquake; (ii) nor can a violent shock at Caen (825 miles) — all the distances are here measured from Lisbon — or a shock at Ponza (1,180 miles) so destructive that two-thirds of the houses were ruined, be so due; nor again (iii) does the oscillation of lamps in churches at Milan (1,045 miles) or the disturbance of the canal waters at Abbiategrasso (1,030 miles) imply that the shocks were actually felt at those places.

13. In France, the earthquake was almost certainly felt at Bayonne (515 miles) and Bordeaux (610 miles), probably at Cognac (660 miles), Toulouse (645 miles) and Angoulême (675 miles). Reports that the shock was felt have come, though without details as to time and nature, from Anduse (775 miles), Caen (845 miles), Vaucluse (820 miles), St. Aubin (920 miles), Lyons (860 miles), Cuers (850 miles) and Strasbourg (1,080 miles), and from the provinces of Poitou, Brittany and Normandy.

14. In Italy, a shock is said to have been felt at San Remo (940 miles), Turin (965 miles) and Lodi (1,055 miles). In Switzerland, some shocks were felt at about 10 a.m. at Neuchâtel (990 miles) and Brieg (985 miles), and, though the time is not mentioned, at Novelle on the Rhone (970 miles) and near Visp (1,010 miles). A shock is also reported to have been felt at Stuttgart (1,170 miles), and strong shocks at Fahlun in Sweden (1,850 miles).

15. Among the islands of the Atlantic, the shock was probably felt at Funchal (605 miles) on the south coast of Madeira, and shocks, it is reported, were observed at Terceira (965 miles), one of the Azores.

16. *Reported Observations in the British Isles.* — It is said that the earthquake was both felt and heard in these islands, and the former statement cannot be discredited on account of the distance from Lisbon, for several great earthquakes — such as the Charleston earthquake of 1886, the Assam earthquake of 1897 and the Kangra earthquake of 1905—have been felt at places more than 800 miles from the origin.

In the Scilly Isles (785 miles), the shock is said to have been so strong that several people ran out of their houses. At Cork (905 miles), two shocks were felt at 9.36 a.m. At Poole (895 miles), some persons felt a slight earthquake. At Earley Court (near Reading, 965 miles), at about 11 a.m., a gardener standing by a fishpond, felt a violent trembling of the earth, lasting more than 50 sec., and immediately afterwards saw the water in the pond oscillating.

At Eyam Edge (Derbyshire, 995 miles), at about 11 a.m., an observer on the surface felt a shock that raised his chair sensibly and made pieces of plaster fall from the walls of the room. A fissure, nearly 150 yd. long, 6 in. wide and 1 ft. deep, opened at the same time in a neighbouring field. In the same place, two miners were at work in a lead mine in a drift about 120 yd. deep. A violent shock was felt, followed soon after by a still stronger shock, and this again by three slighter shocks, the interval between the first and fifth being about 20 min. Each shock was followed by a loud rumbling sound. As they went along the drifts, the miners noticed that fragments had fallen from the sides and roof.

The shock is also said to have been observed in Scotland. At Leadhills and Wanlockhead (near Dumfries, 1,180 miles), an earthquake was very distinctly felt. Around Drymen (near Glasgow, 1,220 miles), the shock was especially severe. " On that day, Whitefield, the great English divine, was preaching in the adjoining parish of Kilmaronock. . . . The speaker and his hearers occupied the face of an eminence. Instantly the earth heaved, and the people were bent forwards as if by a wave "*.

17. Whatever may have been the origin of these movements, it seems clear for the following reasons (in addition to the frequent omission of the time of occurrence), that none of them was due to the Lisbon earthquake:

(i) Of the writers who describe the seiches in letters read before the Royal Society, only one (at Earley Court) refers to a movement —a violent trembling of the earth. Another observer, in the same place, make no reference to any shock. A few near Durham and in the Lake District, state that no movement was felt (Roy. Soc., **37**, pp. 367, 382, 384 and 386).

(ii) At places between 800 and 1,200 miles from the epicentre, the movement, if it were felt, would have consisted of slow gentle undulations, and not of a trembling or of a series of shocks, violent or slight. It could not have been felt in mines, nor could any sound have been heard, at distances so great.

(iii) The phenomena observed at Eyam Edge closely resemble those of the earth-shakes in mining districts, which are probably due to fault-slips started by mining operations†.

Thus, while it is by no means impossible that the earthquake was felt in the south of England, it would seem that we have no evidence that the disturbed area extended so far to the north.

18. *Extent of the Disturbed Area.*—To sum up, it is clear that the Lisbon earthquake was felt throughout the whole of

---

*Baratta, **9**, pp. 242-243; Bertrand, **10**, pp. 107-114; Bevis, **11**, pp. 283-288, 298, 306-311, 325, 331; *Gent. Mag.*, **17**, vol. 25, pp. 587, 590; Perrey, **28**, p. 40; **29**, p. 287; **34**, pp. 51-52; **35**, p. 46; Roy. Soc., **37**, pp. 365-366, 393; **38**, pp. 398-402; *Edin. Adver.*, 1820; Nimmo, *Hist. of Stirlingshire*, 1880, vol. 2, p. 207.

†Mr. R. D. Oldham, in his report on the Assam earthquake of 1897 (*India Geol. Surv. Mem.*, vol. 29, 1899, pp. 371-376), also concludes that the observations at Eyam Edge refer to a local disturbance, and that there is no evidence to show that the Lisbon earthquake was felt in this country.

Portugal and practically all over Spain. The vibrations from the Lisbon focus may have been observed in North Africa and perhaps confused with those from the Mequinez centre. It is doubtful whether the earthquake was felt in France at distances much greater than 675 miles and whether it was felt at all in the British Isles or in Italy or Switzerland or the rest of the continental area. It may have been felt at Terceira in the Azores, but such isolated observations, without supporting evidence, can hardly be accepted as decisive.

Thus, it would seem that, in France, the earthquake was certainly felt to a distance of at least 610 miles from Lisbon and probably to a distance of 675 miles, but that all observations at greater distances must be received with caution. If the disturbed area were a circle with the former distance as radius, it would contain about 1,170,000 sq. miles; if with the latter distance as radius, about 1,430,000 sq. miles. Roughly then, it may be said that the area shaken by the Lisbon earthquake lies between $1\frac{1}{4}$ and $1\frac{1}{2}$ million sq. miles. It should be added that this estimate takes no account of the tract affected by vibrations from the Mequinez and Algiers centres, a tract as to the magnitude of which there is no evidence.

VII. Nature of the Shocks

19. There were three great earthquakes in Lisbon during the morning of Nov. 1. There is some doubt as to the time at which the first began, but it must have been about 9.40 a.m. (Lisbon time). The interval between the first and second great earthquakes is estimated at from 10 to 15 minutes to an hour after the first ended. The lower estimate, judging from the actions of witnesses, would seem the more nearly correct. The third is said to have occurred two hours later and near noon. Thus, taking into account the duration of the first shock (about 6 or 7 min.), the times of the three great earthquakes were probably about 9.40, 10.0 and noon.

20. All observers agree as to the great duration of the first earthquake. Even if allowance is made for inaccuracy or exaggeration, such estimates as 6 or 7 min. at Lisbon (five observers), 6 or 7 at Oporto, 5 at Cadiz, and 8 at Madrid, all point to an unusual duration.

There were clearly three phases in the movement. At Lisbon, the first consisted of rapid vibrations, too slight to cause alarm, and lasting for about a minute. Then, after about 30 sec., there came a shock, also composed of rapid vibrations, but so violent that houses began to fall. This lasted a little more than 2 min. Then, after a pause of less than a minute, the nature of the movement changed, and buildings were jerked upwards like a waggon driven violently over rough stones. This phase lasted for 2 or 3 min. and laid in ruins all the houses, churches and public buildings in Lisbon, with the loss of thousands of lives. When the clouds of dust that darkened the sky settled, " the whole tract of country about Lisbon was seen to heave like the swelling of the billows in a storm ".

These three phases, though not always recorded, were observed at great distances from Lisbon, at Cadiz and at Funchal in Madeira.

21. Of the other two earthquakes, we possess but few records. At Lisbon, the second shock was said by one observer to be little less violent than the first, by another as of greater violence but shorter duration. Many buildings, already shattered, were thrown down. The master of a ship anchored a few hundred yards from the quay that sank, stated that " he could see the *whole* city waving backwards and forwards ".

22. The third earthquake, though less violent than the others, was so strong that people were unable to keep their feet, and many more shattered buildings collapsed*.

VIII. POSITIONS OF THE EPICENTRES

23. *The Lisbon Centre.*—While the position of the Mequinez centre can be determined approximately, that of the Lisbon centre is uncertain. Unfortunately, it is the one of greatest interest, for it was probably the origin of the seiches and seawaves so widely observed.

From the existence of the great seawave, Michell remarks that the origin must have been submarine, and its great height and the shortness of the interval at Lisbon between the shock and the seawave show that it was not far from that city. The position that he suggests is about a degree from Lisbon and $1\frac{1}{2}$ degrees from Oporto, or at a distance of 10 or 15 leagues from the coast between Lisbon and Oporto.

In 1841, another attempt was made to determine the position of the centre by Mr. David Milne. He assigned it to a point in lat. 39° N., long. 11° W., or about 75 miles from the coast of Portugal. Milne gives no evidence for this estimate, but he seems to have been led to it by the extreme violence of the shock felt on a ship near this point.

In 1911, Pereira de Sousa plotted the directions in which the seawaves reached the coast of Portugal. He concluded that the epicentre lay in an area between the southeast of the Iberian peninsula and the African continent and to the west of the Straits of Gibraltar. This position, he considered, is supported by the arrangement of the isoseismal lines and by the existence of the area of high intensity near Fez and Mequinez.

---

*Bevis, **11**, pp. 315-318, 328-329; Davy, **13**, pp. 15-16, 28, 114-116; *Gent. Mag.,* **17**, vol. 25, pp. 560, 587; vol. 26, p. 67; Pereira, **24**, p. 6.

The best interpretation of the evidence seems to me that the Lisbon focus was of great size and that a part, and a very active part, of it must have been not many miles to the southwest of Lisbon. This may be inferred from the great intensity of the shock at Lisbon, Cascaes and Setuval, from the brevity of the interval between the earthquake and the arrival of the seawaves at Lisbon, and from the number of after-shocks felt in that city.

In the absence, then, of some definite point that may be regarded as the centre, the distances in this chapter have been measured from Lisbon.

24. *The Mequinez Centre.* — At four places in the north of Africa, the intensity of the shock reached the highest degree (10) of the Rossi-Forel scale. At Salle, nearly one-third of the houses were overthrown; at Mequinez, two-thirds of the houses fell and many lives were lost, about 4,000, it is said, in the Jewish quarter; at Fez, more than 300 houses were overthrown and many people were buried in the ruins. Tasso is said to have been completely destroyed. At Ceuta, Oran, Saffé and Morocco, the intensity was at least 9, at Tangier 8, and at Tetuan 7 or 8. The four places first mentioned lie along a band nearly 200 miles in length, roughly parallel to the trend of the neighbouring mountain-ranges, and, if produced, passing through or near Algiers. The centre of the band is in about lat. 34° 7′ N., long. 5° 18′ W., or about 12 miles northeast of Mequinez.

25. It is unfortunate that so little trust can be placed in the estimates of the time. The earthquake is said to have occurred at about 10 a.m. at Tetuan and Tangier and at 10.6 a.m. at Ceuta. If these are referred to local times, it follows that, in Lisbon time, they would be 9.45, 9.47 and 9.51 a.m., or from 5 to 10 min. after the first great earthquake was felt at Lisbon. The evidence is far from decisive, but, so far as it goes, it seems to show that the Mequinez centre was in action at about the same time as the Lisbon centre, or at most a few minutes later.

The duration of the shock was evidently considerable. At Tangier, three shocks were felt, lasting altogether, it is said, 10 or 12 min.; at Tetuan, also three shocks, of 7 or 8 min. in duration.

26. An interesting feature of the Mequinez centre is that it possessed its own series of after-shocks. It is probably responsible for the slight shocks felt at Ceuta every day from Nov. 1 to 17. On Nov. 8, " very violent " shocks were felt at Fez and Mequinez, on Nov. 18 and 19, violent shocks at Tangier and Tetuan, and on Nov. 19 one that entirely destroyed the buildings at Mequinez that were spared by the earthquake on Nov. 1. On Nov. 20, several strong shocks occurred at Tangier and Tetuan.

So far as we know, the great earthquake of Nov. 19 at

Mequinez was not felt at Lisbon, nor were the strong after-shocks of Nov. 8 and Dec. 11 in the Lisbon centre noticed in the north of Africa. The only subsequent earthquake that may have been caused by movements in both centres was that of 1773 Apr. 12, violent at Lisbon, Cadiz, Malaga, etc., also at Salle and probably at Fez. On 1821 Apr. 8, a strong earthquake was felt at Melilla, after which this district seems to have become stable*.

27. *The Algiers Centre.*—As Algiers lies 690 miles to the east of Mequinez, it is difficult to resist the impression that another centre was in action in its neighbourhood. No time is mentioned, and we know little beyond the fact that, on Nov. 1, Algiers was shaken so strongly that not a house in the city was undamaged.

The centre at or near Algiers is one of the most active in North Africa. Omitting all but great earthquakes, there was one on 1716 Feb. 3, followed about three months later by another during which 20,000 persons lost their lives. Others occurred on 1807 Nov. 18, 1867 Jan. 2 and 1885 Jan. 31 and Dec. 3-13[†].

ix. Effects of the Earthquake on the Ground

28. *Uplift of the Coast.*—In two places, the land seems to have been elevated. At Colares, about 16 miles west of Lisbon, the sea retired, for it was possible after the earthquake to walk on dry land where before it was necessary to wade. Again, at some distance from the harbour of Cadiz, a rock was seen that had not before been noticed by sailors[‡].

29. *Sinking of the Quay.*—One of the strangest results of the earthquake was the sinking of a large newly-built quay, called the Cays Depreda, close to the custom-house at Lisbon. The quay was made of a coarse marble and was very strong. According to the fullest account—that given to Braddock by the master of a ship moored within two or three hundred yards of the quay, the river rose at once nearly 20 ft. with the second shock and as rapidly subsided. At the same moment, he saw the quay sink down, with all the people who had fled to it for safety after the first earthquake, and all the boats and small vessels near it were drawn in, and none of the bodies or wrecks was ever seen again. A few days later, Braddock examined the place and could find no trace of the quay. Many years afterwards, in 1841, Lyell was informed that no part of the Tagus was then more than 30 ft. in depth. Thus, though there may have been changes in the interval, the best explanation of the sinking seems to be that given by Lyell, that " perhaps a

---

*Bevis, **11**, pp. 326-328; *Gent. Mag.*, **17**, vol. 25, pp. 564, 587; vol. 26, p. 7; Perrey, **30**, pp. 312-313.

†Perrey, **30**, pp. 299-323.

‡Bevis, **11**, p. 313; Perrey, **33**, p. 472.

narrow chasm opened and closed again in the bed of the Tagus, after swallowing up some incumbent buildings and vessels "*.

30. *Landslips.* — In the absence of detailed accounts of the landslips and rockfalls, the chief interest of such accidents lies in their distribution. They seem to have occurred in two areas, the larger being that within 30 or 40 miles from the coast of Portugal, from about the latitude of Coimbra to about halfway between Setuval and Cape St. Vincent. They were especially numerous in the neighbourhood of Lisbon, along the coast at Colares, in M. Arrabida and M. Cintra, and in two rocky islets near the mouth of the Tagus. In North Africa, a few landslips are recorded in the neighbourhood of Fez. It is worthy of notice that these two landslip areas include or are close to the two main epicentral areas†.

31. *Effects on Springs.*—Springs are said to have been disturbed in many districts and at great distances from the origin. In a few cases, the time is mentioned; in many of them, there is no note of the hour or even of the day, and it is difficult to feel any assurance that the disturbances were in any way connected with the earthquake. Omitting, then, all records of changes of which the time is not definitely given, the following seem worthy of notice.

At Madrid, shortly after the earthquake, the water in the wells rose several fathoms. At 10 a.m., the water of springs at Cuers, Géménos, St. Auban and Vaucluse in Provence became muddy and reddish in colour and did not become clear until 6 p.m. The most remarkable change, if it were connected with the Lisbon earthquake, was that which occurred at Töplitz in Bohemia (1,380 miles from Lisbon). On the morning of Nov. 1, the chief springs in the medicinal baths became turbid and muddy, and having stopped entirely for about a minute, broke out again half an hour later, between 11 and noon, with such violence that, in about half an hour, all the baths overflowed with reddish water. Afterwards, the water became clear again, but, for some time, it flowed in greater quantity than before, its temperature was higher, and its medicinal properties were more pronounced.

Somewhat similar changes also seem to have occurred on Nov. 1 in North Africa, though the exact time is unknown. At Ceuta, the waters of springs ceased to flow on that day, though afterwards they flowed with the same abundance as before. At Tangier, the springs dried up until the evening‡.

---

*Anon, **1**, pp. 33-34; Bevis, **11**, p. 316; Davy, **13**, pp, 27-29; *Gent. Mag.,* **17**, vol. 25, p. 559; vol. 26, p. 67; Lyell, **19**, pp. 147-148.

†Bevis, **11**, pp. 313, 317-319, 327.

‡Bevis, **11**, pp. 305-306, 313, 318-319; Perrey, **29**, p. 288; **34**, pp. 52-53.

x. Seismic Seiches

32. Seiches are rhythmical oscillations of masses of water, often raised in lakes by wind and in open harbours by the swell of the sea. Occasionally, as in the Assam earthquake of 1897 (art. 271), they are caused by the distant slow movements of great earthquakes, but they have never, in any earthquake, been so widely and generally observed as in the Lisbon earthquake of 1755.

In the following accounts, the distances are measured, as before, from Lisbon. In a few cases, the direct distances from the mouths of rivers are also given.

33. *Disturbances of Rivers in Portugal and Spain.*—Many of the rivers flowing into the Atlantic were swollen and disturbed. For instance, at Seville (205 miles), 50 miles from the mouth of the Guadalquiver, the waters were so agitated that all the vessels in the river were driven on shore. In such cases, the disturbances were probably due to seawaves. The river Tagus at Toledo (288 miles), 294 miles from the mouth, rose 10 ft.; and the river Douro at Segovia (315 miles), 240 miles from its mouth, was greatly disturbed. At Valencia (475 miles), on the east coast of Spain, there are said to have been " very terrible agitations of the water." In the absence of time-records, however, the cause of such movements must remain uncertain*.

34. *Seiches in France.* — The seiches in this country were usually observed in rivers. The shock itself was felt at Bordeaux (610 miles), 57 miles from the mouth of the Garonne. It lasted some minutes and was accompanied by an extraordinary agitation of the river. This observation is important, for it shows that the movements were due to seiches and not to seawaves. Similar movements were observed in the Charante at Angoulême (675 miles). At Ouilly Bridge (865 miles), the waters of the Orne and of a lake in the neighbourhood were much agitated, and this was also the case in the same river at Caen (845 miles). At Havre (930 miles), vessels in the harbour were strangely agitated at about 11 a.m. With France may be included the island of Corsica (1,045 to 1,100 miles), in which most of the rivers overflowed their banks and inundated the surrounding country†.

35. *Seiches in Holland.*—In this country, the seiches occurred chiefly in canals, but also in rivers and even in small vessels. At Amsterdam (1,160 miles), the canals were suddenly agitated and so strongly that several boats broke loose. Similar movements were observed at Bois-le-Duc (1,135 miles) and Leerdam (1,135 miles). At Haarlem (1,150 miles), during the morning, the water in rivers

---

*Bevis, **11**, pp. 313-318, 320, 324, 325.
†Bertrand, **10**, pp. 112, 114; Bevis, **11**, p. 306.

and canals and even in tubs was agitated and dashed over the sides, in the rivers and canals rising 1 ft. vertically. At the Hague (1,140 miles), at 11 a.m., the rise of the water in canals was measured and found to be 1 ft. At Rotterdam (1,125 miles) and other places, the water in canals and rivers was agitated so violently that buoys were broken from their chains and large vessels snapped their cables. The agitation of the water lasted 4 min., the rise in rivers and canals being again 1 ft. At Leyden (1,140 miles), the water in some of the canals rose suddenly between 10½ and 11 a.m., and made several undulations*.

36. *Seiches in Italy.*—In this country, seiches were seldom observed. At Abbiategrasso (1,030 miles), the water of a canal rose towards its source and then resumed its course with impetuosity. The water in the canal that surrounds Milan (1,045 miles) was greatly agitated. The Lago Maggiore (1,020 miles) rose and fell considerably†.

37. *Seiches in Switzerland.*—Most of the lakes in this country were agitated. At the east end of Lake Geneva (970 miles), from Vevey to Villeneuve, the water rose abruptly at about 10 a.m. and then fell; nothing was noticed at Morges or Geneva. The Lake of Neuchâtel (990 miles) rose about 2 ft. On Lake Nidau (1,010 miles), fishermen felt their boat swept away and returned by a kind of current and then raised by waves. On Lake Seedorf (1,010 miles), the water rose suddenly and fell. In Lakes Thun (1,015 miles) and Brienz (1,025 miles), the water advanced up the shores and then withdrew; the river Aar, running from the latter lake into the former, was retarded for an instant. The Lake of Zurich (1,070 miles), for 6 or 7 min. rose at different places by from 6 to 12 ft. Lake Constance, near the town of Stein (1,090 miles), rose several feet, and the Rhine, that leaves the lake at this end, increased considerably for some seconds. Besides these, other small lakes, such as Wallenstadt and Etalière, near Neuchâtel, were raised for some moments‡.

38. *Seiches in Great Britain.*—In this country, the seiches were observed in harbours, lakes, rivers and canals, and in a large number of ponds. In the harbours, they were noticed in the morning, and are thus distinguished from the seawaves that swept in late in the afternoon.

At Dartmouth (850 miles), there was a great and sudden swell about 9 a.m. " Though there was but little wind, yet the boats,

---

*Bertrand, **10**, p. 112; Bevis, **11**, pp. 309, 310; *Gent. Mag.,* **17**, vol. 25, pp. 588-589; Perrey, **28**, p. 40.

†Bevis, **11**, p. 311; *Gent. Mag.,* **17**, vol. 25, p. 587; Perrey, **35**, p. 46.

‡Bertrand, **10**, pp. 105-111; Bevis, **11**, pp. 311, 325; Perrey, **29**, p. 287; **34**, p. 52.

riding near the mouth of the river, tumbled and tossed as if they would have leaped into each other; and two of them broke loose from their moorings ". At this time, the tide had ebbed four hours, yet the waters rose as high as they usually do during spring tides. At Poole (895 miles), between 10 and 11 a.m., the sea at the quay was violently agitated; ships were tossed and broke loose from their moorings. At Portsmouth (850 miles), H.M.S. Gosport had just entered the north dock, when, at about 10½ a.m., " she was observed to pitch forwards with her head deep into the water, and immediately to recover it and pitch in as deep with her stern ". At Yarmouth (1,090 miles), shortly before noon, the water in the harbour was violently agitated and suddenly rose 6 ft.

39. At Busbridge (955 miles), near Godalming, in a canal nearly 700 ft. long and 58 ft. wide, the water at the east end was strongly agitated at 10½ a.m. " It rose in a . . . ridge in the middle, which extended lengthwise about 30 yards, and between 2 and 3 feet above the usual level. . . . The ridge heeled to the north side of the canal with great force and flowed above 8 feet over the grass walk on that side ", which was about 2 ft. above the water. It then flowed over the grass walk on the south side, while the bottom on the north side was left bare of water. The oscillations then gradually diminished, until, in about a quarter of an hour, the water became smooth as before. On the Thames at Rotherhithe (985 miles), a barge was suddenly heaved by the swell of the water between 11 a.m. and noon. After it had risen and sunk three or four times, the water again became quiet.

40. Most of the ponds in which seiches were observed lie in the southeast of England, but there were a few in counties farther north. Ponds were disturbed in Sussex at Midhurst (955 miles), and in Surrey at Godalming (955 miles), Lee (955 miles), Guildford (960 miles) and Cobham (970 miles). In Kent, the water in a pond at Cranbrook (975 miles) rose 3 or 4 ft. above its usual level between 10 and 11 a.m.; also at Eaton Bridge (965 miles). At Tenterden (975 miles), between 10 and 11 a.m., several ponds were greatly agitated, water being forced up the banks with violence. In others at the same place, the water whirled round in eddies, drawing down leaves and sticks. In Essex, ponds were agitated at Rochford (1,010 miles) at about 10 a.m., Thaxted (1,020 miles), Wickham Hale (1,048 miles), Bardfield (1,020 miles) between 11 a.m. and noon, Bocking (1,015 miles), Finchingfield (1,025 miles) and Topsfield (1,025 miles); in Suffolk, at Dunstall (1,045 miles) and Framlingham (1,055 miles); near London (985 miles); and, in Hertfordshire, at Albury (1,048 miles) and Royston (1,020 miles). At Luton (1,005 miles), between 10 and 11 a.m., the water of a pond overflowed its banks.

At Earley Court (965 miles), near Reading, at about 11 a.m., the water of a pond moved to the north end, leaving the bottom of the south end bare, then returned and flowed 3 ft. up the bank at the south end, the oscillations lasting about 4 min. At Shirburn Castle (970 miles) in Oxfordshire, the water in the moat surrounding the house was disturbed shortly after 10 a.m. The movement began gently at the northeast corner. At the same time, the water at the southeast corner sank. The swells were unequal in height. Sometimes, after a great swell, there would be two or three small ones. In less than half an hour, the water in the moat was still. Pebbly Dam (1,070 miles) is a large pond covering nearly 30 acres near Barlborough in Derbyshire. Between 11 a.m. and noon, the water rose up the sloping dam at the north end. It then subsided and returned with less vehemence, the agitation lasting for about three-quarters of an hour. From the mark left on a post near the north end, it was seen that the water rose about 8 in. above its usual level. Lastly, in a pool near Durham (1,165 miles), about 40 yd. long and 10 yd. wide, the water, at about $10\frac{1}{2}$ a.m., was seen to rise until it reached a grating about 6 in. above, through which it flowed for some seconds. Then it subsided to the same distance below its usual level, and continued rising and falling four or five times a minute for 6 or 7 min., after which the oscillations became less.

41. The most remarkable seiches were those observed in large bodies of water, such as the lakes of northwest England and Scotland. About 10 a.m., a fishing-boat had been drawn up on the shore of Windermere (1,115 miles). The surface was smooth, when suddenly the water rose, floated the boat farther inshore, and then drew it back. The oscillations lasted 8 or 10 min., and it was estimated that the water rose about knee-deep above its usual level. On Coniston Water (1,105 miles), at about 10 a.m., the water, though quite calm, rose more than a yard upon the bank. The vertical rise was about a foot, and the undulations lasted about 5 min. Esthwaite Water (1,105 miles), a smaller lake, was similarly disturbed at the same hour, but in a less degree and for a shorter time.

In Scotland, still larger bodies of water were put in oscillation. At Queen's Ferry (1,220 miles), on the Firth of Forth, the water rose suddenly at about 10 a.m., through a vertical distance of 12 or 18 in., so that ships and boats then afloat ran backwards and forwards on their ropes with great rapidity. This continued for 3 or 4 min. In Loch Lomond (1,220 miles), at $9\frac{1}{2}$ a.m., the water rose suddenly and with great rapidity, but immediately retired until, in 5 min., it was as low as in the greatest summer drought. The water continued to rise and fall to the same points, taking 10 min. for each complete oscillation, until 10.15, when the movements gradually diminished, and, by 11 a.m., the lake was once more still. The height to which the water of the loch rose vertically was measured and found to be 2 ft. 4 in. Similar movements were observed at the same time in Loch Katrine (1,230 miles) and Loch Long (1,220 miles). At 9½ a.m., a great agitation was observed in Loch Ness (1,305 miles), and, at about 10 a.m., the river Oich (1,305 miles), that runs into the loch from the west, was seen to swell, and a wave, 2 or 3 ft. in height, moved rapidly upstream for about 200 yd. and broke on the north bank of the river. The water ebbed and flowed in this way for about an hour, no wave being so great as the first; but, at 11 a.m., a wave higher than any of the others, came up the river and broke with so much force on the low ground on the north side that it ran over the bank for about 30 ft. At the same time, the river Tarff (1,305 miles), that flows from the south into the west end of Loch Ness, was agitated in the same manner.

42. It may be well here to summarise the phenomena of the seismic seiches, as observed in Great Britain. Though the measurements are only approximate, it would seem that : (i) the oscillations occurred in the north-south, rather than in the east-west, direction; (ii) the water rose and fell from about 4½ in. to 1 foot in pools to 2 ft. 4 in. in Loch Lomond with reference to the former level; (iii) the period of the seiches varied from about 15 sec. in pools to about 10 min. in Loch Lomond; and (iv) the duration of the movement ranged from 2 or 4 min. in pools to 1½ hr. in Loch Lomond*.

43. *Seiches in Germany and Scandinavia.*—At Hamburg (1,360 miles), the water in the canal that passes through the town was agitated. Several gentle whirlpools were formed, and then the water rose more and more impetuously, throwing up mud from the bottom. At Lubeck (1,400 miles), between 11 a.m. and noon, the waters of the river Trave rose suddenly 4 or 5 ft., snapping the cable of a ship and causing great damage to other vessels. The rivers Eider, Elbe, Owe and Weser were strongly disturbed at various places. The river Stohr at Itzehoe rose and fell so much that a large float of timber was thrown up several feet on the bank. Waters were disturbed in the province of Holstein at Brandstadt, Emshorn, Gluckstadt, Kellinghausen, Meldorf and Steinburgh Fort (about 1,360 miles); and, in the province of Brandenburg, in the lakes of Libbese, Muhlgast, Netze and Roddelin. Farther to the east, in the basin of the Danube, the lakes of Walchen (1,195 miles) and Salzburg (1,275 miles), were agitated.

Seismic seiches were traced to the greatest distances from the origin in Norway and Sweden, in which many rivers and lakes were

*Bevis, **11**, pp. 280-304; *Gent. Mag.,* **17**, vol. 25, pp. 534, 541-542, 590; vol. 26, p. 8; *Roy. Soc.,* **37**, pp. 360-361 ; 384; **39**, pp. 551-552, 642-644.

disturbed, especially in the Swedish province of Kopparberg, formerly known as Dalecarlia. Lake Wener is about 1,750 miles from Lisbon, and even beyond this, the river Dal (1,820 miles) overflowed into the adjacent fields, afterwards, with the same rapidity, retiring within its bed.

There can be little doubt that seiches might have been observed at still greater distances. Extraordinary movements were noticed in Lake Ontario on Nov. 1, but, as similar movements also occurred there during October, we cannot feel sure that they had any connexion with the Lisbon earthquake*.

44. *Swinging of Chandeliers.*—In many of the continental churches more than 1,000 miles from the origin, chandeliers were observed to vibrate or swing. In Italy, at Lodi (1,055 miles), the baldacchino above the greater altar and the lamps in the presbytery moved; at Milan (1,050 miles), the lamps in the churches oscillated at about 11 a.m. In Holland, at Rotterdam (1,125 miles), the chandeliers that in one church hung from long iron rods, made several vibrations; at the Hague (1,140 miles), candles hanging from the ceiling of a shop vibrated; at Amsterdam (1,160 miles), chandeliers in several churches shook. In Germany, at Hamburg (1,360 miles), the branched candlesticks hanging from the roof of one of the churches vibrated and the font-cover suspended from the roof of another was moved; at Rendsburg (1,390 miles), three large chandeliers suspended from the roof of a church vibrated greatly, while a smaller one over the font was not so much affected. Chandeliers also vibrated in several churches in Holstein—at Brandstadt, Emshorn, Kellinghausen and Meldorf (about 1,360 miles)†.

45. *Distribution of Seismic Seiches.* — Thus, seismic seiches were observed in France at distances of 610 to 930 miles from Lisbon, in Italy of 1,020 to 1,045, in Switzerland of 970 to 1,090, in Holland of 1,125 to 1,160, in Great Britain of 850 to 1,305, in Germany of 1,195 to 1,400, and in Scandinavia up to 1,820, miles. There is no satisfactory evidence that seiches were observed in either Portugal or Spain, though the disturbances at Valencia (475 miles) may have been seiches. The nearest place to the origin at which they were certainly observed is Bordeaux (610 miles), and the most distant from it the river Dal (1,820 miles). If we may assume that seiches were formed equally in all directions from the origin, there would thus be a central area containing 1¼ million sq. miles practically free from seiches, surrounded by a zone containing 9½ million sq. miles, in the land-area of which they were frequently and distinctly observed.

*Bertrand, **10**, p. 108; Bevis, **11**, pp. 307, 308, 311, 325; *Gent. Mag.,* **17**, vol. 25, p. 589; *Roy. Soc.,* **39**, p. 552.
†Baratta, **9**, p. 243; Bertrand, **10**, p. 115; Bevis, **11**, pp. 307-310; Perrey, **35**, p. 46; *Roy. Soc.,* **39**, p. 552.

XI. Seismic Seawaves

46. It seems clear that the seawaves so widely observed started at or about the time of the first great earthquake. Two independent observers at Lisbon relate that the second earthquake (that of about 10.0 a.m.) occurred and immediately the waves were seen advancing up the river. Now, if the seawaves had been formed with this earthquake, they must, to reach Lisbon so soon, have originated in or near the Tagus estuary, and waves raised within an area so small could not have spread over the ocean to Britain and the West Indies. They must have been connected with a more distant submarine focus that was in action some time before the second great earthquake.

47. *Seawaves on the coast of Portugal.*—The first movement at Lisbon was a retreat of the sea, the bar being laid bare over its whole course. Then, a great wave came in, foaming and roaring, and rushed with impetuosity more than half a mile over the shore, invading the streets and gardens in the lower part of the city. Its height was variously estimated, 50 ft. at Belem Castle according to one observer, about 16 ft. and more than 20 ft. according to others. Bridges were broken down by it, walls overturned, piles of great size were torn up and carried over the shore. Many people were swept away and drowned at Cascaes, Setuval and Algarves. Several large ships that lay high and dry were floated off and carried down the river. The ships were seen tossing about as in a violent storm, some had broken their cables and others were overturned, and the river Tagus was soon converted into a forest of entangled masts. The water rose and fell three times about 16 ft. and by 2 p.m. returned to its normal course.

At Oporto, the river Douro rose 5 to 6 ft. in a minute or two and then fell; the oscillations continuing about 4 hr[*].

48. *Seawaves on the coasts of Spain and North Africa.*—The seawaves were observed at various ports on the southwest coast of Spain, as far east as Gibraltar. About half an hour after the earthquake, at Ayamonte, near the mouth of the Guadiana, the sea and rivers overflowed their banks with great violence and flooded all the adjoining coast. The sea also broke in at San Lucar, at the mouth of the Guadalquiver, and did much damage. At Cadiz, the waves were especially prominent. At 11.10 a.m., the first wave, said to have been 60 ft. in height, tore away portions of the town wall, 8 or 10 tons in weight, and carried them to a distance of 40 or 50 yd. Other large waves followed at 11.30 and 11.50 a.m., 0.30, 1.10 and 1.50 p.m., that is, at intervals of 20 or 40 min. They continued, gradually decreasing in size, until the evening. The

---

[*]Anon, **1**, p. 19; Bevis, **11**, pp. 316-317; Davy, **13**, pp. 25-27, 122; *Gent. Mag.,* **17**, vol. 25, pp. 560-561, 563; Lyell, **19**, p. 147; Pereira, **24**, pp. 6-7.

lower part of the town was inundated to the depth of 3 or 4 ft., and a narrow neck of land from the town to the island of Leon was washed away. Farther east, a great part of the town of Algaraist, at the mouth of the Straits, was overflowed by seawaves, while, at Gibraltar, the sea rose 6 ft. every quarter of an hour, and fell so low that small vessels and boats near the shore were left aground, as well as a number of small fishes. The waves lasted until the next morning, gradually decreasing in height after 2 p.m.

49. On the opposite coast, at Ceuta, the phenomena were the same as at Gibraltar, except that the sea rose to a height of 7 ft. At Tangier, the first wave is said to have been 50 ft. in height, and to have flowed $1\frac{1}{2}$ miles inland. The sea came in 18 times, though continually decreasing in the height of the waves, until 6 p.m. At Azila, the sea rose suddenly and with great impetuosity at 10 a.m. At Salle, the sea flowed into the heart of the city, leaving a great quantity of sand and fishes in the street. Two ferry-boats on the river were upset and all the passengers drowned. At Saffé, the sea flowed a great distance into the town*.

50. *Seawaves in Madeira.*—At Funchal, on the south side of the island, the earthquake was felt at 9.38 a.m. At 11.45 a.m., the sea, though quite calm, retired some paces. It then rose with a great swell and, suddenly advancing, overflowed the shore and entered the city. The height of the wave was estimated to be $18\frac{1}{2}$ ft. above the level of the water at the time. After fluctuating four or five times, it gradually subsided. On the north side of the island, the swell was much greater and lasted longer than at Funchal. At first, the sea retired more than 100 paces, and then suddenly overflowed the shore, breaking down the walls of store-houses, and carrying away their contents. Great quantities of fishes were left on shore and in the streets of the village of Machico†.

51. *Seawaves on the coasts of the British Isles.*—The first seawaves reached the coasts of Ireland and Cornwall shortly after 2 p.m. At Kinsale, near Cork, a large mass of water suddenly poured into the harbour between 2 and 3 p.m. and with such force that it broke the cables of two vessels, each moored with two anchors. The bottom of the harbour was much altered, the mud being washed away from some places and deposited in others. The rise of the water at one quay was measured $5\frac{1}{2}$ ft. The movements continued until 10 p.m., according to one account until 3 a.m. the next day.

At Swansea, a large head of water rushed up the river at $6\frac{3}{4}$ p.m., and floated two vessels, broke their stern-moorings and drifted

*Bevis, **11**, pp. 319-328; *Gent. Mag.*, **17**, vol. 25, pp. 562-564, 587; vol. 26, p. 7; Lyell, **19**, p. 150; Perrey, **30**, pp. 312-313; **33**, pp. 471-472.

†Bevis, **11**, pp. 328-331.

them across the river. The water fell almost as suddenly as it had risen, and in 10 min. returned to its normal level.

On the north coast of Cornwall, the waves reached Hayle at about 4 p.m., and continued for 1½ hr., the greatest rise (of about 7 ft.) being about the middle of that time. At St. Ives, the sea rose between 8 and 9 ft. in the north channel and floated two large vessels that before were dry. On the south coast, at Mount's Bay, a little after 2 p.m., the sea advanced suddenly and rose for 10 min., after which the water fell for 10 min. until it was 6 ft. below the point first reached, and then rose and fell between 5 and 6 ft. always in the same time for about 2 hr., after which the range of movement gradually decreased until, in 5½ hr. from the first rise, the disturbance of the water ceased. At Penzance, the water first retired at 2.45 p.m. and then returned, the greatest rise (of 8 ft.) occurring about 3 p.m. At Newlyn Pier, the water advanced as a high-crested wave, and, after a few advances and retreats (the greatest rise being at least 10 ft.), the sea gradually, in about 5½ hr., became quiet. The first disturbance of the sea at Plymouth occurred at about 3.40 p.m. At 4 p.m., an extraordinary bore advanced up the harbour and drove ships from their moorings and broke some of the hawsers. In the adjoining Stonehouse Lake, the bore drove everything before it, tearing up the mud, sand and banks, and broke a large cable by which the ferryboat was drawn across the lake. At Creston Ferry, near Plymouth, the tide retreated at 4 p.m., leaving two ferryboats stranded in the mud, that before were in 4 or 5 ft. of water. In less than 8 min., the tide returned and refloated the boats in 6 ft. of water. The sea fell and rose, though to a less extent, for nearly half an hour.

It is possible that the seawaves were also observed at three places on or near the east coast of England; but, as the time is not recorded, it is doubtful whether the movements were those of seawaves or of seiches. At Hunstanton, the sea suddenly advanced, and at Hull and Gainsborough, the water of the harbour rose 5 or 6 ft., and fell again in a minute or two[*].

52. *Seawaves on the coast of Holland.*—At Alphen, on the Rhine between Leyden and Woerden, the waters were agitated in the afternoon so violently that buoys were broken from their chains, large vessels snapped their cables, and others lying dry on land were floated. Phenomena similar to these were observed at Boshoop, Rotterdam, Utrecht and Woubrogge[†].

53. *Seawaves in the West Indies.*—The seawaves swept across the Atlantic and were observed in several of the West Indian Islands,

　　*Bevis, 11, pp. 283-303; *Gent. Mag.,* 17, vol. 25, pp. 590-591; *Roy. Soc.,* 37, pp. 376-377.
　　†Bevis, 11, pp. 309-310.

where the usual rise of the tide is little more than 2 ft. At Antigua (3,540 miles), they were first noticed at 7.38 p.m., Lisbon time. The sea rose 12 ft. several times, and every 5 min. afterwards until 10 p.m., when it rose 5 ft. without any violent disturbance on the surface of the water. At St. Martin (3,540 miles), the sea retired so far that a sloop, riding at anchor in 15 ft. water, was laid dry on her broadside. In the island of Saba (3,545 miles), the sea rose 21 ft. At Martinique (3,545 miles) and most of the French islands, the sea overflowed the low land, returning quickly to its former limit. At Barbadoes (3,585 miles), at 5.14 p.m., Lisbon time, the sea flowed over the wharves and streets, and continued ebbing and flowing for 8 hr*.

54. *Velocity of the Seawaves.*—Taking the epicentre to be in lat. 39° N., long. 11° W., Mr. D. Milne has calculated the velocities of the seawaves along nine paths, namely, 185 ft. per sec. to Plymouth, 238 to Kinsale and Mount's Bay, 317 to Cadiz, 326 to Funchal, 440 to Ayamonte, 484 to Lisbon, 528 to Antigua, and 642 ft. per sec. to Barbadoes. Figures somewhat similar have been obtained for the Arica earthquake of 1868, ranging from 479 ft. per sec. (to Valdivia) to 746 ft. per sec. (to Honolulu), and for the Iquique earthquake of 1887 from 231 ft. per sec. (to Callao) to 579 ft. per sec. (to Kahuliu in the Hawaiian Islands)†.

XII. After-Shocks

55. On Nov. 1 and the three following days, many shocks were felt in Lisbon, and, for a whole year, few days passed without a shock. According to A. Pereira, in addition to the three strong earthquakes on Nov. 8 and Dec. 11 and 23, about 250 slighter shocks were noticed within the first six months. Of these, few but those that were strong enough to cause some alarm are now known to us. These are briefly described in the following list, founded on the catalogues of Mallet and Perrey and on the accounts of various contemporary writers. They were all felt mainly in Lisbon.

1755

Nov. 8, 5.30 a.m., a shock of short duration, strong enough to throw down some houses still standing in Lisbon.

Nov. 16, fresh shocks, during which the sea rose.

Nov. 18, shocks equal in strength to that of Nov. 8.

Dec. 9, the most violent shock in Lisbon since Nov. 1.

Dec. 11, several shocks in Lisbon, one at about 4¾ a.m. being the greatest since Nov. 1, throwing down many shattered buildings.

---

*Bevis, **11**, pp. 328-331.

†Milne, **22**, pp. 361-366; J. Milne, *Japan Seis. Soc. Trans.*, vol. 2, 1880, pp. 82, 87.

Dec. 23, 9 a.m., two shocks, of which the second was the stronger. They caused much destruction in the city.

1756

From Jan. 18 to Feb. 3, many slight shocks were felt in Lisbon, of which the strongest occurred on Jan. 20.

Feb. 18, a shock that lasted nearly 3 min.

Mar. 1, the strongest earthquake felt so far this year in Lisbon, followed by many others during March.

Mar. 11, one shock; some houses were thrown down in Lisbon.

Mar. 29, a violent shock; the waters of the Tagus rose considerably.

During April, more than 30 strong shocks were felt in Lisbon, those of Apr. 15, 27 and 30 being the most remarkable.

July 10 and 11, two strong shocks.

Oct. 10, a shock strong enough to cause slight damage.

Oct. 29, a strong shock.

Nov. 1, a shock that, owing to its occurrence on the anniversary of the great earthquake, caused some alarm.

1757

Mar. 1, 17 and 18, rather violent shocks at Lisbon. At Cascaes, houses were thrown down.

About Nov. 20, a violent shock was felt at Lisbon, Alcantara, Viana and Evora, thus disturbing an area of about 60,000 sq. miles.

Dec. 31, 6 a.m., a shock lasting 30 or 32 sec., said to have been the most violent since the great earthquake.

After 1757, the series of after-shocks of the earthquake of 1755 may be regarded as closed. On 1761 Mar. 31, the second principal earthquake occurred. In the interval, shocks were felt at Lisbon in 1758 during Jan. and Feb. and on July 3, in 1759 on Apr. 25, and in 1760 on Jan. 11 and Aug. 31*.

XIII. Lisbon Earthquake of 1761 Mar. 31 and later Earthquakes

56. *Earthquake of 1761 Mar. 31.*—With the exception of the earthquake of 1755, this was probably the strongest of the whole series. Though violent in Lisbon, there was little, if any, loss of life there, a few old houses were shattered or thrown down and the walls of some new ones cracked.

The shock is said to have been felt at Oporto and all along the coast of Portugal, in Spain at Madrid and Aranjuez, in France

---

*Bevis, **11**, pp. 316-317; Davy, **13**, p. 120; Mallet, **20**, pp. 172-176, and *Brit. Ass. Rep.*, 1853, pp. 119-137; Pereira, **24**, pp. 7-8, 13; Perrey, **33**, pp. 473-478.

at Bayonne, Bordeaux and Rousillon, and even so far as Amsterdam, Cork, Funchal and through Madeira, the Azores and the Canary Islands. Little confidence can be placed in reports from such outlying places. Possibly, the epicentre lay some distance to the west of Lisbon, an inference that seems supported by the clearly great extent of the disturbed area (of, say, half a million or a million sq. miles), the comparatively slight intensity of the shock there, and the small number of recorded after-shocks.

The earthquake occurred at o.5 p.m., and, as in that of 1755, it was of great estimated duration—5 min. at Lisbon, 3 min. at Aranjuez and Bayonne, and $2\frac{1}{2}$ min. at Madrid.

57. The effects of the earthquake were manifest far beyond the bounds of the disturbed area, but were much less widely noticed than in 1755. At Fort Augustus, at about 2 p.m., the surface of Loch Ness rose suddenly about 2 ft. and continued to rise and fall for 45 min. According to another account from the same place, the movements began between noon and 1 p.m. and lasted half an hour, the rise in the level being nearly 30 in. In Amsterdam, the chandelier in one church was seen to vibrate at some time between 1 and 2 p.m., that in another moved about a foot from the vertical line through the point of support.

58. At Lisbon, the agitation of the sea was very great, the water rising and falling many feet vertically. Ships at anchor in the river, though riding in some fathoms of water, were left dry at intervals. According to another account, the sea began to fall and rise about $1\frac{1}{4}$ hr. after the earthquake, about 8 ft. vertically; the movements continued until night.

At Penzance, about 5 p.m., the sea rose suddenly about 6 ft. five times within one hour. At the pier of St. Michael's Mount, the sea rose and fell about 4 ft. at the same time. At Newlyn, the sea rose nearly 6 ft. In the Scilly Isles, it rose 4 ft. at this time, the movements continuing for two hours. Along the Irish coasts, the same phenomena were observed. At Kinsale, at about 6 p.m., the sea rose suddenly 2 ft. and retreated rapidly in 4 min., this being repeated, though to a less extent, several times. At Carrick, at 4 p.m., the surface of the river Suir rose 1 ft. in five minutes. At Dungarvan, the sea ebbed and flowed five times between 4 and 9 p.m. At Waterford, the sea advanced 30 ft. along the shore, while at Ross (Co. Wexford), a violent agitation of the river occurred at 7 p.m.

To the south and west, similar movements were observed. At Terceira, in the Azores, the sea rose to a great height and then fell so low that the quays were left dry. At Barbadoes, at about $8\frac{1}{2}$ hours after the earthquake, the sea, then near low water, suddenly retired from the shore and in about 3 min. returned, rising to the height of nearly 4 ft. This flux and reflux continued until 6 a.m. the next day.

59. The number of after-shocks felt in Lisbon must have been small, and this points to a considerable distance between the city and the epicentral area. Several shocks were felt during the next three days, all of them slight but one, a severe shock, on Apr. 3 at 2 a.m.*

60. *Later Earthquakes.*—The remainder of the Lisbon record must be passed over rapidly. Confining ourselves to strong or violent shocks, we have those in the following list, all felt more or less severely in Lisbon :—

1761 Apr. 30.

1763 Oct. 11.

1764 Dec. 26, 11 a.m., an instantaneous vertical shock of great violence. The sea, though very low and quite calm, rose considerably.

1765 May 25.

1768 June 9, several violent shocks.

1772 Apr. 5-6, about midnight, two violent shocks, the second of which was the stronger and lasted 2 min. It was also felt at Cadiz, Sta. Maria, San Lucar-de-Baremeda, and other places.

1772 Apr. 10.

1773 Sep. 24.

1796 Jan. 10, 17 and 27.

1800 Feb. 26, a strong shock, some buildings in Lisbon being injured.

1807 June 6, 4 p.m., a violent shock, followed immediately by a second, lasting 10 or 12 sec.

1816 Feb. 2, 0.40 a.m., a severe shock of duration of 1 min., followed, at 6.45 a.m., by another shock of shorter duration.

1822 July 6, 6.45 a.m., a violent shock, lasting 6 or 7 sec. at Lisbon.

1858 Nov. 11, 7 a.m., a strong shock lasting 48 sec. The damage at Lisbon was slight, but at Setuval (18 miles southeast of Lisbon) many houses were destroyed and some lives were lost.

1915 July 11, an earthquake that Pereira de Sousa assigns to the centre placed by him near the Straits of Gibraltar.

Thus, so far as destructive movements are concerned, the great earthquake of 1755 seems to have relieved the strain in the Lisbon focus for nearly two centuries, and that of 1761 to have performed the same office for some neighbouring portion of the earth's crust.

---

*Mallet, *Brit. Ass. Rep.,* 1853, pp. 140-141; *Phil. Trans.,* vol. 52, 1761, pp. 142-143, 155-156, 418-433.

XIV. Bibliography

1 Anon. " An account of the late dreadful earthquake and fire which destroyed the city of Lisbon, the metropolis of Portugal. In a letter from a Merchant resident there, to his friend in England." (London, 1755, 45 pp.)

2 Anon. " An account of the earthquake at Lisbon, 31st March, 1761." *Phil. Trans.*, vol. 52, pt. i, 1761, pp. 141-142.

3 Anon. " A particular account of the effects of the late earthquakes in Africa." *Gent. Mag.*, vol. 26, 1756, pp. 7-8.

4 Anon. " Further particulars relating to the earthquake at Lisbon." *Gent. Mag.*, vol. 25, 1755, pp. 591-594.

5 Anon. " Further account of the effects of the late earthquake." *Gent. Mag.*, vol. 26, 1756, pp. 67-68.

6 Anon. " New phenomena attending the earthquake at Lisbon." *Gent. Mag.*, vol. 26, 1756, pp. 99-100.

7 Anon. " Rélation historique du tremblement de terre survenu à Lisbonne le premier Novembre 1755. Avec un détail contenant la perte en hommes, eglises, convens, palais, maisons, diamans, meubles, marchandises, etc." (The Hague, 1756, pp. 181-216.)

8 Anon. " A new and faithful account of the earthquake experienced in Lisbon and over Portugal on the 1st of November, 1755, with a few curious remarks and explanations of its causes." (Lisbon, 1756; reprint in the *Comercio de Portugal* for Oct. 31, Nov. 6, 7 and 11, 1886; summary in *Japan Seis. Soc. Trans.*, vol. 12, 1888, pp. 5-13.)

9 Baratta, M. *I Terremoti d'Italia,* 1901, pp. 242-243.

10 Bertrand, E. " Mémoires Historiques et Physiques sur les Tremblemens de Terre, 1757. Troisième Mémoire. Rélation de ce qui a été observé en Suisse le premier de Novembre 1755. Avec un détail de quelques faits, qui y ont du raport et qui se sont passés ailleurs," pp. 103-116.

11 Bevis, J. " The History and Philosophy of Earthquakes, 1757. Phænomena of the great earthquake of November 1, 1755, in various parts of the globe," pp. 280-334.

12 Borlase, W. " Some account of the extraordinary agitation of the waters in Mount's Bay, and other places, on the 31st of March 1761." *Phil. Trans.*, vol. 52, pt. ii, 1762, pp. 418-433.

13 Davy, Rev. C. " Letters, addressed chiefly to a young gentleman, upon subjects of Literature, etc.," vol. 2, 1787, pp. 12-60 (letter from Mr. Braddock to the Rev. Dr. Sandby, Chancellor of the Diocese of Norwich), 114-127 (summary of a pamphlet by Antonio Pereira published in 1756).

14 Fournet, J. " Notes additionelles aux récherches sur les tremblements de terre du Bassin du Rhône." *Lyon Soc. Agric. Ann.,* vol. 8, 1845, pp. 347-370.

15 Fowke, —. " Letter to Mr. Joseph Fowke, from his Brother near Lisbon; dated November 1755. In which is given a very minute and striking Description of the late Earthquake." Dublin, 1755, 8 pp.

16 Gentil, L., and Pereira de Sousa, F. L. " Sur les effets au Maroc du grand tremblement de terre en Portugal (1755)." *Paris Acad. Sci. C.R.,* vol. 157, 1913, pp. 805-808.

17 Gentleman's Magazine, vol. 25, 1755, pp. 534, 535-536, 541-542, 554-564, 587-594; vol. 26, 1756, pp. 7-8, 67-72, 99-100.

18 Heberden, T. " An account of the earthquake felt in the island of Madeira, March 31, 1761." *Phil. Trans.*, vol. 52, 1761, pp. 155-156.

19 Lyell, Sir C. " Principles of Geology," 1st edit., vol. 1, 1830, pp. 438-440; 12th edit., vol. 2, 1875, pp. 147-154.

20 Mallet, R. " Catalogue of recorded earthquakes." *Brit. Ass. Rep.,* 1852, pp. 163-176.

21 Michell, J. " Conjectures concerning the cause and observations upon the phenomena of earthquakes : particularly of that great earthquake of the first of November 1755, which proved so fatal to the city of Lisbon, and whose effects were felt as far as Africa, and more or less throughout all

Europe." *Phil. Trans.*, vol. 51, 1761, pp. 566-634; *Phil. Mag.*, vol. 52, 1818, pp. 186-195, 254-270, 323-340.

22 MILNE, D. ["Times at which the shock of the earthquake of 1st November 1755 reached different places, and the principal phenomena there."] *Edin. New Phil. Journ.*, vol. 31, 1841, pp. 37-40.

23 MOLLOY, —. "An account of the earthquake at Lisbon, 31st March 1761." *Phil. Trans.*, vol. 52, pt. i, 1761, pp. 142-143.

24 PEREIRA, E. J. "The great earthquake of Lisbon." *Japan Seis. Soc. Trans.*, vol. 12, 1888, pp. 5-14.

25 PEREIRA DE SOUSA, F. L. "Sur les effets, en Portugal, du megaséisme du 1er novembre 1755." *Paris Acad. Sci. C.R.*, vol. 158, 1914, pp. 2033-2035.

26 PEREIRA DE SOUSA, F. L. "La raz de marée du grand tremblement de terre de 1755 en Portugal." *Paris Acad. Sci. C.R.*, vol. 152, 1911, pp. 1129-1131.

27 PEREIRA DE SOUSA, F. L. "O terremoto do 1°. de novembro de 1755 em Portugal e um estudo demográfico," 1919, 2 vols., 473 pp. Vol. 1. "Distritos de Faro, Beja e Évora"; vol. 2. "Distritos de Santarem e Portalegre."

28 PERREY, A. "Mémoire sur les tremblements de terre ressentis en France, en Belgique et en Hollande." *Bruxelles Acad. Roy. Mém. Cour.*, vol. 18, 1845, 110 pp.

29 PERREY, A. "Mémoire sur les tremblements de terre ressentis dans le bassin du Rhone." *Lyon Soc. Agric. Ann.*, vol. 8, 1845, pp. 265-346.

30 PERREY, A. "Note sur les tremblements de terre en Algérie et dans l'Afrique septentrionale." *Dijon Acad. Sci. Mém.*, 1845-46, pp. 299-323.

31 PERREY, A. "Sur les tremblements de terre aux Antilles." *Dijon Acad. Sci. Mém.*, 1845-46, pp. 325-392.

32 PERREY, A. "Mémoire sur les tremblements de terre dans le bassin du Danube." *Lyon Soc. Agric. Ann.*, vol. 9, 1846, pp. 333-414.

33 PERREY, A. "Sur les tremblements de terre de la péninsule iberique." *Lyon Soc. Agric. Ann.*, vol. 10, 1847, pp. 461-510.

34 PERREY, A. "Mémoire sur les tremblements de terre dans le bassin du Rhin." *Bruxelles Acad. Roy. Mém. Cour.*, vol. 19, 1847, 113 pp.

35 PERREY, A. "Mémoire sur les tremblements de terre de la péninsule Italique." *Bruxelles Acad. Roy. Mém. Cour.*, vol. 22, 1848, 143 pp.

36 PERREY, A. "Sur les tremblements de terre dans les Iles Britanniques." *Lyon Soc. Agric. Ann.*, vol. 1, 1849, pp. 115-177.

37 ROYAL SOCIETY. "An account of an extraordinary and surprising agitation of the waters, though without any perceptible motion of the earth, observed in various parts of this island, both maritime and inland, on Novem. 1, 1755, chiefly about the time that the more violent motions of both earth and waters so extensively affected many very distant parts of the globe : in several letters transmitted to the Royal Society." (Letters written by S. Adee, —. Allamond, W. Arderon, T. Barber, Rev. W. Borlase, Sir J. Colquhoun, Hon. and Rev. S. Cowper, dean of Durham, —. De Hondt, Rev. J. Harrison, J. Hodgson, J. Huxham, H. Mills, L. Nicola, Visct. Parker, R. Philips, J. Robertson, J. Steplin, Rev. —. Tomlinson, P. C. Webb.) *Phil. Trans.*, vol. 49, 1755 (1756), pp. 351-398.

38 ROYAL SOCIETY. ["Accounts of the earthquake Novem. 1, 1755, in several letters transmitted to the Royal Society."] (Letters written by B. Bewick, Rev. W. Bullock, C. Chambers, Gen. Fowke, T. Heberden, J. Latham, —. Muysson, J. M. Saccheti, —. Stoqueler, A. d'Ulloa, —. de Vautravers, R. Wolfall.) *Phil. Trans.*, vol. 49, 1755 (1756), pp. 398-438.

39 ROYAL SOCIETY. ["Further accounts of the earthquake Novem. 1, 1755."] (Letters written by Capt. Affleck, Rev. H. Holdsworth, J. Pringle, Rev. T. Rutherford.) *Phil. Trans.*, vol. 49, pt. ii, 1756 (1757), pp. 550-552, 643-644, 668-670, 684-686.

40 SHARPE, D. "On the geology of the neighbourhood of Lisbon." *Geol. Soc. Trans.*, vol. 3, 1842, 29-36.

41 VOLGER, G. H. O. "Untersuchungen über des Phänomen der Erdbeben in der Schweiz," vol. 1 (Chronik der Erdbeben in der Schweiz), 1857, pp 153-167.

CHAPTER II

CALABRIA EARTHQUAKES : 1783 Feb. 5—Mar. 27

I. Introduction

58. The shocks that ruined Calabria in the early months of 1783 have long held a prominent place among the great earthquakes of the world. Not by their destructive power alone have they attained this rank, though 181 towns and villages were entirely destroyed and more than thirty thousand people were killed. Nor yet by their varied and striking phenomena, though typical examples of every feature of a great earthquake might be selected from this single province of Italy. The importance of the earthquakes arises from the fact that Calabria, as Lyell says in his well-known chapter, " affords the first example of a region visited, both during and after the convulsions, by men possessing sufficient leisure, zeal and scientific information to enable them to collect and describe with accuracy such physical facts as throw light on geological questions "*.

59. On but few earthquakes, even of modern times, do we possess so many and such valuable reports. (i) The first to traverse the ruined country was F. A. Grimaldi, the secretary of war in the kingdom of Naples. His report, issued in the following year, is a small volume of 87 pages. He gives a list of the more important shocks up to 1783 July 12, five of which exceeded in violence all the others and visited different parts of the province.

(ii) The history of the earthquakes by G. Vivenzio, chief physician in the court of Naples, is the first monograph that we possess on a great earthquake. Much of the two large volumes (containing 569 pages and 21 plates) has no actual concern with the earthquakes, but the detailed accounts of the ruined towns and villages and of the numerous lakes formed by the earthquake are of much value. So also are the tables that fill up the second volume, above all the " Giornale Tremuotico " or list of earthquakes felt at Monteleone by D. Pignataro from 1783 Jan. 1 to 1786 Oct. 1, and Vivenzio's " general index ", in which he describes the condition of every town and village after the earthquakes and gives for

---

*Lyell, **21**, p. 113.

each the population before the earthquakes and the number of persons killed.

(iii) To the Neapolitan Academy of Sciences and Fine Letters belongs the credit for appointing the first scientific commission to investigate a great earthquake. Consisting of five members with several artists, they started early in April 1783 and visited more than 150 ruined towns and villages. In his great report, Sarconi, the director of the commission, described the injury to each place and the number of victims in it, the areas affected by the great earthquakes, the seawaves and after-shocks, and the effects of the earthquake on human beings.

(iv) Besides these national memoirs, we have reports by two well-known foreign men of science. Sir W. Hamilton, British envoy at the Neapolitan court, in a letter to Sir Joseph Banks, describes the ruined places that he visited during a tour of about three weeks in May 1783. He also made many observations on the landslips and on earth-fissures. D. de Dolomieu, the French geologist, spent about two months (Feb.-Mar. 1784) in the central districts. He draws attention specially to the smallness of the areas of ruin, the rapid transitions of intensity within them, the dependence of the intensity of the shock on the nature of the ground, and traced the migrations of the successive foci.

(v) In one other respect, in the careful registration of after-shocks, the students of the Calabrian earthquakes were a century and more in advance of their time. Pignataro's list of those felt by him at Monteleone has already been referred to. It is a work of remarkable value. In addition to this, we have the records kept by A. Gallo at Messina, G. Minasi at Scilla and A. De Leone at Catanzaro.

(vi) All of the above are contemporary records. They were written before the shocks came to an end. To two later students, Prof. G. Mercalli and Prof. M. Baratta, we are indebted for a very careful analysis of all known observations and of the relations of the great earthquakes of 1783 with those that preceded and followed them. Mercalli's monograph on the earthquakes of Calabria (1897) and Baratta's history of Italian earthquakes (1901) are ideal works of their respective kinds and will often be referred to in the present chapter.

11. SEISMIC ZONES OF CALABRIA

60. Within the area of the two Calabrias, which together contain 5,811 sq. miles, there are a number of distinct seismic zones. A somewhat unusual feature of these zones is that several of them may be struck simultaneously or nearly so by a single earthquake such as that of 1905; or several may be struck successively, as in

the earthquake-series of 1783; or, lastly, a single zone may come into action, as in the earthquakes of 1894 or 1907. The boundaries of the zones cannot at present be defined with precision, for the meizoseismal areas of earthquakes apparently originating in one zone are not coincident or concentric, but, rather, overlapping.

FIG. 3.—Seismic zones of the Calabria earthquakes of 1783 (Baratta).

Some idea of the positions of the zones is, however, given by *Figs.* 3 and 10, which represent the meizoseismal areas disturbed by the earthquakes of 1783 and 1905, respectively. Within the small area of the two provinces, which is less than that of Yorkshire, Baratta has determined the existence of eleven seismic zones. Two of these are separated into two distinct zones by Mercalli, who gives the same number of zones in Calabria, as well as three others in Sicily, and four in the adjoining islands.   The following are the zones according to Baratta, with the years of the principal earthquakes occurring in them :—

1. Scilla : 1783.
2. Piano di Calabria or Palmi : 1783, 1894, 1905.
3. Monteleone (including Soriano): 1659, 1783, 1905.
4. Girifalco: 1626, 1659, 1783, 1905.
5. Nicastro : 1638, 1905.
6. Vallo Cosentino (near Cosenza): 1638, 1905.
7. Bisignano : 1638, 1783, 1905.
8. Rossano : 1638, 1836.
9. Cotrone: 1832.
10. Badolato : 1640, 1659.
11. Gerace : 1720, 1784, 1791, 1907.

The meizoseismal areas of earthquakes occurring in zones 1-5 and 11 are shown in *Fig.* 3 and in zones 2-7 in *Fig.* 10.   The three zones 8-10 lie along or near the east coast, outside the districts depicted in *Figs.* 3 and 10.   The most important zones are those which lie along or near the west coast of the peninsula, or, like no. 4, in the centre of the isthmus of Catanzaro*.

III.   Calabria Earthquakes before 1783

61.   According to Mercalli's great catalogue, our knowledge of Calabrian earthquakes begins with the year 1184, when Cosenza was seriously damaged.   During the next four centuries, with the exception of a shock that caused damage to Reggio in 1230, the more important earthquakes were of Sicilian, and especially Messinese, origin.   With the seventeenth century, activity was transferred to the northern part of the province.   In 1609, a ruinous shock occurred at Nicastro (zone 5).   In 1626, from March to October, many earthquakes were felt at and near Girifalco, one of which reduced that town to ruins (zone 4).

During the years 1638-40, a series of earthquakes, inferior in importance only to that of 1783, visited especially the northern districts.   There were three great earthquakes in the series, each connected with a different zone.   The first and strongest occurred on 1638 Mar. 27.   Its meizoseismal area, in which the shock was very disastrous, contained about 425 sq. miles.   Within and near it, 9,571 persons were killed, 6,811 in Calabria citeriore and 2,760 in Calabria ulteriore.   Of these, 1,200 belonged to Nicastro, 796 to Scigliano and 767 to S. Biase.   Mercalli has drawn a map of this earthquake, showing five isoseismal lines.   Though the outer curves are incomplete towards the south and east, it is probable that the disturbed area contained about 84,000 sq. miles.

*Baratta, **13**; Mercalli, **22**, pp. 143-147.

Less than three months later, on June 8, the seat of activity was transferred to the district round Cotrone on the east coast (zone 9), which had suffered but slightly from the first shock. Several places, such as Roccabernarda, Policastro and Terra della Scala, were in great part ruined, with the total loss of 52 lives.

Two years afterwards, on 1640 June 19, a disastrous shock occurred at Badolato (zone 10), resulting in the deaths of 300 persons, and was followed by a ruinous shock three days later with further loss of life.

62. For nearly twenty years, the Calabrian provinces were almost immune from disturbances, until 1659 Nov. 5, when a very disastrous earthquake occurred somewhat to the south in the Monteleone zone. Several places were completely ruined, such as Panaija, Filogasi, Polia, Castelmonardo (now called Filadelfia), Soriano, Vallelonga, Gerocarne, etc. The total number of lives lost was 2,035, 496 of these being at Panaija, 203 at Polia, 193 at Castelmonardo, 161 at Filogasi and 160 at Soriano.

63. Baratta has prepared three maps to illustrate the distribution of seismic activity during the seventeenth, eighteenth and nineteenth centuries. They depend on a scale of nine degrees, the lowest of which corresponds to one very strong shock and a few moderately strong shocks, and the highest to two very disastrous shocks. They show very clearly that, in the seventeenth century, the part of Calabria most frequently visited by disastrous or ruinous earthquakes, was the north in the neighbourhood of Catanzaro, while the district round Reggio was almost immune. During the eighteenth century, the Piano di Calabria held the first place for the number and intensity of its shocks. In the nineteenth century, the province was comparatively tranquil, though important earthquakes occurred in 1832 in the Cotrone zone, in 1835 in the Cosenza zone, in 1836 in the Rossano zone, all in Calabria citeriore, and lastly, in 1894, in the Piano di Calabria zone*.

IV. PREPARATION FOR THE EARTHQUAKES OF 1783

64. Though the first great shock of Feb. 5 occurred without immediate warning, there were slight signs of the coming disturbances for three years and more, both in Calabria and the Messinese district.

In 1779, from June 24 until the middle of July, earthquakes were felt many times in Calabria, two of them strongly. For some months afterwards, the centres of disturbance lay near Messina, that city being shaken on 1779 Dec. 14, 1780 Feb. 13, Mar. 28, Apr. 9 and 10, May 8 and June 10. Towards the close of this series,

---

*Baratta, **6**, pp. 28-261; Mercalli, **22**, pp. 15-83.

3

the centre of activity returned to the Calabrian area. A shock was felt in the south of the province on May 2, and a rather strong shock at Reggio on May 24. In 1781-82, a few shocks were felt in the Piano di Calabria, the scene of the first great earthquake, and on 1782 July 25, nearly the whole province was shaken, from Reggio to Catanzaro. On 1783 Jan. 1, a shock of moderate strength was sensible over southern Calabria. It is the first earthquake recorded by Pignataro at Monteleone, and he adds that, on several nights of the month, other shocks were reported. A slight undulatory shock was felt at S. Sofia (Cosenza) on Jan. 19. Lastly, on the morning of Feb. 5, a few hours before the great earthquake, the sea, though calm near the coast at Bivona and Pizzo, was so disturbed at some distance out that fishermen were obliged to return to harbour. About the same time, on the opposite or Ionian coast, small seawaves were also reported and a slight shock was felt.

65. The series of earthquakes, that began in such strength on Feb. 5, lasted for at least eight years. It consisted of six great or principal earthquakes, all of which occurred within the first two months. Their times of occurrence (in local time)* and central districts are given in the following table :—

Feb.	5, about 0.45 p.m.	Piano di Calabria.
,,	6, 1.15 a.m.	Scilla.
,,	7, 2.5 p.m.	Soriano (Monteleone zone).
,,	7, about 3.45 p.m.	Messina.
Mar.	1, 2.15 a.m.	Polia (Monteleone zone).
,,	27, 7.1 p.m.	Girifalco†.

v. FIRST PRINCIPAL EARTHQUAKE : 1783 FEB. 5

66. Within the limits of our seismic chronicle, that is, for six centuries or more, no disastrous earthquake ever visited the plain of Calabria until shortly after noon on Feb. 5. Then, within two minutes, nearly very town or village within it was reduced to a shapeless heap of ruins. Vivenzio has given two tables that illustrate very clearly the extent of the disaster. In one (vol. 2, pp. xcviii-xcix), he has classified the places under the following graduated headings, the number of places under each being added in brackets : 1. Places entirely destroyed, to be rebuilt on different sites (33); 2. Places entirely destroyed, to be rebuilt on the same sites as before (148); 3. Places in part destroyed and in part ren-

---

*The hours of these earthquakes are usually given in Italian time, which is about 6¼ hours in advance of local time, as follows: Feb. 5, about 19h.; Feb. 6, 7h. 30m.; Feb. 7, 20h. 20m.; Feb. 7, about 22h.; Mar. 1, 8h. 30m.; and Mar 28, 1h. 16m.

†Baratta, 6, pp. 260-261 ; Mercalli, 22, pp. 28-30.

dered uninhabitable (91); 4. Places in part destroyed and in part damaged (44); 5. Places damaged (26); 6. Places in which a few buildings were damaged (4); 7. Places remaining undamaged; etc. Out of 389 places mentioned, 181 were entirely destroyed, 156 were to a great extent destroyed, 49 were damaged more or less seriously, and only 3 escaped entirely unharmed*.

67. The second table (vol. 2, pp. lxxxiv-xcvii) is more detailed. It gives the populations before the earthquake of 381 places in the central area and the numbers of persons killed in 260 of them. It should be remembered that both tables refer to the whole series of earthquakes, for no contemporary writer distinguishes between the effects of the different shocks. The figures in the second table belong, however, almost entirely to the first great earthquake, for, after its occurrence, the survivors forsook their houses, and but few lost their lives in the later earthquakes. Considering that no town in the central area contained so many as six thousand inhabitants, the numbers of deaths in some are unusually great, for example, 3,331 in Bagnara, 2,261 in Polistena, and 2,017 in Casalnuovo. The death-rates in several towns are not often exceeded, even in Italy, as, for example, 76·8 in Terranova, 58·9 in Bagnara, 54·7 in S. Cristina, 50·2 in Oppido, and 49·2 in Polistena.

Vivenzio estimates the total loss of life from the earthquakes alone at 29,451 in Calabria ulteriore (or 6·7 per cent. of the total population) and 5 in Calabria citeriore, but to this number he adds 5,709 who perished from the epidemics that followed. The more recent statistics of A. Grimaldi† increase these figures. He gives the numbers killed in Calabria as 29,515 and in the province of Messina as 630, or altogether 30,145, and of those who died afterwards from the epidemics as 18,876. He estimates that the material damage in Calabria alone amounted to 132,812,500 lire‡.

68. *Isoseismal Lines.* — Mercalli has drawn a series of five isoseismal lines (reproduced in *Fig.* 4), which bound respectively the areas within which the shock was very disastrous, disastrous, ruinous and very strong, strong, and moderate or slight, corresponding to the degrees 10, 9, 7, 5 and 3 of his well-known scale. The innermost curve, bounding the meizoseismal area, is 27 miles

---

*It is interesting to notice that, in the headings quoted above, Vivenzio has drawn up a scale of intensity for destructive earthquakes not unlike that devised by Baratta to represent the distribution of intensity within the meizoseismal area of the Messina earthquake of 1908 ("La Catastrofe Sismica Calabro-Messinese, 28 dicembre, 1908," 1910, pp. 214-215).

†La cassa sacra ovvero la soppressione delle manimorte in Calabria nel secolo xviii.," Naples, 1863, quoted by G. Mercalli, *Mem. della Soc. ital. delle Scienze,* vol. 11, 1897, pp. 111-112.

‡Baratta, **6**, pp. 283-288; Mercalli, **22**, pp. 111-112.

long, 16 miles wide, and contains about 350 sq. miles, that is about the area of the county of Huntingdon. Within it, nearly every place was reduced to a mass of ruins in which streets and the sites of buildings could no longer be recognised, while, in very many of them, one-third or more of the inhabitants were killed. In

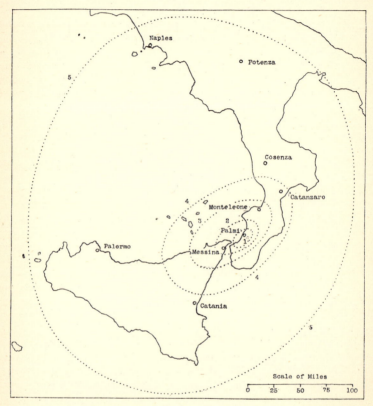

Fig. 4.—Isoseismal lines of the first principal Calabria earthquake, Feb. 5 (Mercalli).

the next, or disastrous, area, the destruction was less complete, but practically all houses were rendered uninhabitable. Its dimensions are 50 miles long and 28 miles wide, and its area about 1,100 sq. miles. The outermost curve, that bounds the disturbed area, includes all Sicily and passes a few miles to the north of Naples. It is about 350 miles long and 320 miles wide, and contains about 88,000 sq. miles. The most important features of these curves are the rapidity with which the intensity decreases from the centre outwards, and the small size of the disturbed area, considering the extreme intensity within the meizoseismal area. On the southeast side, the curves 1 and 2 are separated by only 2·1 miles, the curves 2 and 3 by 3·2 miles.

69. To a great extent, this rapid decline of intensity was due to the nature of the ground. All the towns with high death-rates, as Mercalli remarks, lie on the tertiary and quaternary formations of the Calabrian plain, loose materials superposed on crystalline rocks. Several of the early observers, such as Hamilton and Dolomieu, were struck with the rapid alternations from complete destruction on the plain to only partial ruin on the neighbouring hills. Dolomieu notices, for instance, how Polistena was levelled with the ground on Feb. 5, while S. Giorgio, only 6 miles distant, suffered little on the same day, though later, on Feb. 7 and Mar. 27, it was badly damaged. At Bagnara, again, the death-rate was 58·9 per cent. Only a few miles away, among the hills to the south of the plain, the death-rate fell to 0·3 at Campo (6·8 miles from Bagnara), 2·3 at S. Roberto (7·5 miles) and 1·0 at Rosali (8·3 miles). At Nicotera and Tropea, which are only 8 and 16 miles to the north of the meizoseismal area, the death-rate did not exceed 0·5 per cent.

Yet, taking every account of this important factor, it seems clear, when we think of the high intensity of the shock in the central district and of the small disturbed area, that the intensity of the shock did decrease at an unusually rapid rate, leading to the inference that the focus of the earthquake was situated at a comparatively small depth*.

70. *Nature of the Shock.*—From the large number of accounts given by contemporary writers, a few are here selected. Of the places mentioned, Terranova lies within the meizoseismal area, Scilla near its southern boundary, Monteleone a short distance to the north and Reggio to the south, both within the second isoseismal, and Catanzaro to the northeast within the third.

At Terranova, the shock began with a trembling, and this was followed by an undulatory motion and then by violent upward blows. The vertical component was so marked that masses of the brick floors and foundations of houses were thrown up and overturned. At Scilla, the succession of movements was the same, first a trembling, then an undulatory motion, ending with a vertical and vorticose movement.

At Monteleone, according to Pignataro, the earthquake began with a hollow sound like thunder that very soon was accompanied

---

*Mercalli, **22**, pp. 91-93.

by a slight tremor, to which were added horizontal undulations with strong whirling movements, then a pause, followed by a return of the same vibrations of great vehemence, the whole ending, as it had begun, with a slight tremor. At Reggio, the earthquake consisted of two distinct shocks, the first a strong movement, the second with a more pronounced vertical component and confused vorticose movements that brought down the houses in ruin. At Catanzaro, according to De Leone, the early movements were horizontal from west and southwest, then suddenly a vertical blow, followed by movements in the first direction with interposed trepidations.

All observers agree that the first great earthquake lasted at least 2 min. and that the movements varied much in nature and direction, and that it was to these rapid changes and the long duration of the shock, quite as much as to its violence, that the completeness of the ruin must be ascribed*.

71. *Effects of the Shock on the Ground.*—The meizoseismal area is practically coterminous with the Plain of Calabria. Surrounded by mountain-ranges to the north, east and south, the plain slopes gently towards the west coast, where it ends in a low beach, the Gulf of Palmi. The mountains are very steep, and from them flow down streams which have cut the soil of the plain into deep ravines, sometimes 600 ft. in depth, with steep, almost vertical, sides.

Along nearly the whole chain to the east, the soil slipped over its granite foundation, leaving an almost continuous fissure 9 or 10 miles in length. Close to every ravine and hollow, the soil of the plain was seamed with large parallel cracks, which Hamilton correctly attributed to " the earth rocking with violence from side to side, and having a support on one side only." Even as far as Messina, there were cracks in the earth of the quay, a part of which had sunk more than a foot below the level of the sea.

The soil of the plain, indeed, shared equally with the works of man in the havoc wrought by the earthquake. In many places, large masses of the ground slipped into the ravines often without disturbance of their surface. At Terranova, where the ravine was not less than 500 ft. deep and three-quarters of a mile in width, two huge portions of the earth, on which some hundreds of houses stood, were detached into the ravine and nearly across it, about half a mile from their old position. Some of the inhabitants, Hamilton remarks, were nevertheless dug out alive and a few of them unhurt. Sometimes, as near Oppido, Hamilton " met with a detached piece of the surface of the plain (of many acres in extent) with the large oaks and olive-trees, with lupins or corn under them,

*Baratta, **6**, pp. 272-274; Mercalli, **22**, pp. 89-91.

growing as well, and in as good order at the bottom of the ravine, as their companions, from whom they were separated, do on their native soil on the plain, at least 500 feet higher and at the distance of about three-quarters of a mile ''.

72. In many places, the fall of land from either or both banks formed dams across the rivers below and ponded them back into great lakes. On a smaller scale, such lakes or pools were often caused by the fall of ruined houses. In the plain of Calabria, no less than 215 such lakes are described by Vivenzio, some of the larger being 2 miles long and 1 mile wide*.

73. *Rotation of Bodies.*—In nearly all parts of Calabria, the shock ended with a whirling or vorticose movement, due to rapid changes in the direction of motion. It was only natural, therefore, that the rotation of bodies observed in some Calabrian towns should be regarded as effects of vorti-

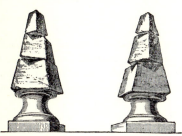

FIG. 5.—Rotation of obelisks at the Convent of San Bruno (Lyell).

cose shocks. One of these, described by the Neapolitan Commission, has become widely known and adopted as the typical example of such rotation from its reproduction in Lyell's *Principles of Geology.* In two obelisks (*Fig.* 5) in the convent of S. Bruno in Stefano del Bosco, the pedestals remained unmoved during the earthquake, but the two upper stones were twisted without falling. It will be noticed that the direction of rotation was different in the two obelisks†. Lyell's reproduction of the illustration had one interesting result, in that it led Mallet to give a simple mechanical explanation of the rotation and thus to mature his views on the nature of earthquake-motion that he has described in his memoir on the dynamics of earthquakes‡.

VI. SECOND PRINCIPAL EARTHQUAKE: 1783 FEB. 6

74. The second great earthquake occurred more than twelve hours after the first, at 1.15 a.m. on Feb. 6. It affected an area so

---

*Hamilton, **18**, pp. 189-190; Vivenzio, **33**, vol. 1, pp. 370-421, vol. 2, pp. ii-v, and plates xiv-xix.

†An early, if not the earliest known, example of this rotation occurred in London during the earthquake of 1750 Mar. 19. At Bloomsbury, Mr. Michael Russell, F.R.S., had two china figures placed on a cabinet with their faces towards the west. After the earthquake, they were both found to be facing northeast (*Phil. Trans.,* vol. 46, 1752, p. 632).

‡Lyell, **21**, p. 119; Mallet, *Irish Ac. Trans.,* vol. 21, 1848, pp. 51-105.

nearly the same as that of the first that no attempt has been made to trace its isoseismal lines. No new districts were damaged, but, at several places, such as Reggio and Messina, the ruins caused by the first were increased. At Messina, according to Torreani, the second earthquake was greater in the impetuosity and vigour of its shocks, and this observation lends support to Baratta's conclusion that the epicentral area of the second earthquake lay between Scilla and the Torre del Faro but nearer the latter and certainly beneath the sea.

Little more is known about this second earthquake. It was, however, remarkable for one result, rare even in the annals of earthquakes, namely, the inrush of a destructive seawave caused by a landslip along the coast. During the first earthquake, great masses of earth and stones had slipped down the rocky slopes near Scilla. Less than two hours after it, there was a further fall, of part of the mountain Monasina, and this led the people of Scilla to take refuge in boats or in tents along the coast.

75. About half an hour after the second earthquake, a great landslip occurred from M. Paci to the west of Scilla, along more than $1\frac{1}{4}$ miles of the coast. Falling into the sea for a hundred yards or more, the shattered mass formed three new points and covered an area of more than 10 acres.

With the rush of the landslip, the sea retired. A few seconds later, it returned, swept over the whole encampment on the shore, and reached the height of the first floors of houses at Scilla, sweeping inland for more than 200 yards. It then withdrew, carrying away the ruins of houses and 1,504 persons from the boats and tents. A second and third time, the wave flowed in, afterwards gradually lessening in force. The extent of coast covered by the waves was small. They were hardly sensible at Bagnara, $5\frac{3}{4}$ miles east of Scilla, and at Reggio no abnormal waves were noticed. At Torre del Faro, the northern point of Sicily, the sea, however, invaded the coast and 20 persons, who were sheltering in small boats, were drowned. According to Sarconi, the wave was sensible at Messina, but caused no damage there. At Catania, the water was disturbed, though without any flooding of the coast*.

VII. THIRD PRINCIPAL EARTHQUAKE : 1783 FEB. 7, 2.5 P.M.

76. On Feb. 7, two violent earthquakes occurred, one at about 2.5 p.m. and the other at about 3.45 p.m. By all the writers of the time, they were regarded as one and the same earthquake, though Pignataro noticed the discrepancy in the times, while Dolomieu remarked that the earthquake of Feb. 7 " was felt the

---

*Baratta, **6**, pp. 275-276; Mercalli, **22**, pp. 94-99.

most at Messina and Soriano, places very distant from each other [they are, in fact, 47 miles apart]; whilst it was mostly less violent in all the intermediate country ". It was reserved for Mercalli, in 1897, to point out that there were in reality two great earthquakes on this day, the earlier, a disastrous shock, with its centre near Soriano, the later, a ruinous shock, with its centre near Reggio and Messina. The isoseismal lines of both earthquakes, as drawn by Mercalli, are shown in *Fig. 6.*

FIG. 6.—Isoseismal lines of the third and fourth principal Calabria earthquakes, Feb. 7 (Mercalli).

In this map, the broken-lines 1-4 represent isoseismals of intensities 9, 8, 7, and 5 of the Mercalli scale, that is, corresponding to shocks of disastrous, ruinous, very strong and rather strong intensities. The epicentre of the earthquake was in the upper valley of the Marepotamo (a tributary of the Mesima) close to Soriano. It caused great damage within a very small district about 13 miles long and 70 sq. miles in area, that had suffered little from the earthquakes of Feb. 5 and 6. The " very strong " area extends to the north as far as, and beyond, Catanzaro, where, according to De Leone, the shock was equal to that of the first principal earthquake in duration and strength.

Sarconi relates that, with this earthquake, there occurred great convulsions of the ground in the hills near Soriano. Many lands were dismantled and sank down. The waters of the river Caridi, he says, disappeared for three days and then returned to follow a new course.

The shock was one of unusual length. At Monteleone, according to Pignataro, it lasted 2½ min. It began with a noise like that of a distant cannonade. Then came a violent shock, and, though there were two momentary pauses near the middle, it recovered and maintained throughout the same intensity*'

---

*Baratta, **6**, p. 276; Mercalli, **22**, pp. 99-101.

VIII. FOURTH PRINCIPAL EARTHQUAKE: 1783 FEB. 7, ABOUT 3.45 P.M.

77. For this earthquake, only two isoseismal lines are traced by Mercalli, represented by the dotted lines in *Fig.* 6. Along and within the inner line, no. 3, the shock was very strong (intensity 7 of the Mercalli scale), the outer line bounds the area within which the shock was strong (intensity 6). The area within the inner curve is 44 miles long, 20 miles wide and contains 690 sq. miles.

FIG. 7.—Isoseismal lines of the fifth principal Calabria earthquake, Mar. 1 (Mercalli).

The shock was felt with greater force at Messina and Reggio. At Messina, according to A. Gallo, until midnight on Feb. 6, not a quarter of an hour passed without shocks. On Feb. 7, the shocks became less frequent, until, at 3.45 p.m., "there burst out at once the terrible noise and gave the last shake to the already destroyed Messina." In this earthquake, more than in the preceding shocks, there was a combination of all the movements — undulatory, sussultory and vorticose—so that people were not able to stand upright and very many buildings fell.

How far to the north of the straits the shock would have possessed destructive power is unknown, for but few houses were left standing in the Plain of Calabria. It seems probable, however, that the epicentre was farther to the south than that of the earthquake of Feb. 5, and not far from the Straits of Messina*

IX. FIFTH PRINCIPAL EARTHQUAKE: 1783 MAR. 1

78. The fifth principal earthquake, of ruinous intensity (degree 8 of the Mercalli scale), occurred at 2.15 a.m. on Mar. 1. Three isoseismal lines, corresponding to ruinous, very strong and strong shocks (intensities 8, 7 and 6 of the Mercalli scale), are shown in *Fig.* 7. The epicentre of this earthquake lay farther to the north than in any of the preceding great shocks.

The innermost isoseismal was unusually small, being only 14 miles long, 9 miles wide, and 48 sq. miles in area. Its centre was

*Baratta, **6**, p. 276; Mercalli, **22**, pp. 101-102.

in the valley of the Angitola, close to Polia, where most of the houses were destroyed. The shock also caused considerable damage at Poliolo, Filadelfia, Vallelonga, Monteleone, Mileto and other places. At Catanzaro, which lies just within the third isoseismal, the shock, according to De Leone " surpassed all the preceding in duration and force ".

At Monteleone, which lies on the innermost isoseismal, the shock, according to Pignataro, lasted about 1 m. 35 sec. It was at first undulatory, and towards the end was transformed, with a hardly sensible pause, into a vorticose movement of greater force than the other*.

x. Sixth Principal Earthquake : 1783 Mar. 27

79. The sixth and last of the principal earthquakes occurred at about 7 p.m. on Mar. 27. With the exception of the first great earthquake of Feb. 5, it was the strongest of the series, though some of the early investigators (Grimaldi, Sarconi and Dolomieu) regarded it as the most violent of all. The number of persons killed by this earthquake, according to Grimaldi, was 1,141, of whom 331 died at Borgia, 184 at Girifalco and 75 at Maida. The total no doubt would have been much higher if the inhabitants had not abandoned their houses and lived in tents and other shelters.

During the earthquakes of Feb. 5-7, no serious damage occurred to the north of the isthmus of Catanzaro, nor was there any loss of life. On Mar. 27, however, the epicentre lay within the isthmus. The three towns already referred to were completely destroyed, while, in many other towns and villages (such as S. Floro, Filadelfia, Cortale, etc.), few houses were left fit to live in. The very disastrous area, enclosed within the innermost isoseismal (*Fig.* 8) was only 17 miles long, nearly 7 miles wide, and contained about 90 sq. miles ; while the areas included within the disastrous and ruinous isoseismals did not exceed 400 and 2,000 sq. miles, respectively. The area included within the sixth isoseismal, in which the shock was moderate or slight, covered about 86,000 sq. miles, or approximately the same as that for the first great earthquake. Both Mercalli and Baratta, however, as well as Sarconi among the earlier writers, state that the earthquake of Mar. 27 disturbed an area notably greater than that of Feb. 5, for, while it was sensible all over Sicily, it was felt, towards the north, in the Basilicata and in the provinces of Otranto, Bari and Terra di Lavoro.

At Monteleone, according to Pignataro, the shock lasted for 2 min. and consisted of undulatory, vertical and vorticose movements combined. Near the river Amato, as Grimaldi states, the

---

*Baratta, **6**, pp. 276-277 ; Mercalli, **22**, pp. 102-103.

earth was shaken for two minutes with a movement so violent that
people were unable to keep on their feet. At Catanzaro, according to De Leone, the vertical blows were so violent that people were
jerked from the ground*.

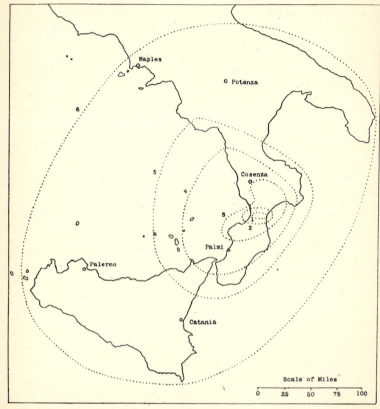

FIG. 8.—Isoseismal lines of the sixth principal Calabria earthquake,
Mar. 27 (Mercalli).

XI.   MIGRATION OF THE FOCI

80.   The most remarkable feature of the Calabrian earthquakes
of 1783 is neither their intensity nor their number, but the rapid
and extensive journeys of the seat of activity. Dolomieu especially, among the early writers, traces the shifting of the foci from
the Calabrian plain to Scilla, then northwards to Soriano, and finally
to Girifalco.

---

*Baratta, **6**, pp. 277-278; Ippolito, **20**, pp. 209-216; Mercalli, **22**, pp. 103-105.

Taking the centres of the innermost isoseismals drawn by Mercalli as representing the positions of the epicentres, the origin of the first shock was about 3 miles south of Palmi beneath the Plain of Calabria. In little more than twelve hours, it moved to a point between Scilla and the Torre del Faro, about 10 miles to the southwest. A little more than a day and a half intervened before the third principal shock occurred (on Feb. 7) with its centre close to Soriano, about 35 miles northeast of the Scilla centre. In less than two hours, the focus retraced its steps by about 36 miles to the southwest, to the neighbourhood of Messina. More than 21 days elapsed before the fifth principal earthquake occurred on Mar. 1, with its centre near Polia and about 46 miles northeast of the Messina focus. Lastly, after the lapse of nearly 27 days, the focus moved about 12 miles still farther to the northeast, close to Girifalco. The distance between the Messina and Girifalco centres is thus about 58 miles.

XII. After-Shocks

81. One of the most valuable sections of Vivenzio's report on the earthquakes is the list of after-shocks felt at Monteleone by D. Pignataro, a physician of that city. During nearly four years (1783 to 1786 Oct. 1), he felt 1,186 shocks, and he not only gives the times of occurrence, but assigns to each its intensity according to a rough scale, that is of interest as the earliest known attempt to devise a scale of intensity. He classifies the shocks as slight, moderate, strong and very strong, denoted in his table by the letters F', F'', F''' and F''''. The five most destructive earthquakes (counting the two on Feb. 7 as one) are arranged in a separate class and are indicated in the table by a Maltese cross. The numbers of shocks for each degree are as follows:—

	Slight	Moderate	Strong	Very Strong	Violent	Total
1783	503	235	175	32	5	950
1784	91	34	16	3	––	144
1785	27	17	4	2	—	50
1786	21	17	3	1	—	42
Total	642	303	198	38	5	1,186

Thus, omitting the five principal earthquakes and one slight shock before Feb. 5, we have a total of 1,180 after-shocks. To this number, Mercalli adds 510 shocks recorded by other observers during the same four years, making altogether a total of 1,690 after-shocks.

82. These after-shocks, according to Mercalli, were connected with seven different centres, five of them being those of the Calabrian plain, Soriano, Messina, Polia and Girifalco (the seats of the first and third to sixth principal earthquakes), and the district round

Reggio and the Ionian slope of Aspromonte, in which are seated the origins of the strong shocks of 1783 June 11 and July 20, respectively.   Most of the after-shocks were of slight intensity. For instance, in 26 months from 1783 Oct. to 1785 Nov., Pignataro recorded 280 shocks at Monteleone, of which 179 were slight, 68 moderate, 27 strong and 6 very strong.   During the same interval, Minasi felt 230 shocks at Scilla, but only 28 were common to both places.

83. Among the after-shocks, of which lists are given by Mercalli and Baratta, the following were the most important :—

1783 Apr. 26, 27 and 28, three shocks at Milazzo (20 miles west of Messina), the first of which was almost ruinous and the others caused some damage in that town.

1783 June 11, at Reggio, resulting in damage to buildings in that city.

1783 July 29, a very violent earthquake connected with the Gerace centre, causing damage at Gerace (by which the town was in part destroyed and in part rendered uninhabitable), Reggio and even at Catanzaro.   This earthquake is regarded by Mercalli as the seventh principal earthquake.

1784 Jan. 7, near Roccella, accompanied by a seawave.

1784 Jan. 19, seawaves that caused damage at Fossa and Catona.

1784 Oct. 14, a destructive shock connected with the Gerace centre, and causing further damage to houses at Gerace and Reggio. At Gerace and Canolo, this earthquake was considered to be stronger than that of 1783 Mar. 27.

1785 Feb. 6, at Scilla, where some damage to property was caused.

1789 Feb. 7, two very strong earthquakes at Messina, with damage to houses at Reggio and Monteleone.

1791 Oct. 12, a very disastrous earthquake, with its meizo-seismal area in the Monteleone district and its centre close to Soriano, almost coinciding with that of the third principal earth-quake (1783 Feb. 7).   Either totally or in great part, the shock ruined 39 villages, and 15 persons were killed.   This earthquake was followed by a series of after-shocks that continued frequent until Oct. 24.   It is usually regarded as the last prominent member of the 1783 series of earthquakes*.

84. *Periodicity of After-Shocks.* — It is interesting to notice that, in the first column of his list of after-shocks observed at Monteleone, Pignataro gave not only the dates of the four lunar

---

*Baratta, **6**, pp. 289-292 ; Mercalli, **22**, pp. 110-111 ; Vivenzio, **33**, vol. 2, pp. i-lxxxiii.

phases, but also those of perigee and apogee. He was careful to state, however, that he did not wish to imply that the moon can have any influence on the occurrence of earthquakes. His list was used by Perrey in the studies that led to his third law, that earthquakes are more frequent when the moon is near the meridian than when at a distance of 90° from it. It may also be used to show the existence of the lunar periods of 29·6 and 14·8 days. If, in order to smooth away inequalities, we take 14-day means of successive daily numbers of after-shocks as given by Pignataro, the resulting curve shows a series of maxima, that lie on an average of 29·7 days apart and agree closely with the times of new moon. In the same way, by taking 7-day means of the same numbers, we obtain another series of maxima at an average interval apart of 14·6 days, and agreeing very nearly with the times of new and full moon.

XIII. CALABRIA EARTHQUAKES AFTER 1783

85. After the earthquake of 1791, Calabria had rest from earthquakes for more than forty years, and, for more than a hundred years, no great earthquake disturbed the southern part of the province. Until 1894, all the destructive earthquakes, four in number, occurred near Cosenza or Bisignano. In this section, are given brief accounts of five earthquakes from 1835 to 1887, and somewhat fuller descriptions of the important earthquakes of 1894 Nov. 16, 1905 Sep. 8 and 1907 Oct. 23.

86. *Miscellaneous Earthquakes from 1835 to 1887.*—On 1835 Oct. 12, a disastrous earthquake visited the upper valley of the Crati. Castiglione was levelled with the ground, with the loss of 100 lives, the total number of persons killed in the central district being 126. The isoseismal 9, as drawn by Baratta, is 5·6 miles long from north to south, 3·6 miles wide, and 16 sq. miles in area. Its centre is close to Castiglione and 3·6 miles northeast of Cosenza.

On 1854 Feb. 12, a very violent earthquake occurred in the same district. At Cosenza itself, many houses were shattered or ruined, all were more or less injured, and 41 persons were killed. At Donnici, all the houses were destroyed and 191 persons lost their lives, at Rende 96, and at Castelfranco 68, the total number of deaths from the earthquake being 472. The meizoseismal or disastrous area is elliptical in form, 15 miles long, 9 miles wide, and about 100 sq. miles in area. Its longer axis is directed north-northwest, and its centre lies about midway between Cosenza and Rende or about 2½ miles west-northwest of Cosenza.

On 1869 Nov. 28, a very violent shock was felt at Monteleone, where some poorly built houses were ruined. The centre of the innermost isoseismal lies close to Monteleone.

Nearly a year later, on 1870 Oct. 5, the centre of activity returned to the Cosenza zone. More than 100 houses in Cosenza, and more than 1,600 in the surrounding district, were damaged more or less seriously. The total number of persons killed was 117, of whom 36 belonged to Mangone and 30 to Longobucco. According to Baratta, the centre coincided with the village of Cellara, a short distance to the southeast of Cosenza.

On 1887 Dec. 3, the centre migrated 16 miles northwards to the Bisignano zone. The centre lay close to Bisignano, where most of the houses were seriously injured and many ruined.

Thus, for more than a century, seismic activity in Calabria was confined to the northern part of the province, with the exception of the Monteleone earthquake of 1869, and, it may be added, of a shock of intensity 7 at Gerace on 1886 Apr. 5 and of another of intensity 8 on 1893 Apr. 22, the centre of which lay about $8\frac{1}{2}$ miles southwest of Milazzo*.

87. *Earthquake of 1894 Nov. 16.*—This disastrous earthquake was investigated by Mercalli and by a Government Commission consisting of A. Riccò, E. Camerana, M. Baratta and G. Di Stefano, of whom Riccò contributed the seismological portion of the joint report.

The earthquake was preceded by several shocks, by a weak one on Nov. 1 at Mileto and Pizzoni, by slight but frequent shocks on Nov. 13-15, and by three of greater consequence on Nov. 16 at 6.15 a.m., about noon, and about 6 p.m. The shock at 6.15 a.m. was strong enough to be felt generally at Scilla, Delianova, Polistena, etc., slightly at Monteleone, and very slightly at Capo Spartivento.

The principal earthquake occurred at 6.52 p.m. In 23 districts with a total population of 160,350, 101 persons were killed, of whom 48 belonged to S. Procopio. The two inner isoseismal lines, 1 and 2, correspond to shocks of disastrous and ruinous strength (intensities 9 and 8 Mercalli scale). They are represented by the broken-lines in *Fig.* 9. The boundaries of the meizoseismal area, according to Baratta and Riccò, occupy nearly the same position as the innermost isoseismal of Mercalli, and all three writers agree in assigning a position for the epicentre, or one of the epicentres, close to S. Procopio. From a study of the directions of the shock, Mercalli concludes, however, that there were two epicentres, one on the western slope of Aspromonte, between S. Cristina and Delianova, the other in the sea off Palmi. To the corresponding foci, he assigns the movements that gave rise to the two principal phases of the shock that were observed in many places, the movement from the Palmi focus being the stronger. The total disturbed area, as outlined by Riccò, contained about 44,000 sq. miles.

*Baratta, **6**, pp. 377-379, 389-390, 410-412, 416-418, 448-453, 505-507, 520-522, 554-555; Mercalli, **22**, pp. 50, 61, 63-64, 69.

88. The relations of the meizoseismal area with the corresponding areas of 1783 Feb. 5 and 1905 Sep. 8 are of great interest. It will be seen from *Figs.* 4 and 10 that the area of 1894 is nearly the same as the southern area of 1905, but that it occupies the southern portion of the area of 1783. The greatest ruins in 1894 did not occur in the Plain of Calabria, but among the hills to the south. In 1783, 26 places possessed a higher death-rate than S. Procopio, which suffered most in 1894. Polistena and S. Giorgio, that was razed to the ground in 1783, were only slightly damaged a century later; but Bagnara and S. Cristina were seriously damaged on both occasions. Thus, while the epicentres of the two earthquakes were not coincident, the meizoseismal areas were partly superposed.

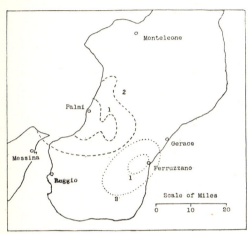

FIG. 9.—Isoseismal lines of the Calabria earthquakes of 1894 and 1907 (Mercalli).

89. The numbers of after-shocks during Nov., Dec. and Jan. were 33, 21 and 53, respectively, and, during the next ten months, 73. Six of them attained an intensity of 6 or 7 of the Mercalli scale, namely, those of 1894 Nov. 16 (11.34 p.m.), Dec. 9, 1895 Jan. 20, Feb. 10, July 26 and Nov. 18*.

90. *Earthquake of 1905 Sep. 8.*—During the last three centuries, 20 ruinous or disastrous earthquakes have occurred in Calabria, and, of these, Mercalli estimates that the earthquake of 1905 occupied the fifth place as regards intensity, while, in the extent of its damaged area, it was equal to the two great earthquakes of 1638 Mar. 27 and 1783 Feb. 5. The earthquake has been studied by G. Mercalli and M. Baratta, and its seawaves by G. Platania.

The earthquake occurred at 2.45 a.m. on Sep. 8. It was preceded by several shocks, by one on Aug. 29, generally felt throughout western Calabria, on Sep. 3 by a sensible shock at Tito near Potenza, and on Sep. 8 by a slight shock at Muro Lucano at 0.15

---

*Baratta, **6**, pp. 567-571; Mercalli, **22**, pp. 116-148; Riccò, **29**, pp. 127-167, 222-234.

a.m., and another about 1.45 a.m. in the central area of the great earthquake, while, immediately before the latter, a sound was heard like that of a strong wind.

The central disastrous area, within which 557 persons lost their lives in 44 communes, includes the districts of Monteleone, Nicastro, Catanzaro, Cosenza and Paolo. It is thus about 60 miles in length, while its greatest width was only about 25 miles. Within this area, the shock was sensible for 40 sec. It consisted of three principal phases, separated by brief intervals of rest or slighter motion. In the first phase, the movement was chiefly vertical; the second phase was the longest and was undulatory; the third phase was the strongest and, while it lasted, the direction changed so much as to give the impression of a vorticose movement. Outside, in the very strong area, three phases were perceptible, but in each the movement was undulatory. Near the boundary of the disturbed area, as at Naples, only two phases were felt.

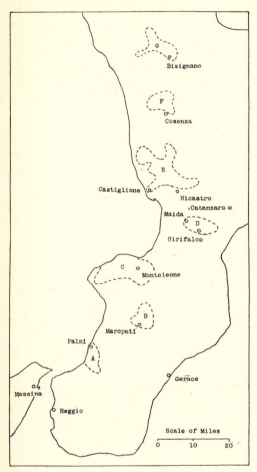

FIG. 10.—Seismic zones of the Calabria earthquake of 1905 (Baratta).

91. The most remarkable feature of the earthquake was the discontinuity of the meizoseismal area. Baratta has mapped as many as seven devastated zones, which are represented in *Fig.* 10. The figure bears a close resemblance to the corresponding map for the Calabrian earthquakes of 1783 (*Fig.* 3). Indeed, several of the areas

in 1905 overlap those of 1783. In the latter year, however, the areas were struck in succession from Feb. 5 to Mar. 27. In 1905, they were struck simultaneously or nearly so, and the distance between the extreme zones was much greater than in 1783. The zones, from south to north, with dates of important earthquakes occurring in them, are :—

A. Palmi : 1783 Feb. 5, 1894.
B. Maropati.
C. Monteleone : 1659 (in part), 1869, 1886.
D. Girifalco : 1626, 1783 Mar. 27.
E. Serrastretta : 1638 (in part).
F. Castiglione : 1835, 1854.
G. Bisignano : 1887.

Thus, with one exception, all of these zones correspond with well-known seismic zones. The distance between the centres of the Palmi and Bisignano zones is about 82 miles.

92. It would seem that the epicentral area of the earthquake was in part submarine. The cable from Milazzo to Lipari was broken at the time of the earthquake at a point in lat. 38° 21′ 50″ N., long. 15° 7′ 30″ E., or 7½ miles east of the south end of the island of Vulcano. From the appearance of the broken ends, it was inferred that the rupture had occurred through mechanical action. After the earthquake, the sea rose and fell for some hours along the west coast of Calabria, at one point to a height of about 5 ft. above its normal level. The seawaves were sensible as far as Ischia, and were recorded at several distant stations, for example, Ischia (186 miles), Naples (207 miles) and Civitavecchia (348 miles). The actual velocity to each of these places was less than that given by the usual formula ($v^2 = gh$), where h is the mean depth of the sea along the paths followed by the waves[*].

93. *Earthquake of 1907 Oct. 23.*—This earthquake occurred in the small and not very sensitive zone of Gerace-Siderno, on the southeast coast of Calabria. Violent earthquakes connected with the zone are those of 1720 Sep. 12, 1783 July 29, 1784 Oct. 14, and 1806 Oct. 6. At Gerace, the earthquake of 1784 was regarded as stronger than the great earthquake of 1783 Mar. 27.

The earthquake of 1907 occurred during an epoch of comparative calm in the whole of Calabria. It was, however, heralded by five shocks within the Gerace zone, on 1905 Sep. 9 and 26, 1906 Jan. 16, 1907 May 25 and Oct. 23, 9.25 p.m. The disastrous earthquake closely followed the last shock, at 9.28 p.m.

The two inner isoseismal lines (corresponding to intensities 9 and 8-7), as traced by Mercalli, are represented by the dotted lines

---

[*]Baratta, **9**; Mercalli, **23**, pp. 1-9; Platania, **26**; Phil. Mag., vol. 43, 1897, pp. 33-36.

in *Fig.* 9. The epicentral area, within which the intensity was 9, was very small, and included only one town (Ferruzzano), where many houses collapsed almost completely, and 158 persons, or 8·0 per cent. of its population, were killed. How rapidly the intensity declined outwards is evident from the fact that at Bruzzano Zefferio, only 1¼ miles from Ferruzzano, no houses were ruined and no lives were lost. The total disturbed area was about 41,000 sq. miles.

In the central area, the shock lasted from 10 to 12 sec. The movement was continuous throughout, and varied but slightly in strength.

94. Though perfectly calm at the time of the earthquake, the sea soon afterwards advanced about 130 yd. over the shore, the seawaves being perceptible along the coast for about six miles from Capo Bruzzano to the river Careri. The waves left traces of their passages on the mareograms at Messina and Catania, the record at the former place being interrupted by the stopping of the driving clock at 9.28 p.m. At Catania, the first movements were recorded at 9.48 p.m., the last at 6 a.m. on Oct. 24. The amplitude of the largest oscillations was about 4 in. As in the earthquake of 1905, the velocity of the seawaves (325 ft. per sec.) was distinctly less than that in a sea of the same mean depth throughout (394 ft. per sec.)*.

XIV. BIBLIOGRAPHY

1 AGAMENNONE, G. " Importanti particolarita nei sismogrammi del R. Oss. Geod. di Rocca di Papa in occasione dei terremoti Calabri dell 8'sett, 1905 e 28 dic. 1908." *Roma R. Acc. dei Linc. Rend.,* vol. 18, 1909, pp. 339-343.
2 ALFANI, G. " Il terremoto Calabrese." *Pavia Riv. di Fis.,* etc., 1905, 8 pp.
3 ALFANI, G. " Primi appunti sul terremoto Calabrese del 23 ottobre 1907." *Pavia Riv. di Fis., etc.,* 1907, 4 pp.
4 ANON. " Dreadfull Newes : or a true relation of the great, violent and late earthquake " [1638 Mar. 27].
5 BARATTA, M. " I terremoti nelle Calabrie." *Roma Uff. Centr. Meteor. Geod. Ann.,* vol. 19, 1897, 32 pp.
6 BARATTA, M. " I terremoti d'Italia," 1901, pp. 268-292, 567-571.
7 BARATTA, M. " Calabria sismica." *Ital. Soc. Geogr. Boll.,* 1905, pp. 1074-1081.
8 BARATTA, M. " Le nuove costruzioni in Calabria dopo il disastroso terremoto dell' 8 settembre 1905." *Ital. Soc. Sism. Boll.,* vol. 12, 1907, pp. 249-337.

*Baratta, **12**; Mercalli, **24**; Platania, **27**. An earthquake of intensity 8 (Mercalli scale), strong enough to cause the partial ruin of some houses, was felt on 1928 Mar. 7 in southern Italy and eastern Sicily. The earthquake has been studied by G. Imbò of the R. Geophysical Observatory of Catania (*Ital. Soc. Sism. Boll.,* vol. 29, 1930, pp. 9-25). The meizoseismal area is an elongated ellipse directed N.E. and S.W., and it coincides almost exactly with the corresponding curve of the first great Calabrian earthquake on 1783 Feb. 5. The centre of the curve is in lat. 38° 31′ N., long. 16° 0′ E., a position that agrees closely with that obtained from the records at distant observatories, or lat. 37° 59.6′ N., long. 15° 55.4′ E.

9 BARATTA, M. " Il grande terremoto Calabro dell' 8 settembre 1905 : alcune considerazioni sulla distribuzione topografica dei danni." *Toscana Sos. di Sci. Nat.,* 1906.

10 BARATTA, M. " I terremoti di Calabria." *Ital. Soc. Geogr. Boll.,* 1906, pp. 432-459.

11 BARATTA, M. " A proposito del nuovo codice de edilizia sismica per le Calabrie," 1907.

12 BARATTA, M. " Il nuovo massimo sismico Calabrese (23 ottobre 1907)." *Ital. Soc. Geogr. Boll.,* 1907, 6 pp.

13 BARATTA, M. " Sopra le zone sismologicamente pericolese dell Calabrie " (no date), 12 pp.

14 CAMERANA, E. " Il terremoto del 16 novembre 1894 in Calabria e Sicilia : Relazione technica." *Roma Uff. Centr. Meteor. Geod. Ann.,* vol. 19, 1897, 32 pp.

15 DI-STEFANO, G. " Il terremoto del 16 novembre 1894 in Calabria e Silicia." *Roma Uff. Centr. Meteor. Geod. Ann.,* vol. 19, 1897, 24 pp.

16 DOLOMIEU, D. DE. " Mémoire sur les tremblements de terre de la Calabre pendant l'année 1783." Rome, 1784. Translated under the title, " A dissertation on the earthquakes in Calabria Ultra in the year 1783," in Pinkerton's Voyages and Travels, vol. 5, 1809, pp. 273-297.

17 GRIMALDI, F. A. " Descrizione de' Tremuoti accaduti nelle Calabrie nel 1783." Naples, 1784, 87 pp.

18 HAMILTON, SIR W. " An account of the earthquakes which happened in Italy, from February to May 1783." *Phil. Trans.,* vol. 73, 1783, pp. 169-208.

19 HOBBS, W. H. " The geotectonic and geodynamic aspects of Calabria and north-eastern Sicily." *Beit. zur Geoph.,* vol. 8, 1907, pp. 219-362.

20 IPPOLITO, COUNT F. " Account of the earthquake which happened in Calabria, March 28th, 1783 " (in a letter to Sir W. Hamilton). *Phil. Trans.,* vol. 73, 1783, pp. 209-216.

21 LYELL, SIR C. " Earthquake of Calabria, 1783." *Principles of Geology,* 1st edit., 1830, vol. 1, pp. 412-435 ; 12th edit., 1875, vol. 2, pp. 113-144.

22 MERCALLI, G. " I terremoti della Calabria Meridionale e del Messinese." *Ital. Soc. Sci. Mem.,* vol. 11, 1897, 154 pp.

23 MERCALLI, G. " Alcuni risultati ottenuti dallo studio del terremoto Calabrese dell' 8 settembre 1905." *Accad. Pont. nella Tornata,* 1906.

24 MERCALLI, G. " Sul terremoto Calabrese del 23 ottobre 1907 (Nota preliminare)." *Ital. Soc. Sism. Boll.,* vol. 13, 1908-09, pp. 9-14.

25 OMORI, F. " The Calabrian earthquake of Sept. 8, 1905, observed at Tokyo." *Imp. Earthq. Inv. Com. Bull.,* vol. 1, 1907, pp. 47-51.

26 PLATANIA, G. " I fenomeni in mare durante il terremoto di Calabria del 1905." *Ital. Soc. Sism. Boll.,* vol. 12, 1907, pp. 43-81.

27 PLATANIA, G. " Il maremoto del 23 ottobre 1907 in Calabria e la propagazione delle onde di maremoto." *Ital. Soc. Sism. Boll.,* vol. 16, 1912, pp. 166-174.

28 RICCÒ, A. " Riassunto della sismografia del terremoto Calabro-Siculo del 16 novembre 1894." *Ital. Soc. Sism. Boll.,* vol. 5, 1899, pp. 157-180.

29 RICCÒ, A. " Il terremoto del 16 novembre 1894 in Calabria e Sicilia : Relazione sismologica." *Roma Uff. Cent. Meteor. Geod. Ann.,* vol. 19, 1897, pp. 1-261.

30 SARCONI, M. " Istoria de' fenomeni del tremoto avvenuto nelle Calabrie e del Valdemone nell' anno 1783." Naples, 1784, 372 pp.

31 TACCHINI, P. " Terremoto Calabro-Messinese del 16 novembre 1894." *Roma R. Acc. dei Linc. Rend.,* vol. 3, 1894, pp. 275-278.

32 TACCHINI, P. " Sulla registrazione a Roma del terremoto Calabro-Messinese del 16 novembre 1894." *Roma R. Acc. dei Linc. Rend.,* vol. 3, 1894, pp. 365-367.

33 VIVENZIO, G. " Istoria de' Tremuoti avvenuti nella Provincia della Calabria ulteriore, e nella Città di Messina nell'anno 1783." Naples, 1788, 2 vols., 427+144 pp.

CHAPTER III

NEW MADRID EARTHQUAKES : 1811 and 1812

I. Introduction

95. That the New Madrid earthquakes of 1811 and 1812 rank among the great earthquakes of the world is clear from the extent of the areas disturbed and the changes that they wrought on the earth's surface. No other shock of the same order has visited the United States within historic times.

The principal States affected by the earthquake were Missouri, Arkansas, Kentucky and Tennessee. In the beginning of the nineteenth century, the whole district was thinly populated. New Madrid itself was a village of less than one thousand inhabitants. Most of the dwellings were cabins, strongly built, and houses of brick and stone were rare. So far as we know, only one life was lost on land, though a few persons were drowned through the upsetting of canoes and the caving of river-banks. Had it not been for their physical effects—the remarkable domes and sunken lands, etc.—the earthquakes would have attracted but little attention at the present day*

II. Seismic History of the District

96. Of early earthquakes in the central area, we have little evidence. Fuller gives a list of five earthquakes in the Mississippi valley from 1776 to 1804, but none of them can have been closely connected with the New Madrid earthquakes.

According to Lyell, the Indians of the Mississippi valley had a tradition of a great earthquake that, in some long past time, devastated the same district.

The only conclusive evidence that we possess of former earthquakes is that given by the structure of the district. Fissures as large as any of those produced in 1811-12 have been seen with trees fully two centuries old growing on their slopes and bottoms. The Tiptonville dome (art. 106) was partly uplifted in 1811. The remainder must have been raised with some earlier shock or shocks. To the south of Lake St. Francis are several sloughs possessing

---

*Fuller, **6**, pp. 43, 99-100.

all the features but one of the sunk lands of 1811. The absence of
dead timber in them points to an origin long before that year*.

III. Investigation of the Earthquakes

97. Towards the close of 1811, a number of careful observers
happened to be in or near the central area. Among them may be
mentioned J. J. Audubon the naturalist, J. Bradbury an English
botanist, and L. Bringier a well-known engineer, as well as E.
Bryan, A. N. Dillard and G. Le Sieur, residents in the district.
S. L. Mitchell collected records from all parts of the country, and,
like Pignataro at Monteleone, D. Drake at Cincinnati and Jared
Brooks at Louisville, kept careful records of the after-shocks.

98. At various times within the century following, the district
was visited and the effects of the earthquakes described by well-
known travellers and naturalists. Mr. T. Flint, the American
geographer, traversed the central area about 1820. His observations are described in his " Recollections of the last Ten Years,"
published in 1826. In March, 1846, Sir C. Lyell, during his second
visit to the United States, examined the sunk lands and other effects
of the earthquake still clearly preserved in the neighbourhood of
New Madrid. Prof. W. J. McGee in 1891 crossed a large part of
the epicentral area and traced the effects of the earthquake on the
surface layers. In 1902, Mr. G. C. Broadhead collected and published many of the accounts referred to above. Two years later,
Prof. E. M. Shepard and Mr. Myron L. Fuller examined closely a
large part of the central area, a work that was continued in other
parts by Fuller in 1905. The report written by him is by far the
most full and valuable account that we possess of the New Madrid
earthquakes.

IV. The Series of Earthquakes

99. In the lists of shocks recorded by different observers, three
were evidently of higher intensity than the rest and may be regarded
as the principal shocks of the series. Their times were:—

    A. 1811 Dec. 16, shortly after 2 a.m.
    B. 1812 Jan. 23, about 9 a.m.
    C. 1812 Feb. 7, about 3.45 a.m.

Drake, living at Cincinnati, places these three, and no others, in
his first class. In the second class, he includes the following
shocks :—

    D. 1811 Dec. 16, 7.20 a.m.
    E. 1812 Jan. 27, 8.45 a.m.
    F. 1812 Feb. 8, 10.40 p.m.

---

*Fuller, **6**, pp. 11-13.

The relative strength of the earthquakes varied at different places, a result no doubt of the continual migration of the focus. For instance, E. Bryan at New Madrid, regarded the earthquake D as more violent than A, the earthquake B as equal to any preceding shock, and one on Feb. 4 as only less strong. At Cincinnati, Drake considered the earthquake B as nearly equal in strength to A. At Louisville, Brooks describes the earthquake A as violent and B as very violent. All three observers, however, agree in placing the earthquake C at the head of the series. We may thus infer, I think, that the principal earthquakes of Dec. 16 and Jan. 23 were nearly equal in strength, while that of Feb. 7 was distinctly of greater intensity.

v. Nature of the Shocks

100. Little is known about the nature of the shocks at places near the epicentre. At Cincinnati (328 miles from New Madrid), the first earthquake of Dec. 16 occurred at 2.24 a.m. The motion was a quick oscillation or rocking, the average of several estimates of the duration being 6 or 7 min. At Louisville (237 miles), the shock was felt at 2.15 a.m. It seemed as if the surface of the earth was afloat and set in motion by a slight application of immense power, then a boiling action succeeded, houses oscillated, gables and chimneys of many houses were thrown down. From the earliest tremor to the last oscillation was about 4 min.

101. Visible waves were noticed by several observers. Audubon, who felt one of the shocks while riding in Kentucky, says that " the ground rose and fell in successive furrows like the ruffled waters of a lake. . . . The earth waved like a field of corn before the breeze ". According to G. Le Sieur, an old inhabitant of New Madrid, " the earth was observed to roll in waves a few feet high, with visible depressions between. By and by these swells burst, throwing up large volumes of water, sand and coal. . . . When the swells burst, fissures were left running in a northern and southern direction, and parallel for miles. Some were 5 miles long, 4½ feet deep and 10 feet wide "*.

vi. Intensity of the Shocks

102. At this distance of time, it is impossible to disentangle the effects of the different shocks. Most of the distant observations seem to refer to the first great earthquake of Dec. 16, so that the estimates of the total disturbed area may correspond to this shock alone. The two inner isoseismal lines drawn by Fuller (*Fig.* 11) depend on the effects of all the great earthquakes.

---

*Broadhead, **2**, pp. 80, 86; Fuller, **6**, p. 31; Shepard, **10**, p. 47.

Fuller divides the whole disturbed area into three regions, (i) an area of marked earth disturbances, (ii) an area of slight earth disturbances, and (iii) an area of tremors only.

(i) The first district (bounded by the inner dotted line in *Fig.* 11) contains the domes and sunk lands, to be described afterwards, the fissures and sand blows and the large landslides. It includes the New Madrid region, and reaches from a point west of Cairo on the north to the latitude of Memphis on the south, and from

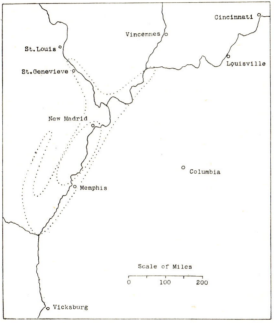

FIG. 11.—Map of the central area of the New Madrid earthquakes (Fuller).

Chickasaw Bluffs on the east to Crowley Ridge on the west. It is thus more than 100 miles long and more than 50 miles wide. The total area of the region lies between 30,000 and 50,000 sq. miles. Within it, the land was ruined for years. Seven years later, when it was visited by Flint, the country " exhibited a melancholy aspect of chasms, of sand covering the earth ", in places to a depth of 2 or 3 ft., " of trees thrown down, or lying at an angle of 45°, or split in the middle ".

(ii) The second district (bounded by the outer dotted line) is marked by minor disturbances such as the caving of river banks.

It reaches nearly to Herculaneum on the north, to a point beyond the Wabash on the northeast, and to the mouth of the Arkansas on the south. The White River region may also be included.

(iii) To the north, the shock is said to have been felt in upper Canada; to the northeast, at Detroit (530 miles from New Madrid); to the east, at Washington (720 miles), and Boston (1,080 miles); to the south, at New Orleans (460 miles); to the southwest, in the Red River settlements and on the Washita River (500 miles); while, to the northwest, it is reported to have been felt by Indians in the upper portions of the Missouri country and between the head waters of the Arkansas and Missouri (more than 500 miles). Thus, the total disturbed area must have contained more than one million sq. miles[*].

VII. Position of the Epicentre

103. There can be little doubt that, as Fuller concludes, the epicentre lay within the area of great destruction (*Fig.* 11). The directions of the shock in outlying towns, which are fairly concordant, also point to the same area. Partly, however, from the directions of the shock at New Madrid and along the Mississippi, Fuller infers that the epicentre must have lain, not as contemporary writers believed, near New Madrid and Little Prairie (now Caruthersville) but along a northeast-southwest fault about 15 miles west of the river. The region of marked disturbance is confined to a definite area, the boundary of which is indicated by the dotted line in *Fig.* 12, and Fuller concludes that the epicentre coincided with the axis of this curve, reaching from a point west of New Madrid to a few miles north of Parkin, Ark. He thinks it probable that the foci of the other principal shocks (Jan. 23 and Feb. 7) also lay along this line, but that the epicentres of some of the other and slighter shocks may have lain elsewhere[†].

VIII. Dislocations of the Crust

104. Although the earthquakes were probably due to movements along a deeply-seated fault, as suggested in the last section, not many scarps were left exposed at the surface. Some of them crossed the Mississippi, giving rise to rapids and waterfalls. W. Shaler notes one such fault, at least 6 ft. high, extending across the river. A similar fault was formed about 8 miles below New Madrid. The roaring of the fall, he says, could be distinctly heard in that village. Such faults, in Fuller's opinion, seem to be con-

---

[*]Flint, **3**, p. 222; Fuller, **6**, pp. 16-17, 33; Lyell, **7**, p. 230; **8**, p. 107; McGee, **9**, p. 200. McGee estimated the extent of the disturbed area at 1¼ million sq. miles.

[†]Broadhead, **2**, p. 84; Fuller, **6**, pp. 14-16,

nected with the fractures involved in the uplift of the Tiptonville
dome.

Most of the scarps formed during the earthquakes of 1811-12
seem to have been worn away. Fuller, however, noticed one along

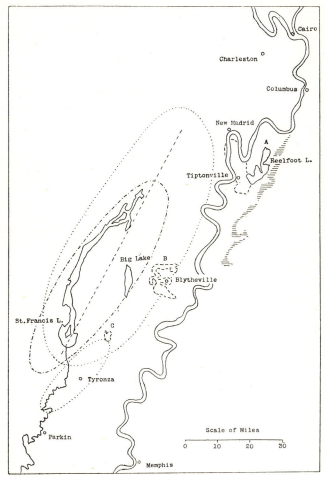

FIG. 12.—Map of the domes and sunk lands (Fuller).

a gently sloping hillside near Campbell, Mo, that had a displacement of 10 ft. or more. Small faults were also seen near Reelfoot
Lake, in one of which the throw amounted to about 6 ft.*

*Fuller, **6**, pp. 58-59.

IX. UPLIFTS AND DOMES

105. We come now to the phenomena that distinguish the New Madrid earthquakes from most other shocks. It was not in their nature alone—though sunk lands and domes are not the result of every great earthquake—so much as in their abundance and wide distribution that the difference lies.

The map in *Fig.* 12 shows the principal features, simplified from the charts given by Fuller (*pl.* 1 and *Fig.* 10). The elevated tracts, known as domes, are represented by the broken-lines A, B and C. The principal sunk lands are occupied in part by Lake St. Francis and Reelfoot Lake, the boundary of the sunk land in which the former lies being indicated by the broken-and-dotted line. Of the two dotted curves, the larger limits the area in which sand blows were chiefly developed, the smaller that in which the largest and deepest fissures occurred.

The more important uplifts and depressions are alone shown in this map. Others occurred in various places. For instance, the left or eastern bank of the Mississippi was raised for some miles below New Madrid, while the opposite bank, on which the village stands, was lowered. Hildreth says that the site of the village before the earthquake was 15 or 20 ft. above the floods of the river. It sank so low at the time of the earthquake that the next rise covered it to the depth of 5 ft. According to E. Bryan, many large ponds were dried up and the beds of some were raised several feet above their former banks. A. N. Dillard states that, before the earthquake, boats would come up the St. Francis River and enter the Mississippi three miles below New Madrid. The channel by which they passed is now dry land.

106. The most important uplifts are the three domes known as the Tiptonville, Blytheville and Little River domes (A, B and C, *Fig.* 12), though only part of their elevation was accomplished in 1811-12. The Tiptonville dome, according to Fuller, reaches from near New Madrid to near Caruthersville, and is about 15 miles long and from 5 to 8 miles wide. Its structure—sandy loam and clays overlying a stiff bluish-green clay—is the same as that of the Mississippi flood-plain. In 1892, great cypresses, sycamores and poplars, two or three centuries old, were growing on the surface of the dome. In the dry channels adjoining it, there were no trees older than 70 or 75 years. Thus, in part at least, the uplift probably occurred with the earthquakes of 1811-12. As the summit of the dome is 10 to 15 ft. above the level of the highest floods, it follows that the total uplift must be about 15 or 20 ft.

The Blytheville dome (B, *Fig.* 12) is from 7 to 10 miles across, and closely resembles the Tiptonville dome. The total uplift is probably not more than 10 or 15 ft.; but there is no evidence that any part of this took place in 1811-12. The Little River dome (C) has a diameter of only 2 or 3 miles, and an uplift of more than 5 or 10 ft. Part at least of this amount seems to have occurred with the earthquake of 1811*.

x. Sunk Lands

107. Just as the domes are local uplifts of the alluvial deposits of the Mississippi basin, so the sunk lands—by far the most conspicuous features caused by the New Madrid earthquakes—are the results of local settling or warping of the same deposits. They are described by all observers, in greatest detail, after existing for nearly a century, by Fuller. There are, he notices, three types :

(i) The sand sloughs, broad troughs not more than a few feet in depth, containing ridges covered by extruded sand and intervening depressions in which all trees have been killed by standing water.

(ii) River swamps or depressed areas along streams, covered by shallow water, in which " wet-land timber " grows, although the stream banks in dry seasons may lie above water.

(iii) The sunk-land lakes, shallow, but permanent, bodies of water lying in depressions of the ground or along the lowered channels of the St. Francis and other rivers. Except in their greater depth, they differ but little from river swamps.

108. As a rule, sunk-land areas are long, narrow, and of irregular form. One of the most prominent, Lake St. Francis, is nearly 40 miles long and less than half a mile wide, though the swampy area on the west side attains here and there a width of 2 or 3 miles. Their general direction, as will be seen from *Fig.* 12, is about N. 30° E., that is, they are roughly parallel to the structural features of the district, the line of the Chickasaw Bluffs, the line of the domes (A-C, *Fig.* 12), etc. The amount of subsidence in the smaller sand sloughs and river swamps may not exceed 2 or 3 ft. below the surrounding areas. In the larger lakes, such as Reelfoot Lake in Tennessee, it may amount in places to 15 or 20 ft.

This remarkable lake is 8 or 10 miles long, and 2 or 3 miles wide†. Originally, the area covered by it was well wooded, most of the trees being of species that grow only on dry land. As a rule, they remained upright after the earthquake, but, though groves of sickly cypresses still line the western side of the lake, the rest were gradually killed by the rising waters. The better timber

---

*Fuller, **6**, pp. 62-64.
†According to Shepard, the lake is from 20 to 25 miles long and 4 to 5 miles wide, and its area is perhaps doubled in times of high floods.

was cut off; the rest were allowed to stand until their branches
fell away, and finally the trunks broke off, leaving only the shattered
stumps, many thousands of which still project above the water*.

XI.　LANDSLIPS

109.　The conditions tending to the production of landslips
were to be found chiefly in two districts—(i) along the banks of the
Mississippi, and (ii) on the steep slopes of the outlying hills, and
especially on those of the Chickasaw Bluffs on the east side of the
river.

(i) The river banks were broken down over great distances,
as far up the Ohio River as Indiana. Lloyd says that the banks
caved in by acres at a time. According to Flint, the graveyard of
New Madrid was precipitated into the river.

(ii) The principal zone of the larger landslips was the western
slope of the Chickasaw Bluffs (indicated by the shaded area in *Fig.*
12), and about 35 miles in length. Landslips were frequent on the
projecting spurs and even on the general slopes of the bluffs.
Slides also occurred on the steep alluvial fans at the mouths of the
gullies that pierce the range. Even after the lapse of a century,
many of these fans showed low scarps due to the slipping of their
material towards the lowlands. A curious feature of this slipping
was the tilting of the older trees, that still remain inclined, except
for the more nearly vertical growth of their upper portions in later
years. From the relative ages of the inclined and wholly vertical
trees, it is clear that the slipping, or a great part of it, occurred
about the time of the New Madrid earthquake†.

XII.　FISSURES

110.　Fissures, in large numbers, were formed during the first
great earthquake on Dec. 16, and, with every strong after-shock,
either the same fissures re-opened or new ones appeared. In every
district, however, they maintained a nearly constant direction, and
Flint and Lyell describe how the inhabitants, recognising this fact,
felled the tallest trees and laid them at right angles to this direction,
so that, by mounting the trunks, they escaped when the earth
opened below them.

The fissures belonged to two very distinct types—(i) simple
fissures like those formed with every great earthquake, especially
near the edges of excavations, and (ii) compound or fault-block
fissures that seem to be peculiar to the New Madrid earthquakes,

---

*Fuller, **6**, pp. 64-75; Lyell, **7**, pp. 235-238; Shepard, **10**, p. 50.
†Fuller, **6**, pp. 59-61.

when a narrow down-faulted block sinks down between two parallel fissures.

111. (i) *Simple Fissures.*—Along the banks of streams, simple fissures are nearly always in concentric curves and parallel to the margins of the excavation. Those in the sand-blow districts seem to tend to a more definite arrangement, their mean direction being about N. 30° E. In length, they vary considerably. Some narrow fissures in both positions may be only a few yards long. Others may have a length of 100 to 200 ft., with a maximum probably of about 300 ft. Their depth is small as a rule, being limited in most cases by the depth of the underlying quicksand, say, from 10 to 20 ft. Such fissures occur in the uplands, but only near the edges of steep bluffs, more frequently in the lowlands, on the flat alluvial lands of the Mississippi and other rivers. They are especially numerous in the broad linear depressions of the sunk lands and at the bottom of river-channels and pools, and in some of the latter led to the draining away of their waters.

Lyell, for instance, describes the draining of a pool or small lake called Eulalie. When he examined it in 1846, the bottom was dry and covered with trees—cottonwood, willows, etc.—all of them less than 34 years old. The lake was formerly filled with clear water, until it was suddenly drained at the time of the earthquake. In the clayey bottom, he was able to trace two parallel fissures, not then quite closed, through which the waters of the lake escaped.

There can be little doubt as to the origin of the simple fissures. Those formed near bluffs were due to the settling of the ground near the excavation. Those in the sand-blow and sand-slough districts opened during the passage of the visible waves described above.

112. (ii) *Compound Fissures.*—Of much more interest are the compound or fault-block fissures. They differ in many ways from the others. They are often straight for considerable distances. Indeed, Lyell remarks that they might easily be mistaken for artificial trenches. They occur as a rule in groups of from two to five, at intervals of from several hundred feet to half a mile, all of them straight and parallel to one another, with an average direction of about N. 30° E. Their length is much greater than in simple fissures, the average seems to be from 300 to 500 ft., those near St. Francis River are said to be half a mile long. Their depth is also greater. Fuller mentions several near that river that were so deep that, when riding on horseback along their floors, he could not see over the surrounding flats. These great fissures occurred within the area bounded by the smaller dotted curve in *Fig.* 12.

There can be little doubt that the compound fissures originated in the manner described by Fuller, by the dropping of the block between two parallel fissures (*Fig.* 13). As Fuller remarks, the

flatness of the bottom of the trench and the presence on it of trees
of a pre-earthquake date imply that the present form of the trench
is due to such dropping.   In order that the block should sink, there
must have been a withdrawal of some of the underlying material,
and, as most of these fissures are near to rivers, it would seem that
the undermining was effected by a creep of the quicksand below
into the rivers*.

FIG. 13.—The formation of fault-block fissures (Fuller).

XIV.   EXTRUSION OF WATER AND SAND

113. Owing to the peculiar local conditions—alluvium in thin
beds overlying quicksand—the quantity of water and sand extruded
from the fissures was enormous.   In some places, the ejections were
violent, the water rising to heights of 10 or 15 ft.; but, in most, the
extrusion was quiet, giving rise to the formation of deposits of sand
known as sand blows and sand sloughs.   Near Little Prairie, to the
south of New Madrid, the ejected water, according to Flint, covered
a tract many square miles in area to a depth of 3 or 4 ft.

114. *Sand Blows.*—These are low patches of white quartz
sand that contrast strongly with the dark alluvium on which they
rest.   As a rule, they are circular in form, from 8 to 15 ft. in
diameter, and from 3 to 6 in. high, with a low rounded profile and
concave slopes.   Some, however, are much larger, the circular
forms reaching a diameter of 100 ft. or more and a height of one
foot, and the linear forms a length of about 200 ft. and a width of
25 to 50 ft.

Sand blows are almost confined to the low alluvial lands bordering the Mississippi and St. Francis Rivers.   They are seldom to be
found on high ground and never within two or three miles of the
Mississippi.   The principal area in which they occur is oval in form
(denoted by the larger dotted curve in *Fig.* 12), and lies to the west
of the river.   It is 65 miles long and 25 miles wide and contains
about 1,420 sq. miles.   They are not, however, confined to this
area, as many are to be seen on the east side of the Mississippi.

115. *Sand Sloughs.*—As a rule, these are low, rather ill-de-
fined, ridges of sand, lying in linear depressions from 3 to 5 ft.
below the level of the plains.   The ridges are roughly parallel to
one another and to the direction of the depression, and are separated

*Fuller. **6**, pp. 47-58.

A. NEW MADRID EARTHQUAKE.
Stumps of timber killed by submergence, Reelfoot Lake (Fuller).

B. OWENS VALLEY EARTHQUAKE.
Earthquake pool on the site of Long Lake near Big Pine (Hobbs).

C. OWENS VALLEY EARTHQUAKE.
Extension of old fault (Hobbs).

PLATE I.   [*To face page* 64.

A. OWENS VALLEY EARTHQUAKE.
Earthquake pool near Diaz Lake (Hobbs).

B. MINO-OWARI EARTHQUAKE.
Overthrown houses along the road from Nagoya to Gifu (Milne and
Burton).

PLATE II.

[To face page 65.

by shallow troughs in which water collects in long narrow pools. They are found only on the lowest ground, mostly on the broad flat bottoms adjoining the uplands, and but very rarely near the river. The principal belts in which they occur are the St. Francis valley, the depression to the west of the Tiptonville and other domes, and in the Reelfoot Lake region.

116. *Causes of Extrusion.*—The violent ejection of water was no doubt due to the closing of fissures, especially of those formed during the passage of the visible waves. The quiet extrusion of sand and water, on the other hand, is probably due to the unequal settling of the surface beds. The absence of sand blows from the uplands seems to be due partly to the greater thickness of the surface deposits there, partly to the fact that the head of water there was powerless to lift it to such heights. Near the Mississippi, the water and quicksand no doubt flowed laterally into the river instead of through fissures to the surface, and thus sand blows would not be formed close to river sides*.

XIV. Miscellaneous Effects of the Earthquakes

117. *Effects on Rivers.* — The principal effects were those caused by the fall of the banks and the formation of scarps across the river bed. When vast portions of the banks broke away, the water receded from the sides; the waves met and rose like a wall in the middle of the stream, and then rolled back with great force, leaving fishes and boats upon the shores. According to Hildreth, the water of the river, clear on the day before, became thick with mud. Through the uplift of its bed and the caving of the banks, the river in a few minutes rose 5 or 6 ft., its current was temporarily checked or even reversed, and then flowed on with increased force†.

118. *Effects on Forests.*—During some of the stronger shocks, trees near New Madrid were seen to bend down as the waves met them, and, in recovering their positions, to become interlocked with others. The passage of the waves through the woods was marked by the crashing noise of countless branches. Dillard saw oak trees split up the centre of the trunk for 40 ft., the two parts afterwards standing on either side of a fissure. Bryan describes how a great wave of the river in receding carried away a grove of cottonwoods that lined its banks.

On the borders of the sunk lands, according to Lyell, all the trees prior to 1811, although standing erect and whole in 1846, were

---

*Bringier, **1**, pp. 20-21; Fuller, **6**, pp. 76-87; Smith, **11**, pp. 93-95.
†Broadhead, **2**, pp. 80-81; Fuller **6**, pp. 89-94; Lyell, **7**, pp. 230-235; Usher, **12**, pp. 294-296.

5

dead. They were chiefly oaks and walnuts with trunks 3 to 4 ft. in diameter and many of them 200 years old. They were supposed to have been killed by the loosening of the roots during the repeated shocks of 1811-12.

The forests submerged in Reelfoot Lake have already been described (art. 108). Fuller estimates that 75 sq. miles of forest were there destroyed. The swamps formed on the west side of the Mississippi probably covered 125 sq. miles of forest land. With the caving of river banks, the total forest area destroyed must amount to 150,000 acres or 230 sq. miles*.

XV. AFTER-SHOCKS

119. As already mentioned, lists of the earthquakes and their after-shocks were kept by D. Drake at Cincinnati (328 miles from New Madrid) and by J. Brooks at Louisville (237 miles), and each observer erected simple pendulums to register the slighter movements.

The numbers of shocks recorded by Brooks during successive weeks from Dec. 16 to Mar. 15 were: 87, 156, 134, 161, 65, 91, 209, 175, 86, 292, 139, 58 and 221.

Of the total number, Brooks gives the times of 178. The numbers during successive hours of the day were 10, 0, 3, 3, 4, 1, 7, 9, 16, 17, 17, 18, 14, 2, 10, 13, 4, 2, 4, 2, 6, 8, 7 and 1. The analysis of these figures gives a marked diurnal period with its maximum epoch at noon.

The after-shocks are said to have continued for nearly two years. According to E. M. Shepard (writing in 1905), a year seldom passes without an earthquake. Somewhat severe shocks were felt on 1895 Oct. 5 and in 1903 Aug. On 1931 July 18, an earthquake occurred with its centre close to New Madrid†.

XVI. BIBLIOGRAPHY

1 BRINGIER, L. " Notices of the geology, mineralogy, topography, productions, and aboriginal inhabitants of the regions around the Mississippi and its confluent waters." *Amer. Journ. Sci.*, vol. 3, 1821, pp. 13-46.
2 BROADHEAD, G. C. " The New Madrid earthquake." *Amer. Geol.*, vol. 30, 1902, pp. 76-87.
3 FLINT, T. " Recollections of the Last Ten Years," 1826, pp. 222-228.
4 FLINT, T. " Earthquakes on the Mississippi: extracted from the travels of Mr Flint." *Amer. Journ. Sci.*, vol. 15, 1829, pp. 366-368.
5 FOSTER, J. W. " The Mississippi Valley: its Physical Geography," 1869, pp. 18-25.
6 FULLER, M. L. " The New Madrid earthquake." *U.S. Geol. Surv. Bull.*, no. 494, 1912, 119 pp.
7 LYELL, SIR C. " A Second Visit to the United States of North America," vol. 2, 1849, pp. 229-239.

*Fuller, **6**, pp. 95-99; Lyell, **7**, p. 235.
†Fuller, **6**, pp. 22-26, 36; Shepard, **10**, p. 59.

8 LYELL, SIR C. " Principles of Geology," 1st edit., vol. 1, 1830, pp. 407-408; 12th edit., vol. 2, 1875, pp. 106-110.

9 McGEE, W. J. " The New Madrid earthquake." *Amer. Geol.,* vol. 30, 1902, pp 200-201.

10 SHEPPARD, E. M. " The New Madrid earthquake." *Journ. of Geol.,* vol. 13, 1905, pp. 45-62.

11 SMITH, E. D. " On the changes which have taken place in the wells of water situated in Columbia, South Carolina, since the earthquakes of 1811-12." *Amer. Journ. Sci.,* vol. 1, 1818, pp. 93-95.

12 USHER, F. C. " On the elevation of the banks of the Mississippi in 1811." *Amer. Journ. Sci.,* vol. 31, 1837, pp. 294-296.

CHAPTER IV

CUTCH EARTHQUAKE : 1819 June 16

1. INTRODUCTION

120. With one exception—the Assam earthquake of 1897—the Cutch earthquake of 1819 June 16 was the greatest of Indian earthquakes during the last century. It disturbed an area that has seldom been exceeded in any part of the world, but, at the present day, its interest lies not in the vastness of that area so much as in the fact that it was one of the earliest in which we have any certain record of marked and extensive changes of level in the crust of the earth.

121. The state of Cutch occupies a peninsular area of more than 7,000 sq. miles on the northwest coast of India, its capital, Bhuj, being about 350 miles northwest of Bombay. To the west, it is bounded by the eastern branch of the Indus, to the south by the Gulf of Cutch and the Indian Ocean; to the east and north lies a nearly level tract, called the Runn of Cutch, that is alternately a dry sandy desert and a muddy inland lake.

When the surface of the Runn is dry, " so imperceptible is the slope ", says Sir Bartle Frere, " that a shower of rain falling on the hard polished surface, neither sinks in nor runs off, but lies, like a vast slop, on the plain. . . . The general surface . . . consists of fine sand and clay, with sufficient salt in it to attract any moisture which the air may possess, and to keep the surface damp when all around is arid. Hence, though sometimes covered with a saline efflorescence, the surface itself never pulverises, even in the hottest weather, and is usually so hard that a horse's hoof hardly dents it in passing ".

In various parts of the Runn, patches of ground rise like low islands a few feet above the level plain and support a scanty growth of grasses, shrubs or small trees. The level portions are called " rann " or " runn," a term that has been extended to cover the whole tract; the patches are known as " bhet ". The cause for the difference between them lies, as Mr. R. D. Oldham points out, in the periodical flooding of the former by water strongly impregnated with salt, and thus destroying all vegetation; while, in the higher ground which has risen through the accumulation of wind-drifted material, the salt is gradually washed out by rain, and vegetation is allowed to establish itself.

The Runn of Cutch extends from the Indus to the western border of Guzerat, a distance of fully 200 miles. Its width is about 35 miles, and its area about 7,000 sq. miles.

122. The Cutch earthquake occurred on 1819 June 16. Before this, we possess the record of only one earthquake in the district. This occurred early in May 1668 in the delta of the Indus. The town of Samawani or Samaji is reported to have sunk " into the ground with 30,000 houses during an earthquake "*.

II. Investigation of the Earthquake

123. For some useful contemporary accounts of the earthquake, we are indebted to Captain J. Macmurdo, who was then stationed at Anjar. In 1827 and 1828, Lieut. (afterwards Sir) A. Burnes visited the central tract and collected evidence from eyewitnesses as to the changes that occurred during the earthquake, in addition to his own valuable observations. Sir C. Lyell, in every edition of the *Principles of Geology,* gave admirable descriptions of the earthquake, somewhat briefly in the first two editions, more fully in the third (1835) and all later editions. In 1880-84, the Survey of India mapped the whole district. The surveyors were concerned only with producing an accurate delineation of the ground, but their maps, under the careful scrutiny of Mr. R. D. Oldham, have shown how extensive were the crustal changes that occurred during the earthquake. Written more than a century later, Mr. Oldham's memoir has restored interest in a neglected earthquake and greatly increased our knowledge of its phenomena.

III. Loss of Life and Property

124. In the capital, Bhuj, nearly 7,000 houses were overthrown and 1,140 bodies were taken from the ruins, though it is estimated that 300 others were never found. Half the town of Anjar is built on its low rocky ridges, and in this part there was comparatively little damage; the other half, erected on a slope leading down to a plain of springs and swamps, was practically ruined, 1,500 houses being destroyed from their foundations and about the same number rendered uninhabitable. Tera, Kothara and Mothala were reduced to heaps of rubbish; while Naliya, Vinghan and many other towns fared nearly as badly. The known total loss of life, according to Macmurdo, amounted to 1,543, namely, 1,140 at Bhuj, 165 at Anjar, 73 at Mothala, 65 at Tera, 45 at Mandir, 34 at Kothara, 13 at Lakhput and 8 at Naliya†.

---

*Burnes, **2**, p. 579; Lyell, **3**, pp. 102-103; Oldham, **5**, pp. 10-15; Oldham, T., *India Geol. Surv. Mem.,* vol. 19, 1883, p. 6.
†Macmurdo, **4**, pp. 112-114.

IV. INTENSITY OF THE SHOCK

125. The earthquake was disastrous over nearly the whole province of Cutch and for some distance beyond its boundary. In *Fig.* 14 (reproduced in part from Oldham's map, *pl.* 15), places at which buildings were destroyed are indicated by small crosses.

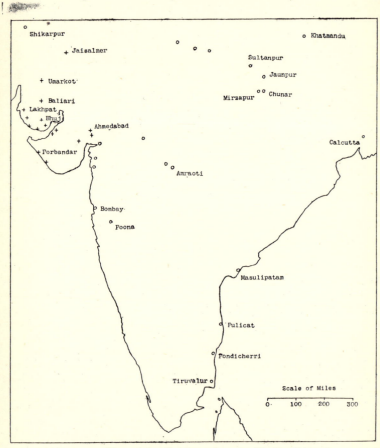

FIG. 14.—Map of the Cutch earthquake (R. D. Oldham).

The other places marked are those at which the shock is said to have been felt.

How far the epicentral area extended is uncertain. Our information is so scanty and can hardly now be increased that it is useless to attempt any definition of its boundary. It certainly included such places as Tera, Kothara, Mothala, Naliya, Bhuj and

Anjar, and it probably extended to Jodiya, Amran and Porbander, and possibly to Ahmedabad towards the east, and Baliari, Umarkot and Jaisalmer towards the north. The area was evidently comparable with that of the corresponding tract in the Assam earthquake of 1897, estimated by Oldham at about 160,000 sq. miles. It may have been two-thirds of that area if Ahmedabad and Umarkot are included, and not less than that area if it spread out as far as Jaisalmer.

Whether there were detached centres beneath Cutch and the districts around Ahmedabad and Jaisalmer cannot now be determined. But there can be little doubt that the intensity throughout this area varied greatly, and it is probable, as Mr. Oldham suggests, that the origin, as in the Assam earthquake of 1897, was widely extended and extremely complex in form.

126. The same uncertainty reigns as to the form and size of the disturbed area. The shock is said to have been felt at Calcutta (about 1,140 miles from Bhuj), and at several towns along the eastern coast of India, such as Masulipatam (860 miles), Pulicat (940 miles), Pondicherri (1,000 miles) and Tiruvalur (1,080 miles). But, in the absence of supporting stations, all of these observations must, I think, be regarded as uncertain. In the Ganges valley, reports have come from places more closely clustered, such as Sultanpur (750 miles), Mirzapur (770 miles), Chunar (780 miles) and Jaunpur (790 miles). In other directions, the limiting distances are much less, but, on negative evidence from such countries as lie to the northwest of Cutch, no conclusions of any value can be based. The average distance from Bhuj of the four places mentioned in the Ganges valley is 775 miles. If we were to regard the disturbed area as bounded by a circle of this radius, it would contain about 1,900,000 sq. miles. As we have no grounds for thinking that the shock was felt at so great a distance except towards the east, all that can be inferred is that the disturbed area was one of the greatest known to us and may have been of the order of one million sq. miles*.

v. Nature of the Shock

127. The earthquake occurred on June 16 between 6.45 and 6.50 p.m. (local time). According to Captain Macmurdo, who was sitting outside at Anjar, there was first a slight motion of his chair, as if it had been lifted up, followed immediately by a second and stronger upheaval. When the shock was at its height, the motion of the earth was so strongly undulatory that it was difficult to stand, and the waving of the surface of the ground was dis-

---

*Lyell, **3**, p. 98; Macmurdo, **4**, pp. 109-111; Oldham, **5**, pp. 38-47, 72-75.

tinctly visible. The total duration of the shock was usually estimated at about 2½ min.*

VI. DISLOCATIONS OF THE CRUST

128. The early accounts collected by Macmurdo hardly touch on the widespread movements of the earth's crust. He himself writes that, according to his observations, " the face of nature has not been much altered by the shocks ". He refers, indeed, to the flooding of Sindri, but ascribes it to the ejection of vast quantities of water all over the Runn. He also states that the branch of the Indus at Lakhput increased in depth from 1 or 2 ft. to 18 ft. in low water.

That we have now so full a knowledge of the changes that occurred in 1819 in the Runn of Cutch, is due, as Oldham points out, to two conditions. The changes affected (i) a region lying almost at sea level and connected with the sea by an open channel, and (ii) a desert region in which changes could still be measured more than sixty years later.

129. The principal changes are clearly described by Burnes, who saw them for the first time in 1827. The little brick fort of Sindri, 150 ft. square, was, he says " overwhelmed at once with a tremendous inundation of water from the ocean, which spread on all sides, and in a few hours completely flooded the country, and converted the tract, which had before been hard and dry, into an inland lake, extending for sixteen miles on each side of Sindri. . . . Of the four towers but one now remains; the inhabitants saved themselves from destruction by ascending it, and only reached the land on the following day by boats "†.

" It was soon discovered ", he adds, " that this was not the only alteration effected . . . ; as the inhabitants of Sindri observed at a distance of five miles northward, a mound of earth or sand in a place where previously the soil was low and level. It extended nearly east and west about sixteen miles. . . . The natives called this ' Allahband ' or the band of God, in allusion to its not being, like the other dams in the Indus, the work of man ".

This embankment, he notes, " is elevated about ten feet from the level of the river, and is composed of soft clay mixed with shells, having all the appearance of being cut through at some late period, the sides being quite perpendicular ". And he adds the important observation that it must not be regarded " as a narrow bar or strip of earth which had been ejected by the earthquake, for it extends very far inland, perhaps sixteen miles, and by gradually sloping to-

---

*Macmurdo, **4**, pp. 106-107.
†Lyell, in his *Principles,* 12th edit., 1875, pp. 100 and 102, reproduces sketches of the fort of Sindri made in 1808 and 1838.

wards the north, unites with the land, which renders it impossible to define its breadth with correctness ".

130. In the following year, Burnes again visited the Allah Bund. It is certainly, he says, " the most singular effect of the earthquake of 1819. To the eye it does not appear more elevated in one place than another, and being covered with a saline soil, has the appearance of the *Runn* in all parts ". Its length, he found, was greater than was at first thought, for he was informed that it could be traced eastwards for 24 miles towards Pachham Island, and westwards as far as Gari, a distance of 18 miles, so that its total length would be between 50 and 60 miles.

131. Sixteen years later, in 1844, Captain (afterwards Sir) W. E. Baker surveyed the Allah Bund and surrounding district and carried a line of levels across the bund. According to this survey, the greatest height of the bund above the level of the Sindri lake was $20\frac{1}{2}$ ft. At a distance of four miles to the north, the height was only 1 ft. above the lake, so that the average slope on the north side of the bund was 5 ft. per mile. On the south side, it amounted to 60 ft. per mile.

Little is known as to the depth of the Sindri lake in the years following the earthquake. In the southern part, the depth, according to Burnes, was 2 or 3 ft. Close to the bund, Baker's section indicates a depth of 10 ft. Assuming, with Oldham, that, before the earthquake, the level of the ground at Sindri was not more than 5 ft. above that of the future lake, this would give an uplift on the north side between 15 and 20 ft., and a depression on the south side between 15 and 10 ft., the change in both directions gradually decreasing to zero. It is possible, as Oldham suggests, that the depression immediately after the earthquake was greater than when Burnes and others made their suveys, and that there was a partial return to the original condition in the months following the earthquake.

The length of the lake was 34 miles, and its area about 150 sq. miles, but that originally flooded may, as Oldham suggests, have amounted to 200 sq. miles.

On the Survey of India map, made in 1880-84, Sindri is not surrounded by water, but by salt. In 1907, according to Mr. R. Sivewright, the Sindri lake had vanished except for some pools of brine that were known to be rapidly disappearing.

132. The rest of this section depends on Oldham's interesting analysis of the Survey map. The course of the Allah Bund and the boundary between the uplift and depression are represented by the broken-line in *Fig.* 15. At its northwest end, the Allah Bund begins about 5 miles from Gari. From this point, it runs in a general S.E. by E. direction, though with some irregularities, for

about 15 miles. Then it trends east-northeast for 7 miles, after which it again follows a southeasterly course for about 15 miles. Throughout this total distance of 38 miles, it forms the northern limit of the area flooded by the earthquake.

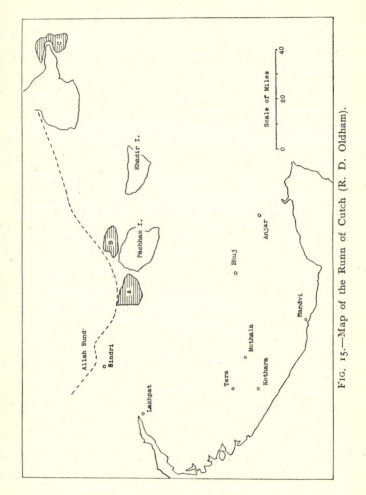

FIG. 15.—Map of the Runn of Cutch (R. D. Oldham).

The dislocation can, however, be traced much farther to the east. To the west of Pachham Island, the uplift may have been perceptible for some time after the earthquake. This, at any rate, is suggested by the report that Burnes quotes from native sources. Still farther, and extending to the northern limit of the Runn, the boundary of the uplifted area was probably less well defined. It can be traced now only by the change in the surface layer from runn to bhet, such as is known to have occurred on the Allah Bund. About 3 miles to the north of Gainda Bet, the Survey map indeed shows a dislocation like the Allah Bund, though on a smaller scale. It can be traced in a southeasterly direction for about 20 miles. At its southeast end, it borders a tract of flooded land.

133. Along the whole southern margin of this elevated land, there are various signs of subsidence. The depression round Sindri is described above. The Survey map also shows two areas of flooded ground. One, lying to the west of Pachham Island (marked A in *Fig.* 15), is about 14 miles long and 8 miles wide. Its northern boundary is roughly straight and runs towards the east-southeast nearly along the continuation of the Allah Bund. The other (B, *Fig.* 15), to the northeast of Pachham Island, is of about the same size, but is more rounded in outline. Beyond this area, the depression cannot be traced with certainty, but the existence of a third flooded area (C, *Fig.* 15) suggests that it may extend still farther to the east.

134. There is thus evidence, as Oldham has shown, of a band of disturbance running rather sinuously across the northern part of the Runn of Cutch, marked by a general elevation of the tract to the north and a general depression of that to the south. Near the western end, the Allah Bund forms a distinct boundary between the two tracts for a distance of about 35 miles. In the eastern section, the slope of the limiting band is so slight that it is revealed as a rule by changes that have taken place afterwards in the surface deposits. At the west end, this band is lost beneath the delta of the Indus. Towards the east, it ceases to be traceable before it leaves the Runn. Thus, the total length of the band cannot be less than 80 miles, and it may be as much as 100 miles or more. In addition to its great length, the most interesting feature of the dislocation is that the vertical displacements to the north and south of it were in opposite directions, greatest in amount close to the boundary and gradually dying away as the distance from it increased*.

vi. After-Shocks

135. Between 7 and 11 p.m. on June 16, three shocks were felt at Anjar, and, according to Macmurdo, there were many slight tremors during the night, of which no record was kept. On June 17, the ground was frequently in motion. Until the beginning of

---

*Burnes, **2**, pp. 552-555, 566-567; Lyell, **3**, pp. 99-101; Oldham, **5**, pp. 16-37, 74.

August, no day passed without one or more shocks. After this they became less frequent, occurring only every third or fourth day, until Nov. 23, when the last distinct shock was felt. After the principal earthquake, only four after-shocks at Anjar—on June 17 at 10 a.m., June 29 at 2 p.m., July 4 at 8 a.m. and at midnight some day later in July—were strong enough to be felt by persons standing, but not to cause material damage to buildings. In his Catalogue of Indian Earthquakes, Mr. T. Oldham records three earthquakes at Bhuj, on 1820 Jan. 27 and Nov. 13, and on 1828 July 20, the last a violent shock*.

BIBLIOGRAPHY

1 BAKER, SIR W. E. " Remarks on the Allah Bund and on the drainage of the eastern part of the Sind basin." *Bombay Geogr. Soc. Trans.,* 1846, p. 186.

2 BURNES, SIR ALEX. " Memoir on the eastern branch of the River Indus, giving an account of the alterations produced on it by an earthquake, also a theory of the formation of the Runn and some conjectures on the route of Alexander the Great; drawn up in the years 1827-1828." *R. Asiatic Soc. Trans.,* vol. 3, 1835, pp. 550-588.

3 LYELL, SIR C. " The earthquake of Cutch in Bombay, 1819." *Principles of Geology,* 1st edit., vol. 1, 1830, pp. 405-407; 12th edit., vol. 2, 1875, pp. 98-104.

4 MACMURDO, J. " Papers relating to the earthquake which occurred in India in 1819." *Phil. Mag.,* vol. 63, 1824, pp. 105-119, 170-177.

5 OLDHAM, R. D. " The Cutch (Kachh) earthquake of 16th June, 1819, with a revision of the great earthquake of 12th June, 1897." *India Geol. Surv. Mem.,* vol. 46, pp. 71-147, i-viii.

6 WYNNE, A. B. " Memoir on the geology of Kutch." *India Geol. Surv. Mem.,* vol. 9, 1872, pp. 29-47, 291-293.

---

*Macmurdo, **4**, pp. 107-109; Oldham, T., *India Geol. Survey Mem.,* vol. 19, 1883, pp. 14, 17.

CHAPTER V

VALPARAISO EARTHQUAKES : 1822 Nov. 19
and 1906 Aug. 16

I. VALPARAISO EARTHQUAKE: 1822 NOV. 19

1. INTRODUCTION

136. For our knowledge of this great earthquake, we are indebted chiefly to Mrs. Maria Graham (afterwards Lady Callcott),
who was then living at Quintero, a small town situated on a promontory about 30 miles north of Valparaiso. A few details, relating
especially to the uplift of the coast, are given by other observers,
such as Mr. H. Cuming, Lieut. Freyer, Capt. Joy, Mr. J. Miers
and Mr. I. Robison, or by travellers, such as Mr. Darwin, Capt.
Basil Hall and Sir F. B. Head, who visited the district within a few
years after the earthquake. General accounts of the earthquake
are given by Sir C. Lyell in his *Principles of Geology* and by Prof.
A. Perrey in his memoir on Chilean earthquakes.

II. PREPARATION FOR THE EARTHQUAKE

137. The first Chilean earthquake known to us occurred in the
year 1550, but of this we have no details. Taking only disastrous
shocks into account, we find that Santiago, the capital of the
country, was either ruined or damaged by a series of earthquakes
in 1562, 1570 and 1647. As, however, the earthquakes of 1570 and
1647 were accompanied or followed by disturbances of the sea, it
is probable that their centres lay 80 miles or more to the west and
not far from Valparaiso*. In 1686, a great earthquake with seawaves occurred in an unknown origin and was felt over a wide area.
The centre of activity then shifted southwards to Concepcion (280
miles from Santiago), visited by destructive earthquakes with seawaves in 1730 and twice in 1751 (Mar. 25 and May 24). After the
lapse of nearly half a century, the centre was transferred to the
north, to Copiapo, where destructive earthquakes occurred in 1796,
1819 and 1822 No. 4-5. Then, again, it moved southwards, to the

---

*Santiago was founded in 1542 and Valparaiso in 1536. There is no men-
tion of the latter city in the accounts of the two earthquakes, but, during the
colonial period, both port and city were of little consequence.

neighbourhood of Valparaiso, where, on 1822 Nov. 19 occurred the great earthquake that forms the subject of the present section.

There was evidently some preparation for this earthquake, during that and the preceding years. A slight shock was felt at Valparaiso on 1821 Jan. 18, two others occurred on 1822 July 16, and, during the four days Nov. 14-17, one or several shocks every day*.

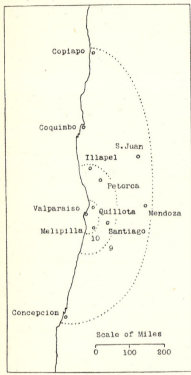

FIG. 16.—Isoseismal lines of the Valparaiso earthquake, 1822.

III. INTENSITY OF THE SHOCK

138. In *Fig.* 16, an attempt has been made to draw three isoseismal lines from the somewhat scanty records still existing. The innermost line, that bounds the meizoseismal area, corresponds to an isoseismal line of intensity 10. Within it, such places as Quillota, Casa Blanca and Melipilla, were converted into little more than heaps of ruins, while in Valparaiso, Almendal and Merced, hardly a house remained habitable. The isoseismal 10, as here drawn, is about 72 miles long from north to south, not less than 60 miles wide, and contains about 3,400 sq. miles. The isoseismal 9 includes such places as Illapel, Petorca, Aconcagua and Santiago, in which many houses were damaged seriously, but the ruin was not complete. The outer line bounds the disturbed area, so far as it is now known. It extends to Copiapo on the north, San Juan and Mendoza on the east, Concepcion on the south, and, it is said, to Juan Fernandez on the west. Assuming these observations to be correct, though they all, especially the last, require supporting evidence from other places, the curve is about 740 miles long from north to south, 450 miles wide, and contains about 270,000 sq. miles. In all probability, the disturbed area extended considerably beyond this curve in all directions†.

---

*Perrey, **12**, pp. 233-259, 289-291.
†Graham, **4**, pp. 308-318; **5**, p. 415; Head, **6**, p. 110; Perrey, **12**, pp. 298-299.

IV. NATURE OF THE SHOCK

139. At Quintero, the first shock was felt at 10.15 p.m., a vertical shock like the explosion of a mine. The vibrations then became so violent that the observer (Mrs. Graham) left the house, when the motion of the earth changed from a quick vibration to a rolling like that of a ship at sea. This shock lasted 3 min., and, within a few minutes more, was followed by two others of less intensity. At Concon, about 15 miles northeast of Valparaiso, the vibrations of the first phase were strong enough to damage buildings; they were succeeded without any pause by the second and much stronger part that lasted 2 min., and this again by a third part less strong and of shorter duration. The three parts together lasted about 5 min. At Valparaiso, the ground rose and fell for about $2\frac{1}{2}$ min., houses reeled like ships on the ocean and trees waved as if bent by a blast of wind, although the night was calm. The sensation felt in the harbour of Valparaiso was as if the ships were driven with violence through the water, striking the rocks occasionally as they went. Even at some distance from the shore off San Antonio (120 miles from Valparaiso), a ship was shaken as though she would fall to pieces. The captain of the same ship afterwards saw great quantities of dead fishes of many kinds floating about[*].

V. UPLIFT OF THE COAST

140. The most remarkable features of the Valparaiso earthquake are those connected with the uplift of the coast. At Quintero, according to Mrs. Graham, it seemed on the morning of Nov. 20 as if the sea had receded in an extraordinary manner during the night. Rocks could be seen above water that were never exposed before. Some distance from land, lay an old wreck of a ship (the *Aquila*) that before the earthquake could not be reached on foot, even at low tide. On Nov. 20, although its place on the shore was unchanged, it was accessible from land. Mrs. Graham estimated the uplift at Quintero at 4 ft. About three weeks later, on Dec. 9, she examined the beach more closely. Although it was high water, the former bed of the sea was laid bare and dry, with beds of oysters, mussels and other shells still adhering to the rocks, " the fish being all dead and exhaling most offensive effluvia ". Three days later, she found a long strip or bed of sea-weed and another of mussels, dead and very offensive, that had not been within reach of the tide since Nov. 19.

On Nov. 24, Mrs. Graham left Quintero for Valparaiso. Along the beach, between the Herradura and Concon, some rocks and

---

[*]Graham, **4**, pp. 305-310; **5**, p. 414; Perrey, **12**, p. 292; Robison, etc., **13**, pp. 111-112.

stones that the lowest tides never left dry had a passage between them and the low-water mark sufficient to ride round easily.

141. At Valparaiso, the change of level, according to Mrs. Graham, was about 3 ft., and some rocks were thus newly exposed on which fishermen collected the scallop-fish, the existence of which in those parts was unknown before the earthquake. Capt. Joy states that the uplift of the shore round the whole margin of Valparaiso Bay was so marked that it was the subject of daily comment. The change was most noticeable on the rocky parts that were found to be elevated from 2 to 6 ft. above the usual tide mark. He states also that the depth of the bay was in places from one to two fathoms less than before the earthquake. Nine years later, in 1831, Dr. Meyen, a Prussian traveller, examined the shore both north and south at Valparaiso, and found remains of animals and sea-weeds adhering to the rocks that in 1822 were raised above high-water mark.

142. How far the elevation extended cannot now be determined. Mrs. Graham gave the total length of coast uplifted as more than 100 miles. Her own observations were confined to the coast between Quintero and Valparaiso (a distance of about 30 miles) and she gives no authority for that statement. Mr. Darwin, however, in 1835, examined the coast from the river Rapel, about 60 miles south of Valparaiso, to Conchali, about 80 miles north of it. Close to the mouth of the Rapel, he found dead barnacles adhering to rocks 3 or 4 ft. above the level of the highest tide, that must have been uplifted within a few years before.

143. Both Mrs. Graham and Mr. Darwin noticed old beaches evidently raised during previous earthquakes. On the coast at Quintero, the former observed " several ancient lines of beach, consisting of shingle mixed with shells, extending in a direction parallel to the shore, to the height of 50 ft. above the sea '. Along the bold granitic coast south of the promontory that forms the Bay of Valparaiso, are numerous horizontal beds of shells elevated from 60 to 230 ft. above the sea. The shells are brittle and of different species, but all similar and in the same proportional numbers to those now living on the beach*.

VI. Seismic Seawaves

144. During the first shock on the night of Nov. 19, the sea in Valparaiso harbour rose to a great height, so as to carry boats farther in than any boat had been before. It then receded so as

---

*Cuming, **1**, pp. 263-265; Darwin, **2**, pp. 446-449; Freyer, **3**, pp. 179-180; Graham, **4**, pp. 308, 310, 313, 321, 329-331; **5**, p. 415; Lyell, **8**, pp. 94-97; Perrey, **12**, pp. 294-295.

A. MINO-OWARI EARTHQUAKE.
Fault Scarp at Midori in the Neo Valley (Milne and Burton).

B. MINO-OWARI EARTHQUAKE.
Fissures in embankment of R. Nagara and damaged railway bridge
(Milne and Burton).

PLATE III.   [*To face page* 80.

A. ASSAM EARTHQUAKE.
Displaced boulders near Kanchi, Khasi Hills (Oldham).

B. ASSAM EARTHQUAKE.
Waterfall formed by the Chedrang fault (Oldham).

PLATE IV.

[*To face page* 81.

to leave the small vessels, that were afloat before, dry on the beach. A few minutes later, there was a second wave, though not reaching the level of the first, possibly on account of the rise of about 3 ft. in the bed of the harbour. The seawaves were of short duration and, after a quarter of an hour, ceased to be noticeable*.

VII. EFFECTS OF THE SHOCK ON THE GROUND

145. On the morning of Nov. 20, the rivers near Quintero and the lakes connected with them were observed by Mrs. Graham to be much swollen, owing to the great slides of snow from the mountain-sides. Similar snow-slides on a much larger scale, as will be seen later (arts. 325-328), occurred during the Alaskan earthquake of 1899.

In all the small valleys, she notices, the earth of the gardens was rent, and quantities of sand and water were forced up through the cracks to the surface. Again, in the alluvial valley of the Viña del Mar, the whole plain was covered with cones about 4 ft. in height, due to the water and sand forced up through the funnel-shaped hollows beneath them, the whole surface being reduced to the consistence of a quicksand. The bed of the lake of Quintero was also full of large cracks, and the alluvial soil on its shore was shaken up so as to look like a sponge. The level of the lake had also sunk considerably.

The swaying of trees during the earthquake has already been referred to. Mrs. Graham adds an interesting observation on this point. At the roots of all the trees, and also at the bases of the posts supporting the verandah, large hollows were seen wide enough to admit the hand, made by the violent swaying of the trunks.

After the earthquake, the granite on the beach of Quintero was found to be rent by many sharp clefts, easily to be distinguished from the old ones, but running in the same direction. Some of the large clefts could be traced from the beach to the distance of $1\frac{1}{2}$ miles across the neighbouring headland.

146. As a general rule, an earthquake is felt much less strongly in mines or tunnels than on the neighbouring surface. In some gold mines near Petorca, however, some remarkable effects were produced. At the time of the earthquake, miners were at work in a lode 200 yd. in depth. During the shock, large pieces of the lode kept falling down and several of the men were killed. The mountain shook so much that it was difficult to ascend the lode. When the survivors reached the surface, there was so thick a dust that they could not see their hands, and large masses of rock rolled down the mountain side†.

---

*Graham, **4**, pp. 310, 321; **5**, p. 414.
†Graham, **4**, pp. 307-308, 313; **5**, pp. 414-415; Head, **6**, p. 111.

VIII. AFTER-SHOCKS

147. Until her departure from Chile on 1823 Jan. 17, Mrs. Graham kept a record of all the more important after-shocks. In the intervals between some of the early shocks, the ground seemed to be constantly trembling, the reality of the tremor being shown by the agitation and occasional spilling of water in a glass. The strongest shocks noted by her occurred at the following times:—

Nov. 20, shortly before 2 a.m., 4 and $6\frac{1}{4}$ a.m., $5\frac{3}{4}$ and $8\frac{1}{2}$ p.m.; Nov. 21, $2\frac{1}{2}$ and 2.50 a.m., 1.40 and $10\frac{1}{4}$ p.m.; Nov. 22, $4\frac{1}{4}$, $7\frac{1}{2}$, 9 and 11 a.m.; Nov. 25, $8\frac{1}{4}$ a.m.; Nov. 27, 10 a.m. and 6 p.m.; Dec. 3, $3\frac{1}{2}$ and 9 a.m., noon, 2 p.m. and midnight; Dec. 4, 4 severe shocks before 8 a.m.; Dec. 8; Dec. 10, midday and $3\frac{1}{2}$ p.m.; Dec. 11, $7\frac{1}{2}$ and 10 a.m.; Dec. 12, noon; Dec. 21; and Dec. 25, 8 a.m.; the strongest of all being those of Dec. 10 (midday) and Dec. 25.

From the latter date until Jan. 17, shocks, more or less severe, occurred every day. In July 1823, they were again violent, and, according to Lyell, they had not ceased by the end of September, for, even then, two days seldom passed without a shock, while on some days three were felt*.

IX. VALPARAISO EARTHQUAKES AFTER 1822

148. After the great earthquake of 1822, no destructive shocks seem to have visited Central Chile for nearly 30 years. On 1851 Apr. 2, however, many public buildings and houses in Valparaiso and Santiago were thrown down, while Quillota and Casa Blanca were seriously injured. This was followed by seven others—on 1873 May 14, July 7 and Nov. 23, 1874 Oct. 26, 1876 Feb. 11 and Nov. 10, and 1880 Aug. 15—four of which were of intensity 1 (Milne scale), two of intensity 2, and only one (that of 1873 July 7) of intensity 3. The areas chiefly affected in all eight earthquakes seem to have differed but little from the central areas in 1822 and 1906†.

II. VALPARAISO EARTHQUAKE : 1906 Aug. 16

X. INTRODUCTION

149. It has been pointed out by Omori that the west coast of the America continent from Alaska to Colombia was almost outlined by the epicentral areas of earthquakes from 1899 to 1906. After the California earthquake of 1906 Apr. 18, he suggested that

---

*Graham, **4**, pp. 308-339; **5**, pp. 413-414; Lyell, **8**, p. 96.
†Perrey, **12**, pp. 218-220.

the next earthquake would probably continue this line to the south or north, and it is a remarkable fact that, on 1906 Aug. 16, earthquakes did occur almost simultaneously at both ends of the line, the earlier off the Aleutian Islands, the later near Valparaiso. Though an arc of 127°, or more than one-third of the earth's circumference, separated the two epicentres, the interval between them was less than half an hour, and, on the seismograms at distant observatories, the records of the two shocks were to a great extent superposed.

150. Our knowledge of the earlier earthquake depends on seismographic evidence. According to Omori, its time of occurrence at the origin was 0h. 11m. 44s. (Aug. 17, G.M.T.), and the epicentre lay in lat. 50° N., long. 175° E. This point lies off the outer or convex side of the Aleutian Islands arc, in a region where the ocean-bed descends rapidly to a depth of more than 3,800 fathoms or 4 miles.

151. The Valparaiso earthquake, according to the same authority, began at the origin at 0h. 40m. 5s., a.m. (Aug. 17, G.M.T.) or 7h. 53m. 29s., p.m. (Aug. 16, Valparaiso time), and its epicentre lay in lat. 31° S., long. 73° W., or about 60 miles off the Chilean coast near the spot where the ocean-bed descends to a depth of more than 4,150 fathoms or about 4¾ miles*.

152. The earthquake was investigated by Comte F. de Montessus de Ballore, the director of the Seismological Service of Chile, and brief reports have also been written by E. Rudolph and E. Tams, by F. Omori, by H. Steffen, and others.

153. The shock caused great destruction in Valparaiso and in the neighbouring towns of Viña del Mar, Le Ligna, Limache, Quilque, Arriaca, Palequin, Meripilla, Quillota, Llaillai, Hierro Viejo, Conchall, Petarda, La Placilla, La Calera, Los Andes, San Felipe and other places†.

XI. INTENSITY OF THE SHOCK

154. The isoseismal lines of the whole disturbed area, as drawn by Rudolph and Tams, are represented in *Fig.* 17, and those in the epicentral area are shown on a larger scale in *Fig.* 18. The innermost isoseismal includes all places, such as those mentioned in the last paragraph, in which great destruction occurred. It corresponds to an intensity 9-10 of the Mercalli scale. The isoseismal 8 bounds the area in which damage to buildings was marked. The land-area included within it was about 15,500 sq. miles. The outermost isoseismal, of intensity 3-4, is rather irregular in form. To the north, it passes through or near Tacna; to the northeast, Corrientes; to the east, Dolores (Buenos Ayres); and to the south-

*Omori, **11**, pp. 75-77.
†Rudolph, etc., **14**, pp. 20-21.

east, Bahia Blanca. The disturbed area is thus about 1,680 miles
long from north to south, and its greatest width about 1,240 miles.
The land-area shaken, within the isoseismal 3-4, was about 785,000

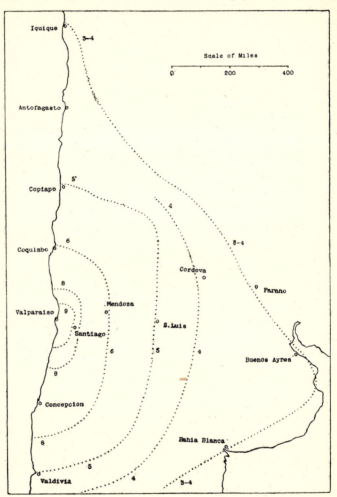

FIG. 17.- -Isoseismal lines of the Valparaiso earthquake, 1906
(Rudolph and Tams).

sq. miles. As the epicentre lay beneath the ocean, the total disturbed area must have been one of the largest known*.

---

*Omori, **11**, p. 104; Rudolph, etc., **14**, pp. 18-23.

XII. NATURE OF THE SHOCK

155. A characteristic feature of South American earthquakes is the large area over which the vertical motion was perceptible. According to Steffen, this area, in the Valparaiso earthquake, extended from lat. 30° to 38° S., or more than 550 miles in length, and from the coast to the mountains. Partly, the sensation of vertical movement may have been due to the uplift of the crust.

As is usual in great earthquakes, the duration of the shock was considerable, at Copiapo amounting, it is said, to as much as 10 min.

XIII. UPLIFT OF THE COAST

156. The elevation of the coast was not quite so great as in 1822, but the evidences of the changes were equally distinct, and the length of coast affected perhaps greater. According to Steffen, to whom we owe much of our knowledge of the uplift, there was no trace of change to the north of lat. $31\frac{1}{2}$° S. or to the south of lat. 35° S. The portions of the coast known to be affected are shaded in *Fig.* 18. They reach, though not continuously, from Llico on the south to Los Vilos on the north, a total distance of 210 miles. The lengths of the various portions, as measured from Steffen's map are: Llico section 43 miles, Valparaiso 15, Papudo 31, Pichidangui 12, and Los Vilos 7 miles, or a total length observed to be uplifted of 108 miles.

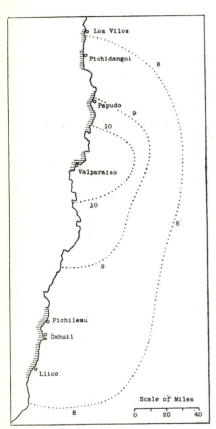

FIG. 18.—Isoseismal lines of the epicentral area, etc., of the Valparaiso earthquake, 1906 (Rudolph and Tams).

The most southerly point from which notices of elevation have come is Llico, a small harbour at the mouth of the canal leading from the Laguna of Vichuquen to the sea. At and near this place, the fords of the canal have been reduced to little more than half their former depth; sandbanks in the lagoon, in the canal, and at its mouth, that used to be covered at low water, now project 16 in. out of the water; while a boat sunk near the mouth of the canal so that its rim was hardly above low-water mark is now at least 10 in. above it. In the same section, a little farther north, near Cahuil and Pichilemu, rocks formerly below water were raised so that fishermen were able to gather shell-fish without difficulty.

At several points in the Bay of Valparaiso, the rocks on the seashore were coated with a white band to a height of 2 ft. above low-water level. The band was composed of molluscs (mostly Balanus) and a coralline that live in shallow water, now, by exposure, killed and bleached.

In the next section, reaching from the Bay of Quintero (uplifted in 1822) to the north of the Rio Ligua, there are clear signs of elevation, the amounts ranging from $27\frac{1}{2}$ to $31\frac{1}{2}$ in. At Papudo, according to an observer familiar with nearly every rock and bay, the seashore looked as if there were always low water. Rocks on which fishermen could venture only at low tide became easily accessible at high-water. Some of the exposed rocks were coated white with bands of dead and bleached mussels.

Still farther to the north, in the coastal districts of Pichidangui and Los Vilos, there has, since the earthquake, been a marked retreat of the sea at low-water.

Thus, the districts affected by uplifts are those in which the intensity of the shock was highest. The amount of the elevation seems to have been somewhat greater towards the north, though at no point did it exceed $31\frac{1}{2}$ in.*

xiv. Seismic Seawaves

157. Though seawaves spread over the Pacific Ocean and were recorded even in Japan, it is remarkable that, along the American coast, they attracted but little attention. To the south of the Bay of Arauco (lat. $37\frac{1}{2}°$ S.), no unusual movements of the sea were observed. Soon after the earthquake, however, waves swept into the harbour of Coronel, in the northern part of the bay. In the harbours of Penco and Tome (in the Bay of Talcahuano), the sea was calm at the moment of the shock, but, after an interval variously estimated from a quarter of an hour to an hour, the sea retreated about 60 yd. and then quietly rose, and this was repeated three or four times. On the coasts of the provinces of Maule, Talca and Carico, unusual waves were observed shortly after the earthquake, the sea rising more than 3 ft. above high-water mark.

*Steffen, 15, pp. 132-138.

Farther to the north, along the coasts of the provinces of Colchagua, Santiago, Valparaiso and Aconcagua, no unusual agitations of the sea were perceived, except that at one or two places, such as the lighthouse on Punta Curaumilla (to the south of Valparaiso), a strong swell was noticed a short time after the earthquake. In the northern provinces of the country, few, if any, movements were observed. Compared then, with the seawaves that followed the Arica earthquake of 1868 or the Iquique earthquake of 1877, those connected with the Valparaiso earthquake of 1906 were insignificant.

158. In the Hawaiian Islands, they were more notable. In the island of Maui, the wave is said to have reached a height of 12 ft. in the enclosed bay of Maalaea. A steamer anchored off the northeast coast of Hawaii was driven forward so suddenly that its cable broke.

The waves were recorded at Honolulu, San Diego and San Francisco, and at four ports on the Pacific coast of Japan, the most distant (Kushimoto) being 10,937 miles from the origin*.

xv. Luminous Phenomena Accompanying the Earthquake

159. From very early times, certain luminous phenomena have been reported as occurring with or shortly before or after earthquakes. The lights take various forms, such as flashes, pillars or beams of light, globes of fire, or diffused lights and luminous clouds. In about 20 per cent. of the examples studied by Galli†, the lights were bright enough to be seen during the day.

During the Valparaiso earthquake, which occurred at 7.55 p.m. (local time), the luminous phenomena attracted much attention, and they were carefully studied by Montessus. He collected reports on the earthquake from 136 observers scattered over an area 640 miles long from north to south. Of these, 44 saw no lights, 16 made no reference to the subject, 38 mention lightning without details, 18 report diffuse lightning, 19 describe luminous phenomena in the form of meteors, 1 a fire or phosphorescence coming from the soil, and 5 saw sparks emitted from telegraph and other wires.

On the night of the earthquake, there was a violent storm of rain, accompanied by thunder, all over the central region. It is thus uncertain whether the phenomena so widely observed were associated with the earthquake or resulted from the disturbed condition of the atmosphere. It will be seen, however, that during the Idu (Japan) earthquake of 1930, the observations were free from this doubt (art. 475)‡.

---

*Honda, etc., **7**, pp. 93-96; Omori, **11**, pp. 108-113; Steffen, **15**, pp. 132-138.
†*Ital. Soc. Sism. Boll.*, vol. 14, 1910, pp. 221-447.
‡Montessus de Ballore, **9**, pp. 7-102; **10**, pp. 187-190.

XI. BIBLIOGRAPHY

1 CUMING, H. "On the earthquake in Chili, Nov. 19, 1822." *Geol. Soc Trans.*, ser. 2, vol. 5, 1840, pp. 263-265.

2 DARWIN, C. "Observations of proofs of recent elevation on the coast of Chili, etc." *Geol. Soc. Proc.*, vol. 2, 1838, pp. 446-449.

3 FREYER, LIEUT. "On the appearance of elevation of land on the west coast of South America." *Geol. Soc. Proc.*, vol. 2, 1838, pp. 179-180.

4 GRAHAM, MRS. MARIA. "Journal of a Residence in Chile during the year 1822," 1824, pp. 305-339.

5 GRAHAM, MRS. MARIA. "An account of some effects of the late earthquake in Chili." *Geol. Soc. Trans.*, ser. 2, vol. 1, 1824, pp. 413-415.

6 HEAD, SIR FRANCIS B., BART. "Rough Notes taken during some rapid Journeys across the Pampas and among the Andes," 4th edit., 1846, pp. 110-111.

7 HONDA, K., TERADA, T., YOSHIDA, Y., and ISITANI, D. "Secondary undulations of oceanic tides." *Imp. Earthq. Inv. Com. Publ.*, no. 26, 1908, pp. 93-96.

8 LYELL, SIR C. "Principles of Geology," 1st edit., vol. 1, 1830, pp. 401-403; 12th edit., vol. 2, 1875, pp. 94-97.

9 MONTESSUS DE BALLORE, F. DE. "Fenomeni luminosi speciali che avrebbero accompagnato il terremoto di Valparaiso del 16 di agosto 1906." *Ital. Soc. Sism. Boll.*, vol. 16, 1912, pp. 77-102.

10 MONTESSUS DE BALLORE, F. DE. "The so-called luminous phenomena of earthquakes and the present state of the problem." *Amer. Seis. Soc. Bull.*, vol. 3, 1913, pp. 187-190.

11 OMORI, F. "Notes on the Valparaiso and Aleutian earthquakes of Aug. 17, 1906." *Imp. Earthq. Inv. Com. Bull.*, vol. 1, 1907, pp. 75-113.

12 PERREY, A. "Documents relatifs aux tremblements de terre au Chili." *Lyon Soc. Agric. Ann.*, vol. 6, 1854, pp. 291-330.

13 ROBISON, I., and JOY, CAPT. "Earthquake and rising of the sea coast of Chili, in November, 1822." *Amer. Journ. Sci.*, vol. 30, 1836, pp. 110-113.

14 RUDOLPH, E., and TAMS, E. "Seismogramme des nordpazifischen und südamerikanischen Erdbebens am 16. August 1906." *Inter. Seis. Assoc.* Strassburg i.E., 1907, 98 pp.

15 STEFFEN, H. "Einige Ergebnisse der Untersuchungen über das mittel chilenische Erdbeben vom 16. August 1906." *Petermann Mittheil.*, vol. 53, 1907, pp. 132-138.

CHAPTER VI

CONCEPCION EARTHQUAKE : 1835 Feb. 20

I. INTRODUCTION

159. About 280 miles to the south of Valparaiso lies the city of Concepcion, destroyed by a great earthquake on 1835 Feb. 20. At that time, Capt. Fitzroy, of H.M.S. Beagle, and Mr. Darwin were on the coast of Chile. Captain Fitzoy measured the uplift of the coast at several places, especially in the island of Santa Maria. Accounts of the earthquake were written by Fitzroy, Darwin, Caldcleugh and others, and summaries of their papers are given in Lyell's *Principles of Geology* and in Perrey's memoir on the earthquakes of Chile.

II. EARLY CONCEPCION EARTHQUAKES

160. On the morning of 1730 July 8, some earthquakes overthrew many houses in Concepcion. The sea retired to a considerable distance and soon returned with violence, inundating the town and country. On July 8, at least three great shocks were felt, and early on July 9 one of such violence that the few houses left by the first shocks and the seawaves were overthrown.

The next great earthquake occurred on 1751 May 24 at 1 a.m., by which the town was ruined. The neighbouring town of Chillan was also destroyed. Shortly after 1.30 a.m., the sea withdrew rapidly from the shore and left the bay dry, returning at 1.37 with such force that it entered the town more rapidly than a horse could gallop and inundated it entirely. It again retired and with such violence that it carried away all the walls, even those not thrown down. The waves returned twice with greater violence and flooded the town, and continued to sweep the coasts, though to a less extent, until about noon the next day. The houses in the islands of Juan Fernandez were entirely ruined, the sea rising far beyond its usual limits.

161. After 1751, few earthquakes of any consequence occurred in the Concepcion area for more than eighty years. From 1834 Jan. 1 to 1835 Feb. 20, some shocks were felt, all feeble with the exception of one at the close of Oct. 1834*.

*Caldcleugh, **2**, pp. 22, 26; Darwin, **5**, p. 602; Perrey, **8**, pp. 259-281, 334, 355-356.

III. Intensity of the Shock

162. The dotted lines in *Fig.* 19 represent, though but roughly, two isoseismal lines. The inner line (shown on a larger scale in *Fig.* 20) includes the places in which most of the buildings were destroyed, reaching from about lat. 34° to 38° S., and thus about 250 miles long from north to south. The towns most severely damaged were Concepcion, Chillan and Talcahuano. In the last-named town, only three houses, built on rocky foundations, were uninjured.

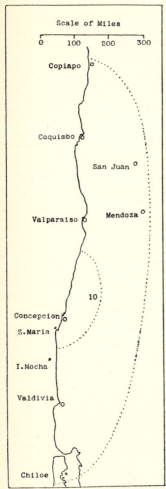

Fig. 19.—Isoseismal lines of the Concepcion earthquake.

The outer line bounds, so far as we know, the disturbed area. The shock was felt from Copiapo on the north to beyond Chiloe on the south, and from Juan Fernandez on the west to Mendoza on the east. As drawn partly in *Fig.* 19, the disturbed area is about 1,160 miles long, 720 miles wide, and includes about 650,000 sq. miles. There can be little doubt, however, that the curve should extend much farther to the west and south. At Juan Fernandez, according to Major Sutcliffe, the earth shook violently. It was said that the trees beat against one another and large masses of rock fell down. In the island of Caucahue (one of the Chiloe group), forest trees swayed so that they nearly touched the ground[*].

IV. Nature of The Shock

163. The first movements were felt at Concepcion at 11.40 a.m. Slight at first, they increased rapidly in strength until at the end of half a minute, the convulsive movements were so strong that it was difficult to stand, and buildings swayed and tottered. Then, suddenly after 1 or 1½ min. came an overpowering shock, and,

[*]Fitzroy, **7**, pp. 406, 415-418; Perrey, **8**, pp. 362-363; Sutcliffe, **9**, pp. 7-9.

ın less than 6 sec., the city was in ruins. This part of the shock lasted with uniform violence for nearly 2 min., so that, including the final vibrations, the total duration cannot have been less than 4 min.*

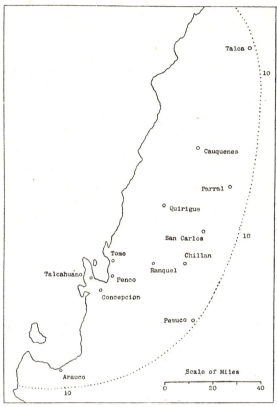

FIG. 20.—Epicentral area of the Concepcion earthquake.

v. UPLIFT OF THE COAST

164. At many points along and near the coast, the uplift of the land was established by the clearest evidence. Opposite Fort Ste. Catherine at Talcahuano, a bank of rocks extended seawards from the coast. Before the earthquake, according to Vermoulin, the whole bank was covered by the sea, but since Feb. 20 it re-

*Caldcleugh, **2**, pp. 23-25; Darwin, **5**, pp. 602-603; Fitzroy, **7**, pp. 402-404, 415-416; Perrey, **8**, pp. 356-359.

mained bare at the highest tides. Along the shore, Fitzroy notes
that, even at high water, beds of dead mussels, chitons and limpets
and withered seaweed, still adhering to the rocks on which they
lived, everywhere met the eye.

165. The greatest upheaval known occurred in the island of
Santa Maria, 25 miles southwest of Concepcion. The island was
visited twice by Fitzroy, who measured the uplift of beds of dead
mussels on large steep-sided rocks. The south end of the island,
he found, was raised by 8 ft., the middle by 9 ft., and the north end
by 10 ft. At one spot, he saw a bed of mussels barely covered at
high spring tides. Before the earthquake, the mussels used to be
collected by diving at low water. Standing on the bed at that time,
a man six feet high could not reach the surface of the water with
his hands. In other parts, beds of dead mussels were found 10 ft.
above the recent high-water mark. A few inches only above what
was then the spring high-tide mark, were putrid shell-fish and sea-
weed that evidently had not been wetted since the upheaval of the
land.

An extensive rocky flat lay round the northern shore of Santa
Maria. Before the earthquake, this was covered by the sea except
for some projecting rocks. After the earthquake, " the whole surface was exposed; and acres of the rocky flat were covered with
dead shell-fish, the stench arising from which was abominable ".
By this elevation, the southern port of Santa Maria was almost
destroyed. There remained but little shelter and very bad landing.
All round the island, the depth of water was lessened by about $1\frac{1}{2}$
fathoms.

166. The length of coast uplifted is unfortunately uncertain.
At Tubul, to the southeast of Santa Maria, the land was raised 6 ft.
(Fitzroy). At Mocha Island (120 miles south-southwest of Concepcion), according to an observer, whose accuracy Fitzroy was
inclined to trust, the land was upheaved about 2 ft. The small
river Tubul, 22 or 23 leagues from Talcahuano, Vermoulin states
was navigable in 1834 for small ships to 330 yd. above its mouth.
After the earthquake, it could be forded. Vermoulin adds that it
was remarked that the beds of many streams and small rivers had
been raised.

167. A point of some interest is that the whole uplift was not
permanent. Fitzroy states that, for some days after the earthquake,
the sea did not rise to its usual marks by 4 or 5 ft. vertically. But,
he adds, this distance gradually diminished until, by the middle of
April, the high-water mark was only 2 ft. above its former level.
Darwin also noticed that, after some weeks, the ground stood lower
than it did immediately after the earthquake, and he suggested that

the later subsidence might be due to the settling down of the uplifted crust*.

VI. SEISMIC SEAWAVES

168. Fifteen minutes after the earthquake, the sea retired about a mile from the coast at Talcahuano, so that all the vessels at anchor, even those that had been lying in 7 fathoms of water, were aground and every rock and shoal in the bay was visible. After an equal interval, a great wave was seen forcing its way through the passage that separates Quiriquina Island from the mainland. It advanced so slowly that the inhabitants had time to reach the higher ground behind. Sweeping the shores up to 30 ft. vertically above high-water mark, it broke over and flooded the greater part of the town, and then retreated with such violence that all moveable articles not buried under the ruins were carried out to sea. In a few minutes, a second great wave swept in, larger and more impetuous than the first. Again, the sea fell, leaving the shipping aground, to be followed by a third and still larger wave that, on retiring, carried away such quantities of household effects, fences, furniture, etc., that the sea appeared covered with wreckage, and the shores of Quiriquina Island were strewn with broken furniture and wood-work. After this third swell, the waves decreased in height, but, for three days following the earthquake, the sea ebbed and flowed irregularly, two or three times an hour.

169. At Talcahuano, marks on the walls of houses showed that the waves reached a height of 25 ft. above the usual level of high water. They penetrated into first-floor rooms and left seaweed hanging to the remains of roofs. The actual height of the waves was of course less. Those who watched them coming in estimated their height as equal to that of the upper part of a frigate's hull, or from 16 to 20 ft. above the usual level.

All along the coast, between the River Itala and Cape Rumena, the waves detached large masses of earth and stones, many thousand tons in weight, from the cliffs. A small schooner of 80 tons at Talcahuano, nearly ready for launching, was lifted over the remains of the walls and left among the ruins 300 yd. from her stocks. Even at Nuevo Bilbao, more than 200 miles north of Concepcion, two schooners, anchored in the port, carried away their cables and were left among the bushes 150 yd. from the beach.

170. The seawaves were observed all along the Chilean coast from Copiapo to Chiloe, a distance of more than 1,100 miles. At Juan Fernandez, 360 miles from the nearest coast, they were unusually high. The first movement there seems to have been a

---

*Darwin, **5**, pp. 618-619; Fitzroy, **6**, p. 329; **7**, pp. 412-414; Vermoulin, **10**.

rise of the water that covered the whole town and reached the first floors of houses, and, on receding, carried away houses, trees and cattle. The sea advanced and receded four times*.

VII. After-Shocks

171. During the remainder of Feb. 20 and the following night, the earth was not quiet for many minutes together. Tremors were frequent, almost incessant, with occasional shocks more or less severe. Between Feb. 20 and Mar. 4, Fitzroy states, more than 300 after-shocks were counted. According to Vermoulin, the number up to May 2 probably exceeded 1,200. The latter writer divides the after-shocks into three classes according to their intensity and duration. (i) In the first class, he includes the strong shocks of 1835 Nov. 11, 1836 Apr. 26 and 1837 Nov. 7. The first and strongest shock lasted for 3 min., and just fell short of destructive intensity. (ii) The second class contains about 150 shocks of much less intensity, but of equal or less duration. (iii) Lastly, the third class consists of more than 1,000 shocks, slight and of brief duration†.

VIII. Valdivia Earthquake: 1837 Nov. 7

172. Although little is known about this earthquake, it is of interest in showing the farther translation of seismic activity by 240 miles to the south of Concepcion.

The shock occurred at 8.5 a.m. and is said to have lasted 10 min., during which the movement of the ground was so violent that it was difficult to stand. Though Valdivia was completely destroyed, it is remarkable that no lives were lost.

An interesting point is recorded by M. Gay, of which similar examples occurred during the Kwanto earthquake of 1923. A great mast, sunk more than 33 ft. into the terrace of the fort of San Carlos, was lifted so as to leave no mark in the soil, the socket remaining as round and regular as before.

173. In the island of Lemus in the Chonos Archipelago, the bed of the sea, according to a sailor who had anchored there two years before, was permanently raised more than 8 ft. In a bay of the same group of islands, a limestone rock was covered to some distance above high-water mark with mussels, limpets and other shell-fish, still adhering to the rock, but in an advanced stage of decay.

Along the Pacific coast, there is apparently no record of sea-waves after the earthquake. Oscillations lasting several hours were, however, observed in various islands of the Pacific Ocean,

---

*Caldcleugh, **2**, pp. 23-25; Fitzroy, **7**, pp. 406-418; Sutcliffe, **9**, pp. 8-9.
†Fitzroy, **7**, pp. 404-407; Perrey, **8**, pp. 360-361.

such as the Gambier Islands, Apia and Intienla in the Samoa group, Mawé and at Honolulu in the Hawaiian Islands, and the Vavao Islands. In Samoa and at Honolulu, the water rose and fell about 5 ft. above and below the mean level of the sea*.

IX. BIBLIOGRAPHY

1 ANON. "Earthquake in Chili, Feb. 20, 1835." *Amer. Journ. Sci.*, vol. 28, 1835, pp. 336-340.
2 CALDCLEUGH, A. "An account of the great earthquake experienced in Chile on the 20th of February, 1835." *Phil. Trans.*, 1836, pp. 21-26.
3 CHEVALIER, E. "Note sur la constitution géologique des environs de Valparaiso et sur le soulèvement du sol de la côte du Chili." *France Geol. Soc. Bull.*, vol. 14, 1843, pp. 396-401.
4 DARWIN, C. "Chiloe and Concepcion : great earthquake." "A Naturalist's Voyage round the world," 1879, pp. 301-312.
5 DARWIN, C. "On the connexion of certain volcanic phenomena in South America ; and on the formation of mountain chains and volcanoes, as the effect of the same power by which continents are elevated." *Geol. Soc. Trans.*, vol. 5, 1840, pp. 601-632.
6 FITZROY, R. "Sketch of the surveying voyages of his Majesty's Ships Adventure and Beagle, 1825-1836." *Geogr. Journ.*, vol. 6, 1836, pp. 311-343.
7 FITZROY, R. "Narrative of the Surveying Voyages of His Majesty's Ships Adventure and Beagle between the years 1826 and 1836, etc.," vol. 2, 1839, pp. 402-418.
8 PERREY, A. "Documents relatifs aux tremblements de terre au Chili." *Lyon Soc. Agric. Ann.*, vol. 6, 1854, pp. 232-437.
9 SUTCLIFFE, T. "The earthquake of Juan Fernandez, as it occurred in the year 1835." Manchester, 1839, 32 pp.
10 VERMOULIN, —. "Voyage au Pole Sud et dans l'Océanie," vol. 3, 1842, pp. 302-312.
11 VERMOULIN, —. "Observations sur certains effets des tremblements de terre qui se sont fait ressentie au Chili depuis quelques années : Lettre de M. Dumoulin à M. Arago." *Paris Acad. Sci. C.R.*, vol. 7, 1838, pp. 705 707.

*Perrey, **8**, pp. 412-419.

CHAPTER VII

OWENS VALLEY EARTHQUAKE : 1872 Mar. 26

I. Physiography of the Owens Valley

174. The valley of the Owens River lies chiefly in Inyo County in the extreme east of California, the small town of Lone Pine, that suffered most from the earthquake, being 260 miles east-southeast of San Francisco. Within the State of California, the valley is linear and runs in the direction of S. 18° E. until the river enters Owens Lake. Both sides of the valley are bounded by steep and lofty mountains. On the west side is the Sierra Nevada, rising to heights of from 12,000 to 15,000 ft. above the sea or 8,000 to 11,000 ft. above the floor of the valley. Outlying this great chain on the east is the low range of the Alabama Hills, 9 miles in length and 1 to 2 miles in width and rising to about 1,800 ft. above the valley. On the east side, are the Inyo Mountains, steeply rising to heights of 8,000 to 11,000 ft. above the sea. In the neighbourhood of Lone Pine, the summits of the Sierra Nevada and the Inyo Mountains are separated by not more than 18 miles, and the floor of the valley itself is only 2 or 3 miles in width. A series of fault-scarps runs along the eastern base of the Alabama Hills, and the most interesting feature of the earthquake of 1872 was the growth of some of these scarps with the important crustal movements that accompanied the shock*.

II. Seismic History of the Owens Valley

175. That violent earthquakes must have visited the valley in past times is clear from the formation of the fault-scarps. According to Holden, whose catalogue of Californian earthquakes is the chief authority for this section, the Indians state that, about 80 years before the shock of 1872, there was a similar earthquake in the same region. From that time, the land seems to have been at rest until Sep. 1868, when numerous shocks were felt in the Inyo County, about 500 at Kern River from Sep. 3 to 6, and 350 at Lone Pine from Sep. 4 to 12. Some of the shocks were strong enough to throw down rocks from the mountains and to make the ground un-

---

*Hobbs, **2**, pp. 355-361.

dulate like the sea. The series seems to have been short-lived, closing during Oct. 1868.

176. The immediate preparation for the earthquake of 1872 may be said to have begun during the preceding year. On 1871 Mar. 6, a weak shock was felt at Carthago, Inyo County; on July 5, a severe shock at Visalia; on July 11, a still stronger shock at 7.30 p.m. at Swansea, Inyo County, a severe shock at 9 p.m. at Bishop's Creek and Owensville (probably Owenyo), and another at midnight at Swansea; on July 12, a strong shock at Bishop's Creek and Owensville; and, lastly, on 1872 Mar. 17, a severe shock at Lone Pine. The great earthquake of 1872, one of the strongest ever felt in the United States, occurred on Mar. 26 at about 2.30 a.m.*

III. Investigation of the Earthquake

177. Two months after the earthquake, the Owens Valley was visited by Prof. J. D. Whitney, of the Geological Survey of California. While the scarps were still fresh, he described them and the earthquake phenomena in two papers published in the *Overland Monthly*†. In 1883, Dr. G. K. Gilbert traversed the same district, but he states that, after only 11 years, the scarps appeared but little fresher than the long-formed Wasatch scarps. Early in 1907, Mr. Willard D. Johnson, of the U.S. Geological Survey, was engaged in the survey of the valley, and, at the suggestion of Prof. W. H. Hobbs, he mapped the faults and photographed the scarps that still retained much of their original clearness. Prof. Hobbs' paper, in which he published Mr. Johnson's valuable results and reprinted the more important sections of Prof. Whitney's papers, is, though brief, one of the most useful reports that we possess of a great earthquake.

IV. Intensity of the Shock

178. Notwithstanding the preparation for the earthquake during the year preceding, the great shock is said to have come without any warning at about 2.30 a.m. on Mar. 26. The first movements were much the strongest, and all the damage caused by them was done within 1 or $1\frac{1}{2}$ min., and probably within the first few seconds.

179. The central area of the earthquake is thinly populated and the losses to life and property were unusually small. At the village of Lone Pine, nearly every house was ruined, and 29 people were killed, but the loss of life was almost confined to this place.

---

*Hobbs, **2**, pp. 361-362; Holden, **3**, pp. 19, 49-50, 57-58.
†This journal exists in but few libraries, and the reserve copies kept at San Francisco were burned by the fire that followed the earthquake of 1906.

At Independence (14 miles north of Lone Pine) and Swansea (14 miles southeast), most of the buildings were destroyed. Outside the Owens Valley, there was little damage to property, except at Visalia (72 miles west of Lone Pine), where some walls were thrown down.

180. Hobbs gives a map of the disturbed area based on records collected by Holden. From this, it appears that observations to the east of the meridian through Lone Pine are almost wanting. To the south, the shock was felt at Anaheim (198 miles from Lone Pine), Los Angeles (188 miles) and Santa Barbara (186 miles); to the west, at San Francisco (260 miles); to the northwest, as far as Red Bluff (339 miles), with numerous observations leading up to it; and, to the north, at Winnemucca, Nev. (303 miles). At about the same time, shocks are said to have been felt at New Madrid, Mo., Paducah, Ky., and the city of Mexico; but, as these places are respectively 1,690, 1,700 and 1,730 miles from Lone Pine, it is hardly possible that the shocks were due to the Owens Valley earthquake, for this would require a disturbed area of about nine million sq. miles or one several times greater than the largest known to us. Taking Red Bluff as the farthest point at which the earthquake was felt, the disturbed area—assuming it to be a circle of 339 miles radius—would thus contain about 360,000 sq. miles, by no means an unusual size for an earthquake of this degree of strength*.

v. Miscellaneous Effects of the Earthquake

181. At the Cerro Gardo and Eclipse mines in Inyo County, the rocking motion underground drove the miners up to the surface. In the Yosemite Valley, on the west side of the Sierra Nevada, the largest trees are said to have waved to and fro " bent about like mere twigs ".

182. *Landslips.*—At the time of the earthquake, and, indeed, for some time afterwards, vast masses of rock fell down the slopes in the central valleys. Near Bishop's Creek, a mass of rhyolite, 200 c. yd. in volume, was thrown down and split in two in falling.

One effect of landslips along the course of the Owens River was to block the main stream near Bishop's Creek temporarily, followed later, when the stream broke through, by muddy floods†.

183. *Changes in the Water-System.*—Near Lone Pine, the Owens River, formerly swift and deep and 60 to 80 ft. wide, is said to have become dry and remained so for several hours after the earthquake. To the north of the same place, the course of the river

---

*Hobbs, **2**, pp. 362-365; Holden, **4**, p. 58.
†Hobbs, **2**, pp. 366-367.

was shifted westward towards the foot of the terrace, probably owing to a tilting of the ground.

At the time of the first great shock, an important water-wave was formed on Owens Lake. The water first receded from the shore, and, after standing momentarily as a vertical north-and-south wall, the wave rolled in over the shore, flowing about 200 ft. beyond its former margin. This was evidently due to a westward tilt of the ground, the lake being a little shallower at the Swansea landing-stage on the northeast side of the lake, while, on the opposite or northwest side, the water has risen so much that the course of the road has had to be carried farther up the slope*.

184. *Formation of Earthquake-Lakes.*—Whitney states that, at the time of the earthquake, a number of pools and lakes were formed. The largest of these lakes near Big Pine (33 miles north of Lone Pine (*Plate* 1B)) was one-third of a mile long and from 200 to 300 ft. wide. About 3 miles south of Lone Pine, was another pool of a different type. It lies on the west side of the main valley. The scarp at this point faces west, instead of the usual easterly direction, and the result has been to dam back the drainage that issues from the hills to the west, and so form a small lake† (*Plate* IIA).

185. *Changes in Springs.*—Several springs in this valley, it is said, dried up permanently at the time of the earthquake. On the other hand, large and important springs opened in various places and especially along the new fault opened in 1872. Even as far as Los Angeles (188 miles from Lone Pine), artesian wells were seriously affected.

For ten years before the earthquake, the level of Owens Lake had been steadily rising. After the earthquake, it fell for a short time and then remained stationary until July. During this month, however, the level of the lake rose rapidly, sometimes by as much as 4 or 5 in. in one night, though, at the same time, the Owens River, apparently its main source of water, was constantly decreasing its supply. It would seem possible that the additional water came from the innumerable springs that broke out all along the foothills‡.

VI. DISLOCATIONS OF THE CRUST

186. Several of the changes described in the preceding section were directly due to the formation of the remarkable fault-scarps in the Owens River valley. These movements are of unusual

---

*Hobbs, **2**, pp. 367-369.
†Hobbs, **2**, pp. 369-370.
‡Hobbs, **2**, pp. 370-371.

interest, and it is worthy of notice that, for, I believe, the first time, horizontal, as well as vertical, displacements were observed. About 3 miles east of Independence, a road running east and west was, as Whitney relates, severed by the fault and the portion on the west side was shifted relatively 18 ft. to the south.

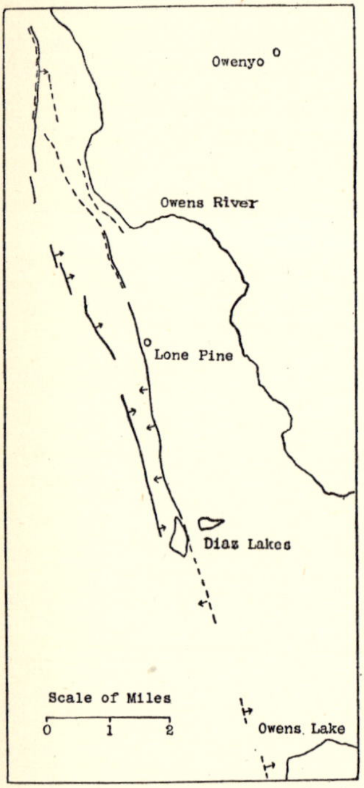

FIG. 21.—Map of the faults in the central districts of the Owens Valley earthquake (Hobbs).

According to Gilbert, who visited the district eleven years later when the scarps had lost some of their freshness, the length of the scarp, or rather series of scarps, was 40 miles, while their height ranged from 5 to 20 ft. The horizontal displacements were still distinct. One tract of land, several sq. miles in area, was not only depressed, but was carried about 15 ft. northwards.

From some distance south of Owens Lake as far as Big Pine Creek, many fissures in the ground were noticed by Whitney, the areas between them being depressed and partly filled with water. As a rule, these fissures were parallel to the base of the mountains, though, in a few places, they ran diagonally across the valley. On the west side of Owens Lake, where the fissures were numerous, the ground between them sank from 2 to 10 ft., the strips so lowered being several hundred yards long and from 10 to 100 ft. wide. Near Lone Pine, the fissures occurred in great numbers, the ground between them being raised or depressed so as to be quite impassable. In no part of the valley were such effects so manifest as in the neighbourhood of Big Pine. The fissures there ran continuously for several miles, and, in on place, an area 200 to 300 ft. wide had sunk 20 ft. or more, leaving vertical walls on either side.

After the lapse of 35 years, much of the original sharpness of the scarps was lost, but the sunken strips were still visible. In several places, Mr. Johnson found that an older fault had been extended either vertically or horizontally or in both directions by the displacements of 1872.

187. *Plan of the Fault-Scarps.*—In 1907, it was still possible

to map the faults, and Johnson has drawn detailed maps, not of the whole district, but of the more important sections, such as that to the west of Lone Pine. In *Fig.* 21, the general map of the district is reproduced in its main features. The continuous lines represents the faults formed in 1872, the broken-lines those of older date. In two places to the north of Lone Pine, where both series coincide, the lines are double. In both places, the new scarp is relatively small and lies at the base of the old one. As a rule, however, the new scarps are the more important. The arrows indicate the directions towards which the scarps face. *Fig.* 22 shows, on a somewhat larger scale, Johnson's map of the faults in the neighbourhood of Lone Pine. The arrows, as before, point to the directions in which the scarps face; the figures indicate the height of the scarps in feet. The dotted line represents the boundary of a spur of the Alabama Hills.

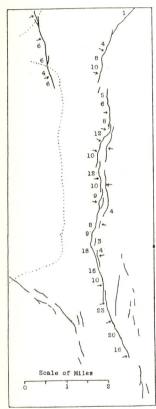

Fig. 22.—Map of the faults near Lone Pine (Hobbs).

188. For some distance, usually one or two miles, the scarps maintain a constant direction. They are, however, subject to abrupt changes of direction, so that the course of each is rather a series of zig-zags. In places, there is a tendency for neighbouring faults to run in parallel directions and to overlap for short distances, the effect being a retreating or an advancing series *en échelon.* These characteristic features of the scarps are represented diagrammatically in *Fig.* 23.

All the scarps, except those that have been much eroded, are steeply inclined, and seem to represent planes that are nearly or quite vertical*.

189. *Horizontal Displacements.*—In addition to the displacements observed by Whitney and Gilbert (art. 186), Whitney noticed

---

*Gilbert, **1**, pp. 51-52, and Lake Bonneville, p. 361; Hobbs, **2**, pp. 371-378, 380-383.

others near Lone Pine and Big Pine, where the severance of fences and ditches indicated horizontal shifts ranging from 3 to 12 ft. According to Whitney, however, they are merely local phenomena and are not to be regarded as representing a general motion of the valley in any fixed direction. Johnson also noticed several horizontal shifts. In one, the fault-line crosses an old fence of trees, the ground, as shown by one tree-stump, having been displaced 9 ft. at the time of the earthquake. Again, in front of the main valley through the Alabama Hills, the fault-scarp is notched by a water-course, the continuation of which on the east side of the fault is now about 20 ft. farther to the south. Lastly, in the west part

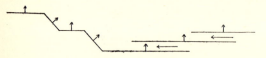

Fig. 23.—Diagram of overlapping faults (Hobbs).

of Lone Pine, a lane was severed by the fault and one portion shifted relatively by 16 ft. Thus, though the examples are few in number, the horizontal displacements range from 3 to 20 ft. The directions in which they occurred are stated or implied in only two cases, and these were opposite to one another, thus confirming Whitney's opinion that they must not be regarded as details of a large-scale movement*.

190. *Vertical Displacements.* — In the district illustrated in *Fig.* 21, the vertical displacement ranges from 1 ft. at the north end of the map to 23 ft. near the south end. The latter, the greatest measured, is at a point on the main scarp west of Lone Pine. Between these two points, the height of the scarp varies rather widely. It usually, however, lies between 8 and 12 ft. When the displacement is great, as near Lone Pine, it is restricted to a single fault-plane. Only a short distance away, the same displacement may be distributed over two or more contiguous planes.

It will be seen also from *Fig.* 21 that, while the main scarps usually face eastwards, there are occasional reversals of throw. For instance, near the northwest end of Owens Lake, there are two old faults facing east. A little more than a mile to the north, the line of these faults is occupied by another old scarp facing west, that runs for 1½ miles to Diaz Lake†.

VII. After-Shocks

191. After the principal earthquake on Mar. 26 at 2.30 a.m., strong shocks, according to one observer more than 50 in number,

---

*Hobbs, **2**, pp. 379-380.
†Hobbs, **2**, pp. 378-379.

continued to be felt during the next four hours. Some of them were powerful enough to move furniture and throw articles off shelves. Between 6 and 6.30 a.m. on Mar. 26, a second violent shock occurred, that was sensible over a large part of California. On May 13, a strong shock was felt at Lone Pine, also at Little Lake, 50 miles to the south. Again, on May 17, occurred the strongest shock at Lone Pine since Mar. 26. The shock lasted about 30 sec. and furniture was much disturbed.

192. From Mar. 31 to May 21, a record of the after-shocks felt at Bishop's Creek (55 miles north of Lone Pine) was kept by Mr. S. G. Sneden. During this interval, hardly a day passed without one or several shocks being felt. At this place, they decreased rapidly in strength, for, during May, none but slight vibrations were felt, while explosive reports, not accompanied by any movement, were often heard. After the close of this month, after-shocks became rare. The last one recorded in the Owens River Valley occurred on Sep. 14*.

VIII. ORIGIN OF THE EARTHQUAKE

193. It is difficult, as Hobbs remarks, to explain the above phenomena except by regarding them as results of the separate movements of crust-blocks composing the floor of the valley.

How small some of the blocks were is clear from the evidence given above. Some of the best farming land in the valley was thrown by them into a confused mass of hillocks and hollows. Near Fish Springs, the earth after the shock was found heaped up in ridges 5 to 10 ft. high and not more than 20 to 30 ft. across. For a month after the Owens Valley earthquake, the cracks in the neighbourhood of Bishop were seen to open and close.

Although the crust-blocks were displaced separately, there seems to be evidence of a westerly tilt of the surface as a whole. In the sunken strip west of Lone Pine, the eastern margin is in places almost undisturbed. The course of the Owens River near Lone Pine was shifted westward to the foot of the fault terrace, and the north end of Owens Lake was tilted in the same direction. As Prof. Hobbs points out, this westerly tilting corresponds with that of the larger orographic blocks of the Sierras during their uplift to form a great mountain range†.

IX. BIBLIOGRAPHY

1 GILBERT, G. K. " A theory of the earthquakes of the Great Basin, with a practical application." *Amer. Journ. Sci.*, vol. 27, 1884, pp. 49-53. See also " Lake Bonneville," *U.S. Geol. Surv. Mem.*, vol. 1, 1890, p. 361.

*Hobbs, **2**, p. 366.
†Hobbs, **2**, pp. 381-383.

2 HOBBS, W. H. " The earthquake of 1872 in the Owens Valley, California."
Beit. zur Geoph., vol. 10, 1910, pp. 352-385.

3 HOLDEN, E. S. " Catalogue of the earthquakes on the Pacific coast, 1769-1897." *Smith. Misc. Coll.*, no. 1087, 1898, 253 pp.

4 HOLDEN, E. S. " List of recorded earthquakes in California, Lower California, Oregon and Washington Territory," 1887, 78 pp., esp. pp. 57-62.

5 WHITNEY, J. D. " The Owens Valley earthquake." *Overland Monthly*, vol. 9, 1872, pp. 130-140, 266-278.

CHAPTER VIII

MINO-OWARI EARTHQUAKE : 1891 Oct. 28

1. Introduction

194. The Mino-Owari earthquake, one of the greatest of all Japanese earthquakes, occurred on 1891 Oct. 28 at 6.37 a.m. The central area, consisting of the provinces of Mino and Owari, is shown in *Fig.* 24, with parts of some of the adjoining provinces that were seriously affected by the earthquake. The continuous, s l i g h t l y curved, line represents the course of the great fault-scarp, to which frequent reference will be made.

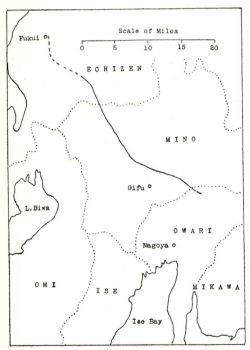

Near the middle of the Pacific coast of the Main Island, the Bay of Ise forms a deep indentation. The depression is continued towards the north as the plain of Owari and Mino. The meizoseismal area includes the whole of this plain, 406 sq. miles in area, as well as the mountainous district of Mino and Echizen farther to the north.

FIG. 24.—Central area of the Mino-Owari earthquake (Koto).

195. The Mino-Owari plain is one of the principal rice-producing districts in Japan, and, as it holds 787 persons to the square mile, it is, with one exception, the most densely populated in the

country. The plain has been described as one of Japan's great gardens. It is covered with rice-fields and is intersected by a network of rivers and canals. The largest towns and chief centres of commerce are Nagoya, Gifu and Ogaki. On its east and west sides, the plain is bordered by low hills of tertiary tuffs lying at the edge of palæozoic mountains that rise to heights of from 2,000 to 4,000 ft.

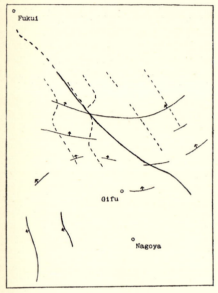

FIG. 25.—Structure of the central area of the Mino-Owari earthquake (Koto).

The structure of the district is shown in broad lines in *Fig*. 25. The strike of the palæozoic formations is represented by the continuous lines, which, as will be seen, form a sigmoidal curve, crossed by the great fault-line. The broken-lines indicate the courses of the valleys of the rivers (from west to east) Tokunoyama, Neo, Mugi and Itatori, all probably coinciding with transverse lines of dislocation. These, again, seem to be crossed by minor fissures, which may be responsible for the zig-zag run of the valley*.

2. INVESTIGATION OF THE EARTHQUAKE

196. The reports on the Mino-Owari earthquake include two notable memoirs that have both taken a place among the classics of seismology. Shortly after the earthquake, Prof. B. Koto, professor of geology in the Imperial University of Tokyo, proceeded to the central district, and traced the great fault-scarp for a distance of 40 miles and measured the horizontal and vertical displacements of the crust along its course. Prof. F. Omori also visited the meizoseismal area more than once and measured the directions of fall of numerous cylindrical bodies at many places. His most valuable contribution, however, was his memoir on the after-shocks of earthquakes, a large part of which is devoted to those of the Mino-Owari earthquake. Some years later, in 1894-1900 and 1916-22, the Military Land Survey Department repeated the precise levelling of the district, several of the routes crossing the important

---

*Koto, **4**, pp. 312-313.

fault-system and throwing light on displacements that would otherwise have passed unnoticed.

3. Loss of Life and Property

197. In the whole of the meizoseismal area (*Fig.* 24), there
was not a building nor an embankment along river or canal that
wholly escaped damage. The road from Nagoya to Gifu was lined
by a serious of villages, each running into the next, so that the
road was a nearly continuous street more than 20 miles in length.
The rows of houses were thrown down, fallen like a row of cards,
so that the road became a narrow lane between two long lines of
debris (*Plate* 2B). Sometimes, according to Milne, there occurred
heaps of rubbish, in which sticks and earth and tiles were so
thoroughly mixed that traces of streets or buildings were entirely
lost.

198. The following Table gives the losses of life and property
in the various provinces :—

Province	No. of persons		No. of houses			
	killed	injured	entirely destroyed	half destroyed	burned	shattered and burned
Mino	4,889	12,311	114,616	30,994	249	5,934
Owari	2,357	4,877	80,428	43,845	196	—
Mikawa	13	49	1,020	1,464	—	—
Echizen	12	48	1,080	1,188	—	—
Omi	6	47	153	366	—	—
Miye	2	11	233	439	—	—
Total	7,279	17,393	197,530	78,296	445	5,934

Complete as was the destruction of houses in many towns and
villages, the loss of life was small, the death-rate being as a rule
less than 5 per cent. In Takegahana, it rose to 5·4 per cent., and
in Kasamatsu to 4·7 per cent. In Gifu, it was less than 1 per cent.,
only 230 persons out of a total of 28,731 having been killed. In
Nagoya, the death-rate was even less, the number of persons killed
being only 190 out of a population of 165,339, or less than one-
eighth per cent.

Other property, besides houses, suffered great damage. It is
estimated that 317 miles of embankment required repairs, and 10·6
miles of railroad. The number of bridges damaged or broken was
10,392. Roads were damaged in 2,067 different places and the
embankments of rivers and canals in 7,177 places. The embankments along the rivers Kiso and Shonai, in Owari, were so greatly
fissured or depressed that it was impossible to count the number of
damaged places, and for the most part they are omitted from the
last figure* (*Plate* 3B).

---

*Koto, **4**, pp. 317-318; Masato, **5**, p. 16; Milne, **7**, p. 197.

4. PREPARATION FOR THE EARTHQUAKE

199. In Sekiya's catalogue of Japanese earthquakes from 416 to 1864, the provinces of Mino and Owari are seldom mentioned. A destructive shock occurred in Mino in 745. Other great shocks disturbed several or many provinces, including Mino in 762, Mino and Owari on 1707 Oct. 28, and Mino on 1819 Aug. 2. An earthquake on 1858 Apr. 9 in Echizen may also have some connexion with that of 1891. On 1889 May 12, a rather strong earthquake occurred with its centre close to Gifu, which shook severely an area of 1,300 sq. miles in Mino and Owari and disturbed a total area of 28,560 sq. miles*.

200. Though apparently not led up to by any other conspicuous earthquake, an analysis of the slight shocks that visited the district during the preceding years shows that the ground was gradually being prepared for the great earthquake of 1891. The materials for this analysis are provided by Milne's valuable " Catalogue of 8,331 earthquakes recorded in Japan between 1885 and 1892." With very few exceptions, Milne gives for every earthquake the time of occurrence, the dimensions of the disturbed area and the position of the epicentre. He divides the whole country into rectangles by north-south and east-west lines one-sixth of a degree of longitude and latitude apart, the position of an epicentre being denoted by the number of the rectangle in which it lies. In order to represent the distribution of the epicentres of the foreshocks and after-shocks (*Figs.* 26, 36 and 37), curves are drawn through the centres of all rectangles in which the number of epicentres is the same or through points which divide the line joining the centres of adjacent rectangles in the proper proportion.

The area included within the maps is bounded by the parallels 34° 40′ and 36° 20′ of N. lat. and by the meridians 2° 10′ and 3° 50′ west of Tokyo, so that ten rectangles adjoin each side of the maps. In each map, the continuous line (broken in its northern portion) represents the course of the great fault-scarp described in a later section. The points A to P denote the centres of the rectangles within which the majority of the epicentres lie.

201. It will be seen from *Fig.* 26 that the meizoseismal area of the earthquake is forked. The more important branch runs towards the south, while the fault-scarp apparently follows only the shorter branch to the southeast. There are, however, other faults in the central area, the existence of which is at first less obvious. The courses of these faults are shown in *Fig.* 31, and one of them lies close to the axis of the southern branch. There can be little doubt that it is responsible for the distribution of many of the minor

---

*Masato, **5**, p. 14; Milne, **6**, pp. 99-101; **7**, p. 149.

shocks   The central points C and D (*Fig.* 26), and possibly also E and F, seem to be connected with the main fault; A and B with the northern end of the fault-scarp; G and H with its southern end; and L and N with a probable continuation of the main fault to the south-east.   The points, K, M and P appear to be related to the fault DD' in *Fig.* 31.

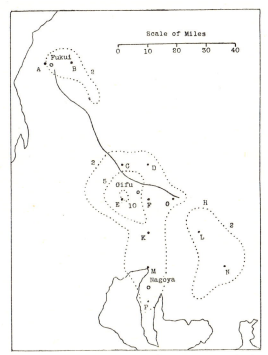

FIG. 26.—Distribution of epicentres of fore-shocks of the Mino-Owari earthquake.

202.   During the five years 1885-89, the number of epicentres lying within the 13 rectangles A-P are respectively 13, 7, 4, 15 and 14; and the numbers occurring outside them are 16, 12, 12, 18·5 and 13·5.   It is remarkable that, during these five years, only one epicentre lies within the rectangle K, which is by far the most prominent seat of after-shocks in Nov. and Dec. 1891, while in the rectangles M and P there were only three during the same interval. At this time, therefore, the secondary fault was almost inactive. At the northern end of the main fault (rectangles A and B) there were no epicentres at all during these years; at the southeastern end

(rectangles G and H) there were 4; and 6·5 in the continuation of the main fault to the southeast (rectangles L and N). The chief seat of earthquakes is the rectangle D in 1885 and E in 1886-89.

Taking into account the fact that the rectangles A-P form only 13 per cent. of the whole area of the map, it follows that the frequency of earthquakes within the fault-region was greater during the years 1885-89 than within an equal area outside, the ratios being 5·4, 3·9, 2·2, 5·5 and 7·0. In the two years before the great earthquake, the ratio rises to 10·6 in 1890 and 10·4 during Jan. 1-Oct. 27, 1891.

203. The distribution of epicentres during the interval 1890 Jan. 1-1891 Oct. 27 is illustrated in *Fig.* 26. While the rectangle E is still the principal seat of activity, it will be seen that the curves follow the lines of the main and secondary faults. In this, as in the other maps, there is a discontinuity in the curves in the portion of the main fault between the points B and C, due in part perhaps to the occurrence of mountain ranges in this area. Otherwise, earthquakes seem to have occurred along the whole fault-system, especially in the secondary fault and the continuation of the main fault towards the southeast. A noteworthy feature is the uniformity in the distribution of epicentres throughout the fault-region. The marked concentration of effort that characterises the after-shocks is hardly perceptible here.

204. The approach of the great earthquake was thus foretold: (i) by the relative increase of shocks within the fault-area during the two preceding years, and (ii) the uniform distribution of epicentres outlining the fault-system during the same interval*.

5. INTENSITY OF THE SHOCK

205. The distribution of intensity throughout the country is represented by the isoseismal lines as drawn by H. Masato, in *Fig.* 27. In the most severely shaken district, which contains about 4,284 sq. miles, the destruction of building and engineering works was nearly complete. This zone is bounded on the map by the curve marked 5. The next zone, the very severely shaken district, bounded by the curve 4, contains 17,315 sq. miles. In it, ordinary buildings were destroyed, embankments and roads were damaged and bridges broken down. The severely shaken district, bounded by the curve 3, is 20,170 sq. miles in area. Some walls were cracked within it, clocks were stopped and furniture overthrown. Within the curve 2, the shock was slight, and within that marked 1 it was weak or just strong enough to be distinctly felt.

---

*Davison, **1**, pp. 2-12; Milne, **8**, pp. 1-367.

The combined area of these two zones was 51,943 sq. miles. Thus, the total land-area disturbed was 93,712 sq. miles.

206. According to Omori, the land-area shaken was slightly larger, namely, 96,500 sq. miles. Moreover, as the mean radius of the outer boundary was about 323 miles, it follows that the total disturbed area, assuming it to be circular, would be about 330,000 sq. miles.

FIG. 27.—Isoseismal lines of the Mino-Owari earthquake (Masato).

207. The boundary of the meizoseismal area, as traced by Koto, is shown in greater detail in *Fig.* 30. The main portion clings to the great fault-scarp, the course of which is indicated by the continuous line. Near the south-eastern end of the fault-scarp, the area forks. The smaller branch runs along the continuation of the fault. The larger proceeds southwards and, as will be seen from *Fig.* 31, follows the course of the important minor fault there marked DD'.

208. Within the meizoseismal area, the movement was so violent that all seismographs were dismounted before many seconds had passed. Estimates of the maximum acceleration could therefore be determined only from the dimensions of well-formed stone lanterns and tombstones. Many observations of such bodies were made at various places by Omori, and the horizontal accelerations required to overthrow them were determined by means of West's formula

$$\alpha = xg/y,$$

where g is the acceleration due to gravity, y the height of the centre of gravity above the base, and x the horizontal distance between that centre and the edge about which it was overturned. The number of places was 22 in Owari, 16 in Mino, 10 in Echizen, and 11 in other provinces. In the province of Owari, the acceleration was found to be 2,600 mm. per sec. per sec. at Nagoya, 4,100 at Bamba, and more than 4,300 at Iwakura and Komaki. In the province of Mino, the corresponding figure was 3,000 at Gifu and Ogaki, and 4,000 or more at Kasamatsu and four other places. At Fukui, the maximum acceleration was 2,500 mm. per sec. per sec., and 1,000 at Kyoto and Osaka. So numerous were the observations that, for the first time, it was found possible to draw isoseismal lines depending on an absolute scale of intensity, and two such lines, corresponding to accelerations of 2,000 and 800 mm. per sec. per sec., have been drawn by Omori and are reproduced in *Fig.* 28.

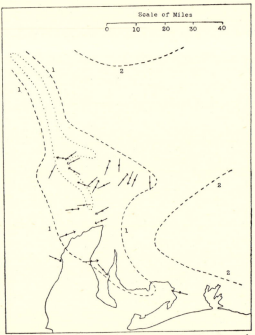

Fig. 28.—Isoseismal lines and mean direction of the shock in the meizoseismal area of the Mino-Owari earthquake (Omori).

At Nagoya, the period of the principal motion was about 1·3 sec., and, from the formula

$$2a = aT^2 / 2\pi^2,$$

it follows that the greatest range of motion in that city was about 223 mm. or 8·8 in.*.

*Koto, **4**, *pl.* 29; Masato, **5**, pp. 16-17; Omori, **11**, pp. 13-17.

6. DIRECTION OF THE SHOCK

209. The stone lanterns and tombstones that provide the materials for estimating the maximum acceleration are also useful for another purpose. The directions in which those at any place fall are variable, but, as Omori has shown, the mean of a large number of observed directions may give a close approximation to the real direction of the shock.   After the Tokyo earthquake of 1894 June 20, he measured the directions in which 245 stone lanterns and other bodies fell. The mean of these directions was S.71° W., while that of the maximum horizontal motion was S.70° W. Now,

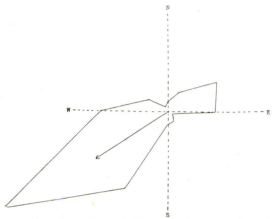

FIG. 29.—Directions of fall of overturned bodies at Nagoya (Omori).

at Nagoya during the earthquake of 1891, of 200 stone lanterns with cylindrical stems, 1 was overturned towards the north, 36 fell between north and east, 6 towards the east, 10 between east and south, 3 towards the south, 119 between south and west, 15 towards the west, and 10 between west and north.   The distribution of the lines of fall grouped between angles of 30° bisected by the cardinal directions, etc., is shown in *Fig. 29.* The arrow represents the mean direction of fall or S. $67\frac{1}{2}$° W.

210.   Similar observations were made at 42 other places within and near the meizoseismal area (*Fig. 28*). The mean directions of fall at different places are indicated by the short lines drawn through them, the arrows marking the direction towards which the majority of the bodies at a given place were overturned. It thus appears that, as a rule, the direction of motion was approximately normal to the meizoseismal zone and directed towards it[*].

---

[*]Omori, **11**, pp. 17-24; *Imp. Earthq. Inv. Com. Publ.,* no. 4, 1900, pp. 25-33; *Ital. Soc. Sism. Boll.,* vol. 2, 1896, pp. 180-188.

7. THE EARTHQUAKE FAULTS

211. Soon after the earthquake, Koto proceeded to the central area and followed the course of the remarkable fault and measured the horizontal and vertical displacements along it for a distance of 40 miles. The course of the fault and the boundaries of the meizoseismal area clinging closely to the fault are shown in *Fig.* 30. Other faults, less manifest to the eye, have been mapped by Omori and Imamura, the complete fault-system, so far as known, being represented in *Fig.* 31. For the present, let us confine ourselves to the more important fracture traced by Prof. Koto.

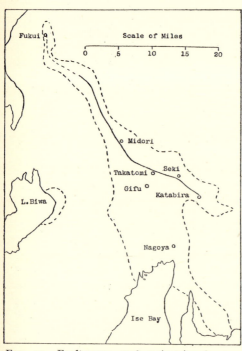

FIG. 30.—Fault-scarp and meizoseismal area (Koto).

212. The most remarkable features of the fault, those which separate it from other and more superficial fissures, were its great length and continuity. It was not confined to soft earth on river banks, but cut indifferently across valley or mountain-spur. Its appearance varied greatly with the nature of the ground traversed by it. When it crossed a mountain ridge, it caused extensive landslips, the crust on one side descending considerably in level. On flat ground, if the throw reached several feet, it formed a terrace, like a railway embankment seen from a distance. If the throw did not exceed a foot or two, the rent left a linear mound, closely resembling the pathway of a gigantic mole or the track of a ploughshare.

213. At its south end, the fault was first seen at the village of Katabira (*Fig.* 30), breaking up a rice-field into clods of earth. A short distance to the northwest, the field was cut sharply by a fissure along which the northeast side had subsided slightly and was shifted from $3\frac{1}{4}$ to 4 ft. horizontally to the northwest. This displacement was shown very clearly by the fact that the straight ridges that separated adjoining fields were cut obliquely and sharply by the line of fault, one or both sides being shifted so that the detached ends no longer met. The rent then takes the direction of N.N.W., traversing the village of Katsu-yama that had been reduced

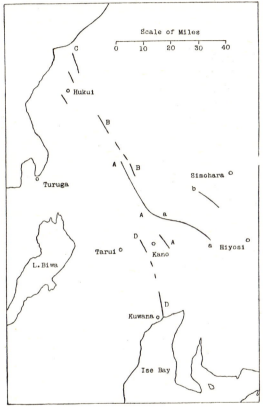

Fig. 31.—Map of earthquake-faults (Imamura).

to a heap of rubbish. A plot of ground here of about half an acre was so thoroughly turned over that at the surface there remained nothing but clods of earth and upturned roots.

Near Takatomi, a tract of land measuring about three-quarters of a sq. mile, together with the bed of the small river Toba, subsided so much that the river lost its outlet, and two villages were transformed into a deep swamp, so that the farmers were obliged to cut their rice from boats. A short distance farther on, the rent passes through the hamlet of Umehara. In a garden here, two persimmon trees formerly stood, and had stood time out of mind, in an east and west line. The line of fault passed between them from southeast to north-west, and the ground was shifted, so that the trees now stand in a north and south line without being in the least injured.

214. Near the south end of Midori, the rent traverses the Neo valley and gives rise to one of the most remarkable effects of the earthquake. A fine new road (*Plate* 3A), leading to Gifu, had been cut obliquely in two, and the crust on the east side was raised relatively by from 18 to nearly 20 ft. and shifted 13 ft. to the north. The earth very regularly took its angle of repose, giving to the scarp a close resemblance to a railway embankment.

215. The total length of the fault from Katabira to the mountain of Haku-san is about 40 miles. Throughout this whole distance, the crust on the east or northeast side of the fault was shifted relatively to the north or northwest, the maximum horizontal displacement being 13 ft. It was also relatively lowered by amounts ranging up to about 10 ft., except at one place (Midori), where it was uplifted nearly 20 ft. Koto was prevented by the coming of wintry weather from following the scarp through the mountain district to the north, but, from reports received, he concluded—and later observations confirmed his inference—that the fault ran along the course indicated by the broken-line in *Fig.* 30 as far as Fukui, its total length being thus about 70 miles.

216. That the great fault traced by Koto was not the only one in action is clear from the form of the meizoseismal area, the main branch of which proceeds towards the south, and also from the distribution of the epicentres of the minor shocks (*Figs.* 26, 36, 37 and 38). Other faults, indeed, though less marked on the surface, were discovered by Omori, who examined the district after Koto. In *Fig.* 31, the main fault-scarp is denoted by the letters Aaa′. An important branch fault BB′ was found to the north by Omori, the northern part of which (B) coincides with the northern extension of the fault-scarp, while the southern part (B′) runs parallel to the scarp, the distance between them being 2·5 miles. Near the north end of the northern segment (B), the crust on the east side was uplifted as at Midori, though on a much smaller scale. Otherwise, throughout the whole course of 57 miles from B to a′, the east side was relatively depressed, with a slight shift to the north or northwest.

A second fault (A″) was also traced by Omori in the southern part of the Mino-Owari plain. When produced northwards, it coincides with the northern portion of the main fault. No actual dislocation was observed, but the ground was tilted along this line, and the triangular block bounded by aa′ and A″ was elevated with respect to the surrounding blocks.

217. The precise levellings of the district before and after the earthquake, though carried out at rather long intervals, have revealed other lines of dislocation. These have been traced by Imamura and are shown in his map reproduced in *Fig.* 31. The line of levels near the coast of the Japan Sea from Turuga by Fukui

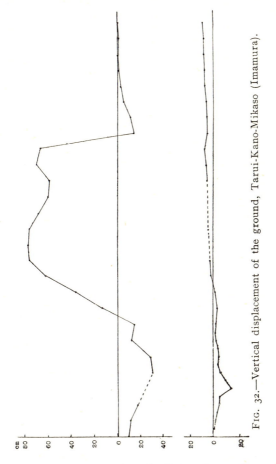

FIG. 32.—Vertical displacement of the ground, Tarui-Kano-Mikaso (Imamura).

to Inoue shows three abrupt, though slight, depressions of 2·0, 2·4 and 3·0 in., which Imamura attributes to small faults, one of which (C) lies along the continuation of the fault BB′ (*Fig.* 32). The changes of level along the second route from Tarui by Kano to Mikasa are shown in *Fig.* 32, the upper curve representing the variations between 1886 and 1896, the lower those between 1896 and 1917. The principal feature of the earlier interval is the upward bulge of as much as 32·6 to 35·8 in. of the triangular block included between the faults aaʹ and Aʺ. The second interval shows a depression of 6·1 in. not observed in the earlier survey. Otherwise, the two curves are somewhat similar, implying that the great

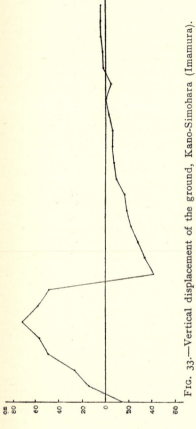

FIG. 33.—Vertical displacement of the ground, Kano-Simohara (Imamura).

movements that occurred with the earthquake were continued, though on a smaller scale, to a much later date. The triangular block between the faults aaʹ and Aʺ is also crossed by the fourth line of levels from Kano to Simohara, depending on observations made in 1890 and 1896 (*Fig.* 33), the uplift near the centre being as much as 45·3 in. Farther to the east, about 12 miles from Simohara, the same line of levels shows a subsidence of 1·9 in., changing at the next bench-mark to the east to a rise of 0·8 in., during the interval 1890-95, due, according to Imamura, to the effect of a small fault b. Imamura also infers from similar evidence the existence of another fault DDʹ, that is of interest as it runs near the axis of the principal branch of the meizoseismal area. The vertical displacement along this fault is comparatively small. Between 1885 and 1896, there was a subsidence of 12·1 in., at the north end (D). At the south end (Dʹ), there was a depression of 8·2 in. between 1888 and 1895, and a further depression of 3·6 in. between 1895 and 1918. The total length of the fault-system from the Sea of Japan to Ise Bay would thus be about 100 miles.

218. That the fault-system also extends beneath the sea at both ends seems clear from the distribution of the submarine epicentres. These are given by Milne in his catalogue of Japanese earthquakes from 1885 to 1892. In the interval before the earth-

quake, 33 shocks were probably connected with the continuation of the fault to the south and 4 with that to the north, the epicentres ranged so far as 10 miles to the south and 20 miles to the north, and the mean areas disturbed were 466 and 619 sq. miles, respectively. In the interval after the earthquake, 26 shocks were probably connected with the southern continuation of the fault and 7 with the northern, the epicentres were distributed over the same ranges as before, and the mean areas disturbed were respectively 2,249 and 13,509 sq. miles. Thus, after the earthquake, the mean frequency was 4·6 times that before the earthquake to the south and 10·0 times that to the north, while the mean disturbed area was 4·8 times that before the earthquake to the south and 21·8 times to the north.

219. The comparative smallness of the displacement at both ends of the fault-system is assigned by Imamura to the relief of the stresses by previous earthquakes. On 1819 Aug. 2, a semi-destructive earthquake was felt along a narrow belt trending north-wards from Kuwana. Again, on 1858 Apr. 9, two earthquakes occurred near the north end of the system in the provinces of Hida, Echizen, etc. During the second shock, many houses collapsed at Maruoka (6 miles north-northeast of Fukui) and in the neigh-bouring villages.

220. The re-survey of the district was confined to the precise levellings, and we have thus no knowledge with respect to the absolute horizontal movements of the ground. Besides the relative horizontal shifting towards the north and northwest of the crust on the east side of the main fault, there was, according to Prof. Milne, evidence of the permanent compression of the ground. Plots that were 48 ft. in length before the earthquake measured only 30 ft. after it. It would seem that the whole Neo valley had become narrower, for the piers of bridges over the river were brought closer together than they were at the time of building*.

8. After-Shocks

221. The after-shocks of the Mino-Owari earthquake were re-corded at five stations within a hundred miles from the origin— Gifu (17 miles), Nagoya (37 miles), Tsu (61 miles), Kyoto (61 miles) and Osaka (88 miles)—as well as at Tokyo (166 miles). The seismographs at Gifu and Nagoya were put out of action a few seconds after the shock began, but, notwithstanding the danger of remaining indoors, the observers at both places re-installed instru-ments within a few hours, and after-shocks were registered at Nagoya from 1.10 p.m., and at Gifu from 1.55 p.m. on Oct. 28. The loss of the first six hours was probably of little consequence,

---

*Imamura, **3**, pp. 49-69; Koto, **4**, pp. 330-353; Milne, **7**, p. 131.

for after-shocks at that time occurred so frequently that it would
have been impossible to separate their records.

222. The number of shocks following the Mino-Owari earthquake was unusually great. At Gifu, 720 after-shocks were

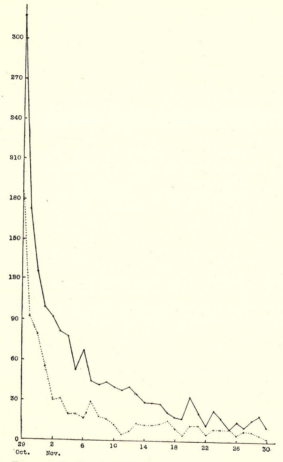

FIG. 34.—Decline in daily frequency of after-shocks at
Gifu and Nagoya (Omori).

recorded during the remainder of October, 1,087 in November and
416 in December, or 2,223 in little more than two months. In successive years from 1892 to 1899, the numbers were 867, 308, 229,
172, 118, 137, 101 and 62, the total number until the end of 1893

being 3,398 and, until the end of 1899, 4,217. At Nagoya, 483 shocks were recorded during the last four days of October, 416 in November and 113 in December, the total for 1891 being 1,012

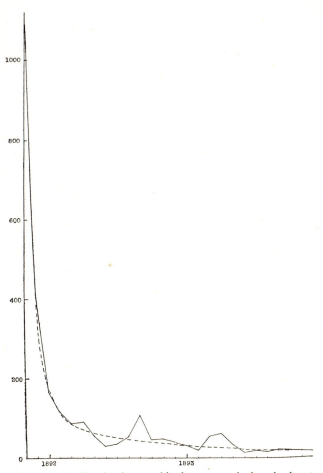

Fig. 35.—Decline in the monthly frequency of after-shocks at Gifu (Omori).

In the following years, the numbers were 188 and 110, the total number until Dec. 1893 being 1,310. The total numbers until the same date at the other observatories were much smaller, 316 being recorded at Tsu, 126 at Kyoto and 71 at Osaka.

223. Of the 3,365 after-shocks recorded at Gifu during the first

two years after the earthquake, 10 were violent, 97 strong, 1,808 weak, 1,041 feeble, and 409 earth-sounds without any tremor. In the days following the great earthquake, violent and strong shocks were frequent, but they became rarer as time advanced. All but one of the violent shocks occurred within the first 4 months, all the strong shocks within the first 13, and all the weak ones within the first 20 months*.

224. *Decline in Frequency.*—The figures already given show how rapidly the frequency of after-shocks declined as time advanced. The rates of decline are represented graphically in *Figs.* 34 and 35. In *Fig.* 34 are shown the curves of daily frequency at Gifu and Nagoya from Oct. 29 to Nov. 30. *Fig.* 35 gives the curve of monthly frequency at Gifu from Nov. 1891 to Dec. 1893.

Though the curves show many fluctuations, representing for the most part the trains of minor shocks following the violent earthquakes, Omori has represented very closely the rate of decline in the frequency of after-shocks by a simple formula. If y is the number of after-shocks within a given interval, the middle of which is separated by x units of time from the epoch of the earthquake, he finds that

$$y = \frac{k}{x + h}$$

where h and k are constants. Taking successive intervals of 12 hours during the first five days Oct. 29-Nov. 2, and applying the method of least squares to the ten equations so given, he obtains the equation

$$y = \frac{440\cdot7}{x + 2\cdot31},$$

Or, taking successive intervals of one month from Nov. 1891 to Apr. 1893, he finds that

$$y = \frac{16\cdot9}{x + 0\cdot397}$$

The latter equation is illustrated by the broken-line in *Fig.* 35, and it shows how closely, in spite of the many fluctuations, the equation does represent the declining rate of occurrence.

225. Though the former equation depends on observations made during the first five days only, Omori shows that it gives satisfactory results for some years afterwards. For instance, he found from this equation that the total number of shocks recorded at Gifu during the years 1898 and 1899 should be 160. The number actually recorded was 163†.

---

*The dates of the violent shocks were 1891 Oct. 30 (3 shocks), Nov. 21 and 28, Dec. 3, 4 and 24, and 1892 Jan. 3 and Sep. 7.

†Omori, **9**, pp. 118-121, 158-191; **12**, pp. 27-31.

226. *Distribution in Space.*—The distribution of after-shock epicentres for two intervals—Nov.-Dec. 1891 and May-June 1892— is represented in *Figs.* 36 and 37, the mode of mapping being the same as that used for the fore-shocks. They are sufficient to reveal the principal features of the distribution, namely (i) the spread of epicentres over the whole fault-region with intense concentration in

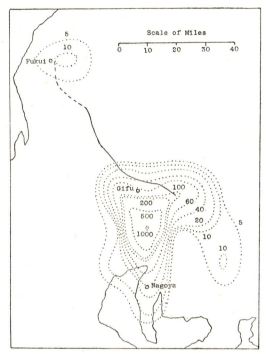

Fig. 36.—Distribution of epicentres of after-shocks, 1891 Nov.-Dec.

the rectangle K near the middle of the secondary fault area, and (ii) the gradual, though fluctuating, contraction of the area of activity towards the central districts. The marked activity within the rectangle K lasted only for two months. In November 65·3 per cent. of all the after-shocks, and in December 63·0 per cent. originated within it. In Jan. 1892, the percentage fell to 7·1, rose to 18·1 in March; but, during the rest of that year, never exceeded 9·2. During the whole of 1892, shocks were most frequent in the rectangles E and F in the neighbourhood of Gifu, the two rectangles including between them three out of every four epicentres in 1892.

227. The seismic activity of the terminal districts was not only less marked, it was also of shorter duration, than in the central district. At the northern end of the main fault, as well as at the south-eastern end of its continuation, all action practically died out before Apr. 1892. In the southern terminal region of the fault-scarp it lasted until, if not after, the close of the same year. A

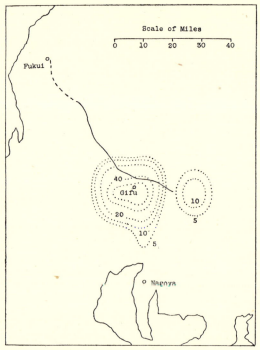

Fig. 37.—Distribution of epicentres of after-shocks,
1892 May-June.

similar withdrawal of activity from its southern end characterises the secondary fault, only two epicentres lying in its neighbourhood after Mar. 1892*.

228. *Periodicity of After-Shocks.* — In the after-shocks of a great earthquake, it is only possible to trace variations of frequency that are comparatively short in period, such as those of 42 minutes, 24 hours and even 14·8 and 29·6 days.

The lunar periods are rather clearly marked. Taking 7-day means of the daily numbers of after-shocks at Gifu, the results show maxima on Dec. 2, 11, 27, Jan. 10, 26, and so on, the mean of 13

*Davison, 1, pp. 9, 13-15.

intervals from 1891 Dec. 2 to 1892 June 9-10 being 14·7 days. In the Nagoya series of means, the average interval is 14·8 days. The 14-day means of the same series reveal traces of a period of about double the length of the latter, the Gifu series showing maxima on Dec. 9, Jan. 3, 29, Feb. 25, Apr. 1 and May 3, the average of the five intervals being 29·3 days. In the Nagoya series, it is somewhat less, or about 28·8 days. It is important to notice that the maxima of the longer period fall close to the times of new moon, and those of the 14·8 day period to the times of new and full moon.

229. In the ordinary earthquakes of Japan, the diurnal period has its maximum epoch at or shortly after noon. The results for the after-shocks of the Mino-Owari earthquake are given in the following Table :—

	Interval	Number of shocks	Epoch	Ampl.
Gifu	1891 Oct. 29-Nov. 10	1,257	12 mid.	·20
,,	1891 Nov. 11-Dec. 31	839	do.	·32
,,	1892	865	do.	·19
,,	1893	272	2 p.m.	·11
,,	1894-99	882	5 p.m.	·11
Nagoya	1891 Oct. 29-Nov. 10	572	3 a.m.	·35
,,	1891 Nov. 11-	1,282	11 p.m.-3 a.m.	·14
,,	1899 Dec. 31			

Thus, at Gifu, more than a year elapsed before the return of the epoch to the neighbourhood of noon.

230. The period of 42 min. duration is of much greater interest, for it is no doubt connected with the throbbing of the earth due to the great displacement. In 21 minutes, the earthquake-movement would reach the antipodes; in 42 minutes, it would return to the focus. If the slips that gave rise to the after-shocks took place in the same direction as the original movement, the maximum-epoch of the 42-minute period should recur at intervals of 42 min. after the great earthquake. If the slips took place in the opposite direction, the epochs should recur about 21 minutes after the ends of the 42-min. intervals. intervals reckoned from the great earthquake. The results for the Mino-Owari earthquake are given in the next table, the epoch being expressed in minutes after the close of each 42-minute interval:

	Interval	Number of shocks	Epoch min.	Ampl.
Gifu	Oct. 28-Nov. 2	863	$18\frac{1}{2}$	·09
,,	Nov. 2-6	201	$9\frac{1}{2}$	·22
,,	Nov. 6-10	177	$3\frac{1}{2}$	·22
Nagoya	Oct. 28-Nov. 2	507	$3\frac{1}{2}$	·11
,,	Nov. 2-6	91	$9\frac{1}{2}$	·47
,,	Nov. 6-10	65	$21\frac{1}{2}$	·41

231. The number of shocks recorded at Gifu is so great that the period can be traced in shorter intervals than those given above. In the next table, the elements of the period are shown for thirteen daily intervals beginning at 2.0 p.m. on Oct. 28, each interval being, however, 12 minutes less than one day and thus containing 34 periods of 42 minutes.

Day	Number of shocks	Epoch min.	Ampl.
1	310	21	·19
2	227	3	·11
3	127	21	·19
4	111	3	·19
5	89	24	·19
6	82	9	·35
7	83	6	·25
8	63	0	·27
9	82	0	·22
10	59	0	·13
11	47	39	·57
12	42	21	·52
13	42	0	·22

Thus, denoting epochs of or about 21 and 0 or 42 min., respectively, by $\frac{1}{2}$ and 1, we have the following series of epochs:

$$\frac{1}{2}, 1, \frac{1}{2}, 1, \frac{1}{2}, \text{ about } 1, 1, 1, 1, 1, 1, \frac{1}{2}, 1,$$

showing that there were no less than seven reversals of epoch during the first thirteen days. It would seem that these reversals were due to the tilting of the triangular crust-block between the faults aa' and A'' (*Fig.* 31 and art. 218), first in one direction and then in the other. Such reversals of tilting have been shown, by repeated lines of levelling, to occur after the Tango earthquake of 1927 (arts. 668, 669). The tilting of this block in different directions along adjoining faults may also be responsible for the opposition in epoch at Gifu and Nagoya during the first and third intervals, as shown in the first of the above tables.

9. SYMPATHETIC EARTHQUAKES

232. The object of the present section is to inquire whether the Mino-Owari earthquake had any effect on the seismic activity of the surrounding regions. The effect that we might anticipate would be a decrease in frequency if the stress were thereby diminished over the whole district, an increase if the stress were relieved in the central area and partly transferred to the adjoining country.

In the accompanying map (*Fig.* 38)*, the district in which the Mino-Owari earthquake and its after-shocks originated is enclosed between the undulating dotted lines. The neighbouring regions are bounded by straight dotted lines and are denoted by the letters A-F. The curves within them are constructed in the same way as those which represent the distribution of fore-shocks and after-shocks. They correspond to 10 and 5 epicentres during the years 1885-1892.

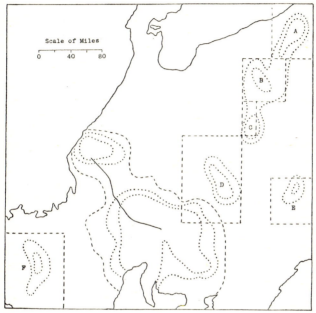

Fig. 38.—Distribution of sympathetic earthquakes in adjoining regions.

The curves in the region marked D and F seem to point to the existence of a pair of transverse faults, one on each side of the Mino-Owari fault-system and roughly parallel to it. The earthquakes in the regions A and E are probably connected with strike-faults and those in the region B with another transverse fault.

233. In the following Table are given the numbers of epicentres that lie within each of these regions from Jan. 1885 to 1891 Oct. 27, and from Nov. 1891 to Dec. 1892. The last line of the table gives the ratio of the average annual number after, to the average annual number before, the principal earthquake.

---

*The map is bounded by the parallels 34° 40′ and 37° 20′ of N. lat. and by the meridians 1° and 4° 30′ W. of Tokyo.

	A	B	C	D	E	F
Before the principal earthquake	66	35·5	5·5	29·5	18·5	20·5
After the same	3	13	31·5	30·5	5	36·5
Ratio	0·3	2·1	33·5	6·1	1·6	10·4

234. The last line shows that in every region but one (A) the frequency of shocks after the Mino-Owari earthquake was greater than it was before. In two other regions (B and E), the ratios are 2·1 and 1·6, a change too slight, perhaps, to have much significance. The ratio is greatest of all in the region C, but this is chiefly due to the large number of shocks that occurred during the months of January and September 1892, and it is uncertain how far these were connected with the Mino-Owari earthquake.

It is in the regions D and F, those nearest the central area, that the change of frequency is most distinct. Moreover, (i) it took place during the month following the great earthquake, the ratios of increased frequency for those months being 20 and 34, respectively; and (ii) the curves representing the distribution of epicentres change from an apparently aimless form before the earthquake to a very regular form after it. It is thus difficult to resist the conclusion that the greatly increased frequency in these two regions, the centres of which lies about 40 and 70 miles from the fault-line, is due to the sudden increase of strain within them after the great earthquake*.

235. Whether the Mino-Owari earthquakes affected the activity of more distant regions is uncertain. Milne, in his study of the earthquakes of 1885-92, divided the whole country into 15 districts. In the two districts containing the main fault and its continuation to the north, the ratios of the average monthly numbers of shocks after the earthquake to those before were 54·3 and 24·0. Two districts on the northeast coast showed a ratio of 3·6, but this was clearly the result of strong earthquakes at the close of 1891. In the two districts to the southwest of the main area, the ratio fell to ·5 on the northwest side of the island and rose to 1·5 on the southeast side; while, in those to the northeast of the main area, it rose to 2·7 on the northwest side, but remained unaltered on the other. In the former, there was a strong earthquake on Nov. 6, which may itself have been a result of the great earthquake. But, on the whole, the absence of any change in the important district surrounding Tokyo seems rather to limit the effects of the earthquake to within a distance of 100 miles from the fault-line.

---

*Davison, **2**, pp. 23-27.

X. Bibliography

1 Davison, C. " On the distribution in space of the accessory shocks of the great Japanese earthquake of 1891." *Geol. Soc. Quart. Journ.*, vol. 53, 1897, pp. 1-15.

2 Davison, C. " On the effect of the great Japanese earthquake of 1891 on the seismic activity of the surrounding districts." *Geol. Mag.*, vol. 4, 1897, pp. 23-27.

3 Imamura, A. " Topographical changes accompanying earthquakes or volcanic eruptions." *Imp. Earthq. Inv. Com. Publ.*, no. 25, 1930, pp. 49-69.

4 Koto, B. " On the cause of the great earthquake in Central Japan, 1891." *Tokyo Imp. Univ. Coll. Sci. Journ.*, vol. 5, 1893, pp. 297-353.

5 Masato, H. " Report on earthquake observations in Japan." *Tokyo, Centr. Meteor. Obs. of Japan,* 1892, pp. 16-18.

6 Milne, J. " Report upon earthquakes observed in Japan, 1889." *Japan Seis. Soc. Trans.*, vol. 16, 1892, pp. 83-117, esp. pp. 99-101.

7 Milne, J. " A note on the great earthquake of October 28th, 1891." *Japan Seis. Journ.*, vol. 1, 1893, pp. 127-151.

8 Milne, J. " A catalogue of 8,331 earthquakes recorded in Japan between 1885 and 1892." *Japan Seis. Journ.*, vol. 4, 1895, pp. i-xxi, 1-367.

9 Omori, F. " Of the after-shocks of earthquakes." *Tokyo Imp. Univ. Coll. Sci. Journ.*, vol. 7, 1894, pp. 113-200.

10 Omori, F. " Sull'intensità a sull'ampiezza del movimento nel gran terremoto giapponese del 28 ottobre 1891." *Ital. Soc. Sism. Boll.*, vol. 2, 1896, pp. 189-200.

11 Omori, F. " Note on the great Mino-Owari earthquake of Oct. 28th, 1891." *Imp. Earthq. Inv. Com. Publ.*, no. 4, 1900, pp. 13-24.

12 Omori, F. " Note on the after-shocks of the Mino-Owari earthquake of Oct. 28th, 1891." *Imp. Earthq. Inv. Com. Publ.*, no. 7, 1902, pp. 27-31.

13 Omori, F. " Note on the relation between earthquake frequency and the atmospheric pressure." *Tokyo Phys.-Math. Soc. Rep.*, vol. 2, 1904, no. 8.

CHAPTER IX

SANRIKU EARTHQUAKES : 1896 June 15
and 1933 March 3

236. The two great earthquakes that form the main subjects of this chapter differ from all others described in these pages. The origins of both were submarine and so far from land that their destructive effects were almost entirely due to the great seawaves that followed them and swept over a line of coast about 300 miles in length. This coast-line and the adjoining prefectures are shown in *Fig.* 39.

237. *Past Seawaves on the Sanriku Coast.*—The past tunami or seawaves along this coast have been studied by Prof. A. Imamura. Counting only those that reached a height of 9 or 10 ft., there were twelve at least before 1896, as follows:—

869 July 13, an extremely severe earthquake, followed soon after by seawaves, by which about 1,000 lives were lost and hundreds of villages were ruined. This and the next were probably the largest of all known tunami on this coast.

1611 Dec. 2, a severe earthquake of long duration preceded the tunami. About 4,783 lives were lost. The seawaves flooded the town of Yamada, ¾ miles from the coast. After sweeping up the Koyatori inlet, the waves rushed over the pass beyond into Yamada Bay, so that their height must have been about 80 ft. In the same district, the heights of the waves in 1896 and 1933 were 57 and 39 ft., respectively.

Between 1611 and 1896, seawaves, usually rather small, occurred ten times, in the years 1616, 1640 (when more than 700 persons were drowned), 1677, 1689, 1763, 1793, 1835, 1843, 1856 and 1894. The epicentres of the earthquakes of 1843 and 1894 lay off the southeast coast of Hokkaido, those of the earthquakes of 1896, 1897 and 1933 off the coast of Sanriku. It is worthy of notice that all five epicentres lay on the western slope of the Tuscaroora Deep at depths of from 3,000 to 4,000 metres (1·8 to 2·5 miles).

Imamura also points out that large secondary undulations were observed in the water of the bays of the Sanriku coast a few hours before the arrival of the great seawaves, especially in 1894, 1896 and 1933. They probably indicate that minor crustal deformations preceded by some hours the main displacements*.

1. SANRIKU EARTHQUAKE : 1896 JUNE 15

238. During this great earthquake, the main destruction occurred in the prefecture of Iwate, in the town of Kamaisi and in many neighbouring villages. Notable damage was caused from the prefecture of Miyagi to the prefectures of Hidake and Tokachi along the southern coast of Hokkaido.

The shock was recorded at Miyako at 7h. 32m. 30s., p.m. (10h. 32m. 30s., a.m., G.M.T.), and the first great wave swept in 21 min. later.

239. The first estimate of the position of the epicentre was made by Dr. T. Iki from the directions in which the seawaves arrived at various ports. He assigned it to a spot about 143 miles east of Kamaisi. As Imamura and Kawase have pointed out, however, he overlooked the changes in direction of the seawaves as they advanced into shallow water. Taking these into account, and also relying on the times of transit of the seawaves, the latter authors estimate the distance of the epicentre from Kamaisi as 93 miles, its position being in lat. 39.2° N., long. 143.5° E. This point is represented by the black spot in *Fig.* 40.

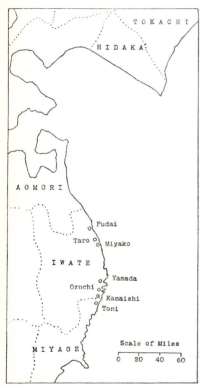

FIG. 39.—Prefectures chiefly affected by the Sanriku earthquakes of 1896 and 1933.

The dotted lines in the sea area (*Fig.* 40) represent isobaths in fathoms. It will be noticed that the epicentre lies close to the 2,000-fathom line, on the western slope of the Tuscaroora Deep. This, as Milne points out, is a well-known source for many great earthquakes.

*Imamura, **4**, pp. 79-93.

240. At Misako and Yamada, two of the places nearest the epicentre, a few houses were damaged by the shock. Otherwise, within the broken-line marked 2, the shock was weak, that is, the motion was well-pronounced, but not strong enough to cause general alarm. In the zone between the broken-lines 2 and 1, the shock was slight, or just strong enough to be felt*.

241. *Loss of Life and Property.*—In the following Table are given the total losses in the prefectures chiefly affected :—

Prefecture	Number of lives lost	Number of persons injured	Number of houses destroyed
Miyagi	2,557	505	688
Iwati	25,413	1,244	5,030
Aomori	346	248	484
Hidaka	5	—	20
Total	28,321	1,997	6,222

In several villages, the losses were very heavy. In the prefecture of Miyagi, 52 per cent. of the inhabitants of Hyori were drowned and 63 per cent. of the houses were washed away; at Toni, the corresponding figures were 78 and 72. In the prefecture of Iwate, the losses were in some places still more serious. At Kamaisi, 4,700 out of 6,557 of the inhabitants, or 72 per cent., were drowned, and 88 per cent. of the houses were destroyed. At Funakoshi, the figures were 58 and 78, at Yamada 28 and 46, at Osawa 53 and 98, at Omohe 47 and 68, at Taro 71 and 20, and at Fudai 50 and 29. The total loss of life thus approached that of 36,380, caused by the seawaves that swept over the coasts of Java and Sumatra during the eruption of Krakatoa in 1883†.

242. *Seismic Seawaves.* — The seawaves thus were highest and most destructive along a line of coast about 100 miles in length from Fudai on the north to Yoshihama (or Hyori) on the south. It is difficult to obtain trustworthy estimates of their maximum height. According to Honda and his colleagues, it reached as much as 24 metres or 94½ ft. at Yoshihama. Milne gives the height of the largest wave at Miyako as 15 ft. and along the coasts of Tokachi and Moyori in Hokkaido as 60 or 100 ft. Half a mile from the shore at Kamaihi, there were no traces to be seen of the waves, but, at a distance of 500 yd. inland, straws adhering to trees showed that the greatest height reached at that point was 8 ft. Even so far as the Bonin Islands (about 900 miles), the sea rose 3 or 4 ft. At Kamaisi, two schooners, each of about 100 tons, floated in on the waves and were left stranded, one of them in a cornfield 200 yd.

---

*Omori, etc., **9**, pp. 164-166.
†Anon, **1**, p. 32; Milne, **7**, pp. 157, 160; Symons, G. J. (ed.), *The Eruption of Krakatoa and Subsequent Phenomena*, 1888, p. 26.

from the shore, the other 50 yd. inland among the debris of the houses.

243. The seawaves were recorded by at least five tide-gauges in Japan, and also across the Pacific at Honolulu (3,641 miles) and Sausalito, near San Francisco (5,000 miles).

The mareogram at Ayukawa shows a series of large waves, that lasted for more than two days. The first movement was a slight fall of 6·5 in., beginning at 8.24 p.m. This was followed by a rise of 55·6 in. and then by a fall of 84·8 in. The greatest movement occurred between 11 and 12 p.m. on June 15, when a rise of 95·5 in. was immediately succeeded by a fall of 97·3 in. In the latter part of the record, there occurs a series of beats, probably due to the period of the incident waves (about 8 min.) being slightly different from that of the free oscillation of the bay.

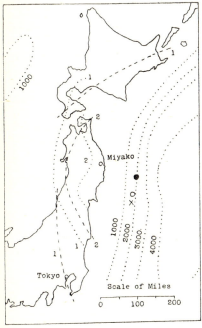

FIG. 40.—Isoseismal lines of the Sanriku earthquake of 1896 (Omori and Hirata).

244. The first movement at Honolulu was a small rise of about ¾ in. at 7.43 a.m. local time (6.15 p.m. G.M.T.). For about two hours, the motion was somewhat irregular, after which the mean distance between crest and hollow of succeeding waves was 1·2 in. At 8 p.m. on June 17, the surface of the water shows signs of returning to its normal steadiness.

Sausalito lies at the entrance to San Francisco Bay. At the time of the earthquake, the gauge here was the only one in operation on the Pacific coast of the United States. In this record, as in that at Honolulu, the first evidence of any change is a rise of 3·7 in. at 1·5 p.m., Pacific standard time (9.5 p.m., G.M.T.). During the first two hours, the waves were larger and of longer period than those that followed, the chief movement occurring between 1.30 and 1.45

p.m., when the water rose 6·8 in. and fell 2·2 in. At 1 p.m. on June 17, there were still very distinct signs of movement due to the Sanriku earthquake.

245. The distance between the epicentre and Honolulu, measured along a great circle, is 3,641 miles, and the times occupied by the waves in crossing was 7h. 44m. The mean velocity of the seawaves was thus 691 ft. per sec. If the ocean were of uniform depth between the two points, the depth corresponding to this mean velocity (as given by the equation $v^2 = gh$) would be 14,833 ft.

Again, the distance from the epicentre to Sausalito is about 5,000 miles, the time-interval was 10h. 34m.; and the mean velocity between the two places was thus 694 ft. per sec. On the same assumption as before, the mean depth of the ocean between the two places would be 14,960 ft.

246. The great circle from the epicentre to Honolulu crosses a part of the ocean that is very variable in depth. That to Sausalito, however, is entirely free from islands and crosses the isobaths approximately at right angles. The mean depth along this line is more than 17,000 ft., the value obtained from the formula being about 88 per cent. of the measured value*.

247. *After-Shocks.*—With an origin so far from land, a full series of after-shocks is not to be expected. Prof. Milne, however, gives a list of 13 weak, and 85 slight, shocks observed in North Japan within 20 hours after the earthquake. During the five days June 15-19, 36 shocks were registered at Tokyo. One after-shock recorded at Miyako at 0h. 46m. 25s., p.m. on June 17, was of considerable strength. The dotted lines 2 and 1 in *Fig.* 40 bound the areas within which the shock was weak and slight, respectively†.

248. Neither list is full enough to throw any light on the diurnal periodicity of the after-shocks. The 42-min. period is, however, shown in both—at 27 min. after the close of the 42-min. intervals (ampl. ·32) according to the first list, and at 15 min. (ampl. ·40) according to the second. It would seem, then, that the minima of the period agreed approximately with the return-movements, that is, that the displacements causing the early after-shocks were in the opposite direction to that which gave rise to the principal earthquake.

249. On 1897 Aug. 5 at 9 a.m., an earthquake was severely felt along the Sanriku coast. It must be regarded as a separate earthquake rather than as an after-shock of the earthquake of 1896,

---

*Davison, **2**, pp. 579-584; Honda, etc., **3**, pp. 90-93; Milne, **11**, pp. 25-31. For an explanation of the above inequality, see *Phil. Mag.*, vol. 43, 1897 pp. 33-36.
†Milne, **11**, pp. 7-8, 22-23.

for its epicentre (indicated by the small cross in *Fig.* 40) lay 66 miles to the south-southwest of the last. About half an hour later, a small seawave swept over the coast. It reached a height of about 10 ft. at Okkirai, Hirota, Onagawa and Oohara (the first and last of which are about 50 miles apart), and flooded houses and fields on low ground, besides causing damage to embankments. The epicentre lay about 20 miles south-south-west of that of the earthquake of 1933, in about lat. 38·3° N., long. 143·2° E.*.

II. SANRIKU EARTHQUAKE : 1933 MAR. 3

250. Less than forty years after the earthquake described above, the same coasts were swept by destructive seawaves following an earthquake that occurred in nearly the same region.

As soon as the news of the disaster reached Tokyo, several members of the Earthquake Research Institute were sent to the districts chiefly affected, to determine the highest levels reached by the seawaves, the areas of the regions inundated, the damage to property, and the relations between the effects of the waves and topographical conditions. Their reports are included in a special volume of the Institute's Bulletin containing 521 pages and 251 plates.

251. The earthquake occurred at about 2.32 a.m. on Mar. 3 (5.32 p.m. on Mar. 2, G.M.T.). From the observations at Tokyo, Imamura and Kawase place the epicentre in lat. 38·5° N., long. 143·3° E. This point, which is represented by the small circle in *Fig.* 40, lies about 50 miles to the south of that of the earlier earthquake, and about 80 miles from the coast.

252. *Loss of Life and Property.*—Owing to this distance, the shock, though widely felt on land, caused only slight damage along and near the coast. The losses of life and property were almost entirely due to the seawaves that swept in after intervals of between 25 and 40 min. These are summarised in the following Table :—

Prefecture, etc.	No. of lives lost	No. of persons injured	No. of houses destroyed
Hokkaido	13	56	61
Aomori	30	70	264
Iwate	2,670	805	7,072
Miyage	309	161	1,454
Total	3,022	1,092	8,851

In addition, more than 8,000 boats and other vessels were destroyed†.

---

*Imamura, **4**, pp. 91-92.
†Imamura, etc., **5**, pp. 33-35.

253. *Seismic Seawaves.*—In Hokkaido, the greatest heights reached by the waves, as shown by marks left on trees, posts, slopes, etc., was 15 ft. In the Main Island, it was 15 ft. at Kamaisi, the town that suffered most in 1896, but, farther to the south, it rose to 62 ft. along the coast at Ryori Sirahama (and 93 ft. inland) and 75 ft. at Hirota Atumari. The waves swept in so rapidly that a motor-boat from Kamaisi, with a speed of 12 miles an hour, could make no headway against them.

254. The propagation of the seawaves was studied by Prof. N. Miyabe. The waves were recorded at 17 stations on the Pacific coasts of Japan. The times at which the first waves arrived at each station cannot always be determined with precision, and there may be errors of as much as 5 min. in the estimates. Taking their probable values and using the formula $v = \sqrt{(gh)}$, Prof. Miyabe drew circles with the stations as centres and radii equal to the distances the waves would travel during the intervals between the time of the earthquake and the times of arrival at the respective stations. These circles do not intersect in a point, but envelop one side of an area about 360 miles long from north to south. Thus, it is possible that the displacement that gave rise to the seawaves may have been several hundred miles in length.

255. The seawaves were also recorded by tide-gauges at Honolulu, San Francisco and Santa Monica (Cal.). The records at Manila and Wellington (N.Z.) show no trace of the waves, perhaps on account of the disturbing effects of intermediate islands. Nor do those at Sydney and Melbourne with certainty. On the other hand, they were registered with considerable amplitude at Iquique, though that station is nearly 9,000 miles from the origin of the earthquake. The times of transit to Honolulu and San Francisco were in each case 12 min. less than in 1896*.

256. A remarkable feature of these seawaves was the series of luminous phenomena exhibited as the waves approached the shore. Among these phenomena, which Mr. K. Musya described and classified in interesting detail, is reported a strong flash of light that seemed to be emitted from the surface of the sea near the mouth of Kamaisi Bay. Prof. Terada shows that the most probable explanation of the flash is that the turbulence of the water in front of the advancing wave excited simultaneous luminosity in a swarm of *Noctiluca miliaris*†.

---

*Miyabe, **12**, pp. 112-126.
†Musya, **13**, pp. 87-111; Terada, **18**, pp. 25-35.

III. BIBLIOGRAPHY

1 ANON. "The great disaster in Japan, June 15th, 1896." A series of letters reprinted from the *Japan Gazette* (Yokohama).

2 DAVISON, C. "On the sea-waves connected with the Japanese earthquake of June 15, 1896." *Phil. Mag.,* vol. 50, 1900, pp. 579-584.

3 HONDA, K., TERADA, T., YOSHIDA, Y., and ISITANI, D. "Secondary undulations of oceanic tides." *Imp. Earthq. Inv. Com. Publ.,* no. 26, 1908, pp. 90-93.

4 IMAMURA, A. "Past tunamis of the Sanriku coast." *Japan. Journ. Astr. Geoph.,* vol. 11, 1934, pp. 79-93.

5 IMAMURA, A., and KAWASE, Z. "The Sanriku tunami of 1933." *Japan. Journ. Astr. Geoph.,* vol. 11, 1933, pp. 17-36.

6 ISHIMOTO, M. "Preliminary notes on the tunami of March 2, 1933 (G.M.T.), and an outline of the investigations now being made concerning it at the Earthquake Research Institute." *Japan. Journ. Astr. Geoph.,* vol. 11, 1933, pp. 1-10.

7 ISHIMOTO, M., and HAGIWARA, T. "The tunami considered as a phenomenon of sea water overflowing the land." *Earthq. Res. Inst. Bull.,* Suppl., vol. 1, 1934, pp. 17-24.

8 INOUYE, W. "On sound phenomena of the Sanriku earthquake of March 3rd, 1933." *Earthq. Res. Int. Bull,* Suppl., vol. 1, 1934, pp. 77-86.

9 MATUZAWA, T., KANBARA, K., and MINAHAMI, T. "Horizontal movement of water in the tunami of March 3, 1933." *Japan. Journ. Astr. Geoph.,* vol. 11, 1933, pp. 11-16.

10 MILNE, J. "The great sea-waves in Japan." *Geogr. Journ.,* vol. 8, 1896, pp. 157-160.

11 MILNE, J. "On the sea-waves and earthquakes of June 15th, 1896, in North Japan." *Brit. Ass. Rep.,* 1897, pp. 25-31.

12 MIYABE, N. "An investigation of the Sanriku tunami based on mareogram data." *Earthq. Res. Inst. Bull.,* Suppl., vol. 1, 1934, pp. 112-126.

13 MUSYA, K. "On the luminous phenomena that accompanied the great Sanriku tunami in 1933. (Part I.)." *Earthq. Res. Inst. Bull.,* Suppl., vol. 1, 1934, pp. 87-111.

14 NASU, N. "Heights of tunamis and damage to structures." *Earthq. Res. Inst. Bull.,* Suppl., vol. 1, 1934, pp. 218-227.

15 OMORI, F., and HIRATA, K. "Earthquake measurements at Miyako." *Tokyo Imp. Univ. Coll. Sci. Journ.,* vol. 11, 1899, pp. 164-166.

16 OTUKA, T. "Tunami damages March 3rd, 1933, and the topography of Sanriku coast, Japan." *Earthq. Res. Inst. Bull.,* Suppl., vol. 1, 1934, pp. 127-151.

17 TAKAHASI, R. "Seiches and surface waves in Ohunato Bay and two other bays." *Earthq. Res. Inst. Bull.,* Suppl., vol. 1, 1934, pp. 198-217.

18 TERADA, T. "Luminous phenomena accompanying destructive sea-waves (tunami)." *Earthq. Res. Inst. Bull.,* Suppl., vol. 1, 1934, pp. 25-35, and *Tokyo Imp. Acad. Proc.,* vol. 9, 1933, pp. 367-369.

19 YAMAGUTI, S. "Abnormally high waves, or 'tunami,' on the coast of Sanriku in Japan on March 3, 1933." *Earthq. Res. Inst. Bull.,* Suppl., vol. 1, 1934, pp. 36-54.

CHAPTER X

ASSAM EARTHQUAKE : 1897 June 12

I. INTRODUCTION

257. Among the great earthquakes of the world, the Assam earthquake holds, and must always hold, a very prominent place. Though it occurred in an unstable region, in one of the most unstable provinces of India, no earlier Assam earthquake has possessed a disturbed area of more than a few hundred thousand sq. miles. It belongs, indeed, to the same order of earthquakes as the Lisbon earthquake of 1755 and the Kansu earthquake of 1920.

The area disturbed by the earthquake is shown in *Fig.* 42, and the epicentral area, on a larger scale, in *Fig.* 43.

II. ASSAM EARTHQUAKES BEFORE 1897

258. For our knowledge of Assam earthquakes, we are indebted chiefly to Mr. T. Oldham's report on " The Cachar Earthquake of 10th January 1869 " and his valuable " Catalogue of Indian Earthquakes "*. Confining ourselves to destructive earthquakes only, we find recorded not more than three earthquakes that can be assigned to origins within the province of Assam, as follows:—

1845 Aug. 6, int. 1 (Milne scale), several houses injured in Gauhati and Sylhet.

1852 May, int. 2, Darjiling.

1869 Jan. 10, int. 3, Assam, Silchar, etc.

259. Of these earthquakes, we know little except as regards the Cachar or Silchar earthquake of 1869. The boundary of the disturbed area of this earthquake is represented approximately by the outer dotted line in *Fig.* 41. It is oval in form, about 650 miles long, 400 miles wide, and includes about 200,000 sq. miles. The inner dotted line, drawn in part, surrounds the area in which the shock was severe. Completing the curve, it is about 260 miles long, 135 miles wide, and contains about 27,500 sq. miles. The broken-lines represent the boundary of the epicentral area and the inner-

---

*India Geol. Surv. Mem., vol. 19, pt. i, 1882, pp. 1-98, and pt. ii, 1883, pp. 1-53.

most isoseismal of the earthquake of 1897. The epicentre, according to the observations of Mr. T. Oldham, lies in about lat. 26° N., long. 92° 40ʹ E., on the northern borders of the Jaintia Hills. The epicentral area of the earthquake of 1869 thus lay to the east of that of the earthquake of 1897.

III. INVESTIGATION OF THE EARTHQUAKE

260. Soon after the news of the earthquake reached Calcutta, four officers of the Geological Survey, and later on a fifth, were

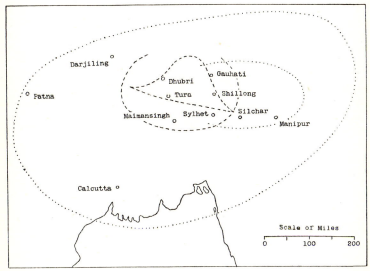

FIG. 41.—Isoseismal lines of the Cachar earthquake of 1869 (T. Oldham).

sent to study the effects of the shock in different parts of the shaken country. During the cold weather of 1897-98, Mr. R. D. Oldham made a tour of the epicentral region, examined the remarkable faults and fractures, and gathered evidence of other dislocations of the crust. The report, in which he embodied the observations of himself and others, is one of the most careful and detailed that we possess. The after-shocks were frequent and were connected with many different centres. They were recorded by a pendulum seismograph at Shillong from Aug. 4, and by various observers at Cherrapunji, Goalpara, Laitlynkote, Mairang, Maophlang, Tura and elsewhere.

261. When it became clear that notable changes of level had occurred in the central district, the Government of Assam and the

Director of the Geological Survey both suggested that the triangulation of the country should be repeated. This was done, so far as was possible, during the cold weather of 1897. Though the results were to some extent disappointing, it is worthy of notice that the Assam earthquake was the first in which such a survey was proposed and carried out*.

IV. LOSS OF LIFE AND PROPERTY

262. The earthquake occurred at about 5.15 p.m., local time, and, as most persons were then out of doors, the death-roll for so great an earthquake was comparatively small. The total number of persons killed was only 1,542, about 600 of these by landslips at and near Cherrapunji, 117 at Cheyla, and 17 in the coal-mines of Cherrapunji.

263. The damage to property must have been very great, for, within an area of 30,000 sq. miles, all brick and stone buildings were practically destroyed, and in this area were to be found all the principal towns of the province—Shillong, Sylhet, Gauhati, Goalpara, Dhubri and Tura†.

V. INTENSITY OF THE SHOCK

264. A great part of the area in which the earthquake was felt is a wild thinly populated country. Brick and stone buildings are rare and widely scattered. Thus, a detailed scale, such as the Rossi-Forel scale, was useless, and the following simple scale was devised by Mr. Oldham for the purpose:—

6. The destruction of brick and stone buildings was practically universal.

5. The damage to masonry or brick buildings was universal, often serious, amounting in some cases to destruction.

4. All or nearly all brick buildings were damaged.

3. The earthquake was universally felt, severely enough to disturb furniture and loose objects, but not to cause damage, except in a few instances, to brick buildings.

2. The shock was strong enough to be generally noticed, but not to cause any damage.

1. The earthquake was only noticed by a small proportion of people who were sitting or lying down or were otherwise favourably placed for observing it.

Roughly, these degrees may be taken to correspond with the

---

*The re-triangulation of Sumatra was in progress when the earthquake of 1892 May 17 occurred (H. F. Reid, *Amer. Seis. Soc. Bull.,* vol. 3, 1913, pp. 72-79).

†Luttnam-Johnson, **1**, p. 55.

following degrees of the Rossi-Forel scale : 10, 9, 8, 7-6, 5-4 and 3-2.

265. Isoseismal lines, corresponding with these degrees, are represented by the dotted lines on the map in *Fig. 42.* Owing to

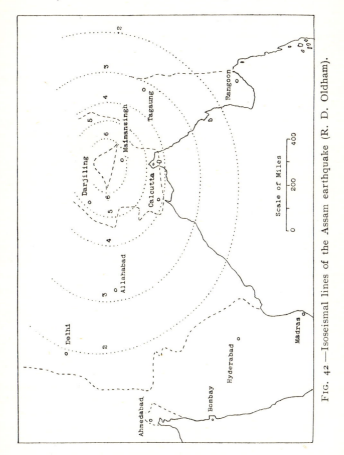

FIG. 42.—Isoseismal lines of the Assam earthquake (R. D. Oldham).

the absence in many parts of the necessary records, Mr. Oldham regards them as purely diagrammatic, as representing what their course would probably be if we might suppose that local conditions were everywhere uniform. It must be remembered that one-third of the area over which the shock was sensible was one from which no observations could be obtained, while another third was inhabited by ignorant and illiterate tribes. With regard to two of the areas, however, those in which serious damage occurred to buildings and in which the shock was sensible to human beings, our information is somewhat more trustworthy. Their boundaries are represented by the broken-lines in *Fig*. 42. The former area contains not less than 145,000 sq. miles, or, if we include the portion from which no reports were procurable, about 160,000 sq. miles— the area of Great Britain is 89,088 sq. miles—while the total disturbed area was about 1,750,000 sq. miles or rather less than half the size of Europe.

266. Within the innermost isoseismal (*Fig*. 42), the broken-line represents the boundary of the epicentral area, as traced by Oldham. Its course is to be regarded as approximate only. It is drawn so as to include all the districts in which dislocations of the crust were observed or measured by the new trigonometrical survey, and all places at which large numbers of after-shocks were observed. As drawn, the length of the area is 200 miles, its greatest width 100 miles, and the area covered by it about 11,050 sq. miles*.

VI. Nature, etc., of the Shock

267. *Nature of the Shock*. — At Shillong, in the epicentral area, a deep rumbling sound was heard, followed, after 2 sec., by the shock. In 2 or 3 sec., the vibrations reached their greatest strength. The ground rocked so violently that it was impossible to stand. The separate movements were sudden, every third or fourth being of greater range. The surface of the ground vibrated visibly in every direction and long cracks appeared in the road. The total duration of the movement was estimated at less than one minute.

In other parts of the area, the estimates of the duration were greater, ranging from about $1\frac{1}{2}$ min. to 8 min., the average of 15 estimates being $3\frac{3}{4}$ min.

268. *Visible Waves*.—These were observed over a wide area. According to an observer at Shillong, the surface of the earth presented the aspect of a storm-tossed sea, with this difference that the undulations were more rapid than any seen at sea. At Nalbari, the waves could be seen following one another, the rice falling and rising as they passed. Their speed, though decidedly faster than a man could walk, was not so fast as he could run. At Mangaldai, the waves came from opposite directions, meeting in a heap, when water and sand were thrown up to a height of 18 in., and then falling back, the ground at the same time opening slightly. Mr. Oldham estimates that, on an average, the waves were about 30 ft. long and 1 ft. in height.

---

*Oldham, **3**, pp. 42-52, 78-85, 129-134, 168-173.

269. *Intensity of the Shock.*—The only direct measure of the range of motion was made at Cherrapunji. From the displacement of two oblong masonry tombs at this place, it is clear that the range lay between 10 and 18 in., and was probably not far from their mean value, namely, 14 in.

270. Estimates of the maximum horizontal acceleration were made at several places in and near the epicentral area by means of West's formula (art. 208). The figures are not unlike those obtained for the Mino-Owari earthquake of 1891, namely, 1,200 mm. per sec. per sec. at Silchar, 2,700 at Dhubri, 3,000 at Cherrapunji, 3,600 at Gauhati, Shillong and Sylhet, and 4,200 at Goalpara. At all of these places and throughout the epicentral area, there was a very large vertical component, greater than that due to gravity or 9,400 mm. per sec. per sec. This is shown by the vertical projection of stones. On the grassy slopes of the Khasi Hills, rounded blocks of weathered gneiss or granite lay partially embedded. Many of them were thrown from their places, leaving a sharply cut mould in the soil, slightly broken down on the side towards which the stone was projected (*Plate* 4A). These moulds were usually seen on slopes, sometimes also on level ground. That the stones were actually projected is shown by the dents made where they fell without any trace in between of their having touched the ground.

At Nongstoin, a block of granite, about 3 ft. long, 1 ft. wide and 9 in. thick, that before the earthquake lay flat on the ground, was thrown to such a height that it broke in two in falling. Near the same place, a splinter of granite about 3 ft. long was thrown to a distance of 8½ ft. Also, a monolith about 6 ft. high was shot out of its socket, and the deep dent where it first struck the ground was at a distance of 6½ ft.

At Tura, the ground, wherever it was sandy, appeared as if a steam plough had passed over it, tearing up the turf and throwing the sods in every direction*.

271. *Seismic Seiches.* — At some distance from the central area, seiches were observed in pools, though not so prominently as during the Lisbon earthquake of 1755. At a spot near Tagaung in Burmah (330 miles from Shillong), there is a shallow reservoir about 300 yd. long, formerly part of an old river-course. Between 5 and 6 p.m. on June 12, the water was seen lapping up against the bank. It was at first thought to be due to elephants bathing, but none were there. The trees shook, but no shock was felt. At Thayetmyo also in Burmah (470 miles from Shillong), the water in a small tank, 40 yd. square, began to oscillate at about 5.30 p.m., the greatest rise of the water at the east end being 18 in. The

---

*Luttnam-Johnson, **1**; Oldham, **3**, pp. 4-8, 20, 26-27, 334.

movement lasted for about 3 min. At this place, also, no shock was felt*.

272. *Rotation of Pillars*.—In no other earthquake have examples of the rotation of pillars been so frequently observed. The most striking was that of the Inglis monument at Chhatak (*Plate* 5A), a short distance to the south of the epicentral area. The monument was an obelisk, made of broad flat bricks, rising from a base 12 ft. square to a height of more than 60 ft. Two portions, altogether 15 ft. in height, were broken off. The part left standing was fractured at a height of about 23 ft. above the ground, and the upper portion, 22 ft. in height, was twisted over the lower through an angle of 30° in the counter-clockwise direction.

273. The rotation in this and other columns was probably due (i) to the rocking of these detached portions during the earthquake, and (ii) to the arrival of vibrations coming in different directions from other parts of the focus†.

VII. Dislocations of the Crust

274. The permanent changes connected with the earthquake take the form of: (i) faults and fractures; (ii) differential changes of level of which we have evidence in the interruptions of drainage without perceptible fault, in other words, warping; (iii) variations of level suggested by reported changes in the aspect of the landscape; and, lastly (iv) changes proved by the re-triangulation of a portion of the epicentral area.

275. Though somewhat limited in size—there are, for instance, no fault-displacements of the magnitude of those that accompanied the Mino-Owari earthquake of 1891 or the California earthquake of 1906—they are distributed over an area in the northern part of the Assam Hills at least 100 miles in length from east to west. Near the southern boundary of this area, the changes seem to have been long low rolls, the variation of slope not being sufficient to cause any appreciable change in the drainage. Beyond this, lies a zone in which the changes are more abrupt, the slopes of the stream beds have been tilted so greatly that alterations have been been made in their courses, but no fracturing or faulting extends up to the surface. Lastly, close to the northern edge of the hills, the rocks have been fractured and faulted, and perceptible scarps have been left as evidence of the surface movement. These changes are most conspicuous along the northern edge of the Garo Hills west of the meridian of 91° E., and it is worthy of notice that the greatest of the faults observed is that which lies farthest to the

---

*Oldham, **3**, pp. 39-40.
†Oldham, **3**, pp. 207-226.

north. It is difficult to believe that the permanent dislocations cease abruptly along this northern slope and do not extend beneath the alluvium of the Goalpara and Kamrup districts. They are masked, however, if they do occur, by the secondary effects of the earthquake, such as the shifting of the superficial layers of alluvium.

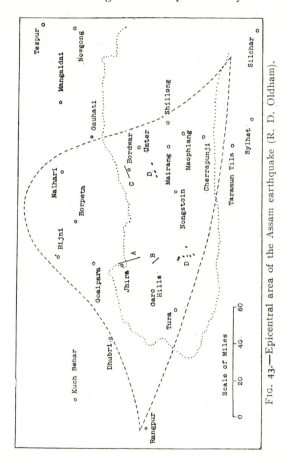

FIG. 43.—Epicentral area of the Assam earthquake (R. D. Oldham).

Thus, the only evidence that we possess of crustal dislocations is the fact that, all down the course of the Brahmaputra, the floods of the latter half of 1897 were more extensive and rose to a greater height than was ever known before the earthquake. And, in no part, were they so disastrous and so long-continued as in the neighbourhood of Borpeta*.

---

*Oldham, **3**, pp. 138, 160-163.

276. *Faults and Fractures*. — Of the fractures with a perceptible throw at the surface, the most important is that known as the Chedrang fault (A, *Fig.* 43), from the river to the course of which it clings. The path of the fault is traced in *Fig.* 44, the numbers at different points denoting the upward throw of the east side in feet. At its southern end, as shown on this map, the fault has no throw on the surface, but the hillside is much fissured and small trees are snapped across. Farther to the south, the fault is lost in thick jungle. Towards the

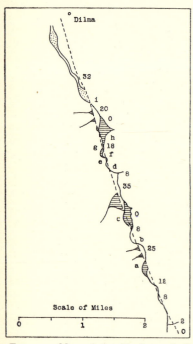

FIG. 44.--Map of the Chedrang fault (R. D. Oldham).

north, it crosses a small tributary of the Chedrang river, where the east side has an upward throw of about 2 ft. Continuing to the north-northwest, the fault keeps to the river-valley, crossing and re-crossing the stream. At every point at which it crosses from east to west (as at b, d, f, i in *Fig.* 44), a waterfall was formed (*Plate* 4B). At places where it crosses from west to east (as at a, c, e, g), the water is ponded back into small pools.

About half a mile below this waterfall, the fault enters a broad sheet of water (c, *Fig.* 44), the recent origin of which is shown by a number of dead trees and bamboo clumps standing in the water. The pool is about half a mile long, from 300 to 400 yd. wide, and its greatest depth is 18 ft. At the point where the fault leaves the pool, its throw is almost zero. There is no apparent barrier, the bed of the pool sinking gradually below the water. In other words, the natural slope of the channel has been reversed and a depression formed in which the water accumulated. The greatest width and depth of the pool occur at the point where the fault has no throw and its northern margin at a part of the fault where the throw is rapidly increasing. Thus, the pool is not directly due to the fault, over which, indeed, it spreads, but rather to an undulation in the surface of the ground. It is worthy of notice that, within half a mile, the uplift of the crust on the east side increases from 0 to 35 ft.

About a mile beyond the north end of this pool, there begins (at h, *Fig.* 44) another large pool on the east side of the fault, more than half a mile in length and in one part nearly as wide. The bed sinks under the water of the lake, the throw of the fault decreasing from 18 ft. to zero, and then increasing, beyond the north end of the lake, to 20 ft.

Less than a mile farther on, the fault has a throw of 32 ft. But, after this, it passes under thick alluvium, and shows no longer as a scarp but as a short slope. When this is forest-covered, the trees have been tilted over in a remarkable manner. Beyond this point, the fault can be traced, though not very clearly to Jhira. North of this village, there is a sheet of water about 1½ miles long, ¾ mile wide, and 12 ft. deep, that spreads over the old river-course. At the north end of the lake, the drainage escapes over a barrier that, on account of the thickness of the alluvium, seems to be a gentle roll or undulation of the surface rather than a scarp.

To the north of Jhira, the throw of the fault decreases and possibly dies out before reaching the hills to the north and west of the village. The total length of the Chedrang fault thus cannot be less than 12 miles, while its greatest throw is as much as 35 ft. It is important to notice that: (i) wherever there is any perceptible scarp, the relative upthrow is invariably on the east side; (ii) no pronounced horizontal displacement could be detected at any place; (iii) wherever the plane of the fault could be seen in rock, it was practically vertical; and (iv) the displacement seems to have been principally, if not entirely, an uplift of the east side.

The last conclusion is supported by the position of the two large pools behind undulations formed on the east side of the fault. At the lower of the two pools, the rapids between the outlet and point where the stream rejoined its former channel maintained the appearance of those in a mountain stream, even though it flowed over alluvium instead of rock. Moreover, the whole of the alluvial plain of Lower Assam is raised but little above the level of the sea, so little, indeed, that, if the changed gradient of the stream-bed were due to subsidence, the whole area depressed must have been flooded.

277. Another fault, much smaller than the Chedrang fault, passes near the village of Samin, about 10 miles to the south of the other. The general direction of the Samin fault (B, *Fig.* 43) is N. 60° W., its total length is about 2½ miles, and the relative upthrow—always on the south side—is about 10 ft. near the middle of the fault, dying off towards either end.

278. Fault-scarps, such as those described above, are not uncommon features of a great earthquake. One, however, that seems to be peculiar to the Assam earthquake, is the occurrence of

great fractures without any accompanying throw of the crust. The largest known is the Bordwar fracture (C, *Fig.* 43). The fissure itself is only a few inches wide, but it has rent the solid rock, great slabs of weathered gneiss having been split in two. In the immediate neighbourhood of the fracture, the violence of the shock was extreme. Trees have been thrown down or killed, and large masses of rock dislodged from the hill. The fracture can be traced in both directions from Bordwar by the numerous landslips that occurred along it and by the overthrow of trees and the breaking of bamboo clumps in its neighbourhood. Trees up to 6 in. in diameter have been snapped across by the violence of the shock. The Bordwar fracture has been traced for a distance of 7 miles, and along its whole course no decisive evidence of any relative movement, either vertical or horizontal, could be detected*.

279. *Formation of Pools.* — As along the Chedrang fault, pools were formed by changes in the gradient of the river-beds, but without any faulting perceptible at the surface. One important group of pools lies in the northeast portion of the Garo Hills, to the south and southeast of the Chedrang and Samin faults. One of these, a pool in the Rongtham river near the village of Dobrukhol, may be described as typical of the rest. Before the earthquake, there was no pool there. Proceeding upstream, the water became gradually deeper, but the bed of the pool was covered with coarse sub-rounded boulders, such as are to be found in streams with a rapid current. As the water deepened, the lower line of vegetation on the banks came down to the surface of the pool, and then trees were seen standing in the water and killed by the submergence of their roots. The greatest depth of 12 ft., occurred at a point where a pathway crossed the stream and where the depth before the earthquake was not more than a foot. The general slope of the stream-bed was such that the total change of level at the point referred to must have been at least 24 ft. In the same valley, two or three miles higher up, is another lake about 1½ miles long with a maximum depth of 18 ft. Here, again, a footpath crossed the stream at a point where the depth before the earthquake was less than a foot and after it about 9 ft. The positions of these and other pools are represented by the oval black spots D, D on the map of the epicentral area (*Fig.* 43)†.

280. *Changes in the Landscape.*—Though they are not susceptible of precise measurement, there can be little doubt that changes have occurred at several places in the aspect of the landscape. For instance, from Maophlang a road goes round a hillspur

*Oldham, **3**, pp. 138-151.
†Oldham, **3**, pp. 152-157.

about 3 miles off to Mairang.   Before the earthquake, only a
short stretch of this road was visible.   Afterwards, a much longer
stretch could be seen.   A few days after the earthquake, an
observer at Maophlang nailed a strip of wood to a stout post so
that its upper edge was in line with the crest of a ridge about $1\frac{1}{2}$
miles to the west.   Six months later, this edge pointed some way
down the slope, though there was no sign of any movement in the
post.   Thus, it would seem that a part of the total movement may
have occurred with some of the stronger after-shocks.   Again, from
a spot on the Garo Hills lying along the continuation of the
Chredrang fault and less than 5 miles from its southern end, it was
formerly just possible to see the Brahmaputra over an intervening
hill.   After the earthquake, the whole width of the river was visible.
Lastly, a battalion of military police at Tura in the Garo Hills used
to signal by heliograph with Rowmari on the banks of the
Brahmaputra.   Before the earthquake, it was just possible to do
so from one spot by means of a ray grazing an intervening hill.
After the earthquake, not only was there no difficulty, but, instead
of Rowmari being just visible, a broad stretch of the plains east of
the Brahmaputra could be seen*.

281. *Re-Triangulation of the Epicentral Area.*—When the re-
survey of the central area was undertaken, it was thought that the
focus lay beneath the southern Khasi Hills, and a group of triangles
extending from their margin to Umter was selected, one of the
principal triangulation points in the Sylhet Plain being also included.   Unfortunately, the whole area of triangulation lay within
the displaced region, and thus no side re-observed could be regarded
as a trustworthy base.   The side that was probably least disturbed was that joining the stations of Taramun Tila and Rang-
sonobo, the former a small hill rising out of the Sylhet Plain and
just outside the meizoseismal area as traced in *Fig.* 43.   Rang-
sonobo lies close to Cherrapunji, near the southern edge of the
Khasi Hills and apparently just within it.   Assuming that the line
was unaltered in length, it would seem that some of the northern
principal stations were displaced by several feet, Dinghei by 9 ft.,
Umter by 11, and Landau Modo by 12, ft., all three to the northwest.   If, however, the line was shortened by a compression of the
district, the result would be an apparent lengthening of the other
sides, the estimated displacements increasing from south to north.
Thus, all that can be inferred with certainty is that crustal changes
of some kind have taken place in a horizontal direction, and, with
some probability, that the principal change was a compression in
the north-south direction.

---

*Oldham, **3**, pp. 157-161.

The same doubt extends to displacements in the vertical direction. If it is assumed that the height of the station at Taramun Tila was unaltered, it would follow that there was but little change in the height of the district, with the exception of two northern stations, Landau Modo and Mautherrichan, which seem to have risen by 11 ft. and 18 ft., respectively*.

VIII. Effects of the Earthquake on the Ground

282. *Landslips*.—Landslips were produced by the earthquake on an enormous scale, the principal conditions for their existence being the violence of the shock, the steepness of the hillsides, the height of the mountains and their mineral constitution. They were especially abundant and conspicuous along the southern slopes of the Garo and Khasi Hills (*Plates* 6B and 7A). From the deck of a steamer sailing up to Sylhet, the southern face of the hills presented a striking appearance. The hills, usually forest-clad from crest to base, were stripped bare, and the white sandstone shone clear in the sun in an almost unbroken stretch of 20 miles from east to west. At Cherrapunji, the valley sides were so scored by landslips that there seemed to be more bare surface than untouched hillside. In the small valley of the Mahadeo, they were, however, developed to an unusual extent. The valley is about 4 miles long from east to west, and about 1½ miles wide. The hills are composed of soft sandstone, the sides are steep, and the hills themselves high and narrow. Moreover, the shock in this district was of unusual violence, the range of motion being not less than 8 in. near the edge of the precipices. The result, as Oldham says, is an indescribable scene of confusion. "Everywhere the hillsides facing the valley have been stripped from crest to base, and the seams of coal and partings of shale could be seen running in and out of the irregularities of the cliffs with a sharpness and distinctness which recalled the pictures of the cañons of Colorado. At the bottom of the valley was a piled up heap of debris and broken trees, while the old stream course had been obliterated and the stream could be seen flowing over a sandy bed, which must have been raised many feet above the level of the old watercourse".

This exposure of hillsides hitherto protected by forests has naturally led to much weathering of the sandstone in the Khasi and Garo Hills. Every large stream carried down enormous quantities of such weathered sand and spread it out in great fans covering many square miles of country along the southern foot of the hills. In the hill country itself, the streams were unable to carry off their burden of sand, and everywhere within the sandstone area their beds have been raised and altered†.

---

*Oldham, **3**, pp. 361-371.
†Oldham, **3**, pp. 111-123

283. *Displacements of the Alluvium.* — Fissures were abundant, wherever the local conditions were favourable, over the whole area bounded by the isoseismal 5 (*Fig.* 42), an area about 400 miles long from east to west and 350 miles wide. They were naturally most numerous and conspicuous near the margins of river-channels and the artificial reservoirs known in India as tanks. But they were also to be found far away from excavations of any kind, and especially near roads and railway-lines, to which they were always parallel. In such places, their formation may be connected with the passage of the visible waves so often observed in the epicentral area.

In sandy ground, the fissures were usually single. In clayey districts, the fissures as a rule were double, and the soil between them had sunk to a depth of 12 or 18 in. (see art. 121).

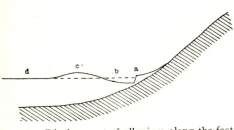

FIG. 45.—Displacement of alluvium along the foot of a hill (R. D. Oldham).

284. A peculiar result of the compression of the alluvium was the low cliff formed along the bases of the Khasi and Garo Hills, a nearly vertical cliff (a, *Fig.* 45) from 1 to 5 ft. in height, that might have been mistaken for a fault-scarp were it not that it followed all the windings of the hill-foot. From the base of the cliff, the alluvium was slightly depressed throughout a band b from 10 to 20 ft. wide, in which the water used for irrigating the plain had collected. Beyond this was a strip c raised above its original level and standing out of the water, and this was succeeded by the level plain d, undisturbed except by fissures. Oldham's explanation is that the thrust of the hill and plain against each other had raised the low ridge at c, while, during the return movement, the alluvial soil between the ridge and hill was lowered and broke away from the cliff.

285. Other examples of compression were seen in the formerly level rice-fields of northern Bengal and Lower Assam. These had been flooded during the spring, and, after the earthquake, were in many places thrown into gentle undulations, the crests of which might be 2 or 3 ft. above the troughs. Telegraph poles were displaced by as much as 10 or 15 ft. from the straight lines along which they were erected. All over the fissured areas, the span of bridges was shortened. The piers were also shifted parallel to the streams and to such a distance as to deprive the end of the girders of their

support.   Railway-lines were crumpled, but this shortening of the rails was probably due to local compression of the alluvium compensated by expansion within a distance of a few hundred yards.

286.   The ejection of sand and water took place during the earthquake and for half an hour afterwards.   From the fissures in the plains, innumerable jets of water rose, like fountains playing, to heights of from 2 to 4 ft., sometimes carrying with them pieces of coal, peat, etc.   The sources of the jets afterwards appeared as circular saucers from 2 to 8 ft. in diameter (*Plate* 6A).   These miniature craters were to be seen all over the country, in places closely packed, as in one strip 100 yd. long and 20 ft. wide near Maimansingh, in which 52 craters were counted.

This outpouring of sand was in part responsible for the filling-up of river-channels, tanks and wells, but to a much less extent than the actual forcing up of their beds.   In the low tract between the Garo Hills and the Brahmaputra, there were numerous drainage channels from 15 to 20 ft. deep.   During the earthquake, the bottoms of these channels were forced up until they became level with their bounding banks.

287.   Immediately after the earthquake, rivers rose in height from 2 to as much as 10 ft.   At Gauhati, the river-gauge is fixed to solid rock.   At 6 p.m. on June 12, or three-quarters of an hour after the earthquake, the water stood 7 ft. 7 in. above its level at 7 a.m. of the same day.   On June 13, at 7 a.m., it had fallen 1 ft. 11 in.; on June 14 3 ft. 2 in. more, and on June 15 another 2 ft. Thus, in 2½ days, the barrier had been scoured away and the river had regained its former level.   At Goalpara, the Brahmaputra rose at once 10 ft. and remained at 8 ft. above the old level when the earthquake was over.   At Maimansingh, the same river rose 4 ft. and at Jamalpur from 5 to 6 ft.

288.   Another remarkable effect of the earthquake was the loosening of the soil, so that at Tura many houses sank into it bodily, the roofs alone remaining above ground*.

IX.   AFTER-SHOCKS

289.   The number of after-shocks was very great, and they originated in many different centres scattered over a very wide area.   For the first few days, no complete record exists.   Even if seismographs had been in action within the epicentral region, it would have been difficult to separate the records of shocks so incessant.   The earth there was hardly ever at rest.   At the Bordwar tea estate, traversed by the great fracture, the surface of a glass of water standing on a table was never still for a whole week after

---

*Oldham, **3**, pp. 10-16, 20, 25-26, 85-111, 334.

the earthquake. At Tura, in the Garo Hills, a hanging lamp was kept constantly swinging for the first three or four days.

Besides these innumerable tremors, the ground was shaken at short intervals by more sensible shocks, and, at somewhat longer intervals, by severe earthquakes. Two of the latter on June 13 (at 1.30 a.m. and 1 p.m.) would have caused great destruction within the central area if there had been anything left to destroy. Both of them were felt at Calcutta and the earlier one at Sutna, more than 600 miles from the epicentral region. In addition to these great earthquakes, after-shocks strong enough to be felt at Calcutta, 240 miles from the nearest edge of the epicentral area, occurred on June 13 (10.40 p.m.), June 14 (0.47 a.m.), June 22 and 29, Aug. 2, and the last on Oct. 9.

290. For about a month after the earthquake, to July 15, the lists of after-shocks are incomplete. Records were, however, kept at four places, the numbers of after-shocks felt from June 15 to July 15 being 209 at N. Gauhati, 98 at Maimansingh, 95 at Kuch Bihar, and (from June 15 to 30) 57 at Kaunia. From the middle of July onwards, lists were kept by interested observers at several places. For instance, during the interval Aug. 1-15, 182 shocks were felt at Goalpara, 151 at Darangiri, 94 at Lakhipur and the same number at Krishnai, these places being near the north foot of the Garo Hills. In the same time, 124 shocks were recorded at Tura, 48 at Dhubri, 28 at Rangpur and 12 at Kuch Bihar; while, farther to the north of the alluvial plain, 105 shocks were felt at Bijni during Aug. 1-15, and 113 at Borpeta during Aug. 1-9.

291. In a supplementary memoir, Mr. Oldham has given lists of after-shocks—most of them until the end of 1898—at Cherrapunji, Goalpara, Laitlynkote, Mairang, Maophlang, Shillong and Tura. Though they are naturally incomplete during the night hours, and though the times given are only approximate, it would be difficult to over-estimate the value of these records. In July 1897, Mr. T. D. La Touche erected a duplex-pendulum seismograph at Shillong that gave the range of motion, though not the time, of every shock recorded. In addition to the separate lists, Mr. Oldham has compiled from them a catalogue of 1,328 after-shocks from 1897 June 12 to 1898 Dec. 31, all of which were strong enough to be felt outside the epicentral area.

292. A more detailed study of the various records has been made by M. F. de Montessus de Ballore. He has drawn the boundaries of the disturbed areas and fixed the position of the epicentres of as many as 5,307 of the total number (5,523) of after-shocks. These he finds to belong to 275 different origins, some of which have been in action several hundred times up to the close of 1898: Maophlang 801 times, Mairang 583, Rangamahal 552,

Tura 510, Goalpara 427, Shillong 319, Laitlynkote 207, and so on.

The region of greatest instability is that bounded by the polygon of which the angular points are Shillong, Gauhati, Goalpara, Bogribari, Dhubri, Tura and Cherrapunji, and especially along the axis of the Khasi and Garo Hills near Shillong,

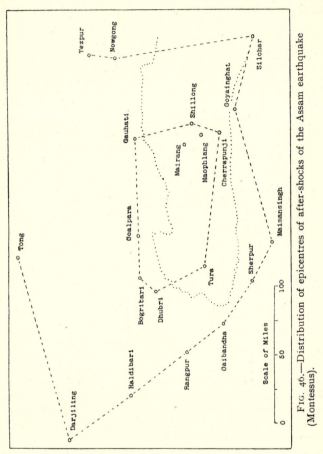

Fig. 46.—Distribution of epicentres of after-shocks of the Assam earthquake (Montessus).

Maophlang, Laitlynkote and Mairang (*Fig.* 46). Within this polygon 3,669 after-shocks, or 69·2 per cent. of the total number, originated. All round this unstable zone, there extends another of distinct but less violent agitation bounded by the lines adjoining Tong, Darjiling, Haldibari, Rangpur, Gaibandha, Sherpur, Maimansingh, Goyainghat, Karimganj, Silchar, Nowgong and

Tezpur, except that its extent towards the north is quite unknown. Within this area, 601 after-shocks, or 11·3 per cent. of the total number, had their centres.

293. Some of these after-shocks disturbed areas of vast size. Montessus gives about 750,000 sq. miles for that shaken by the earthquake of Aug. 2, a value that would entitle it to a place among the great earthquakes of the world. Other high figures are 263,000 sq. miles for the shock of Sep. 21, 406,000 for that of Oct. 9, and 237,000 for that of Nov. 17. In the following year, the areas occa-

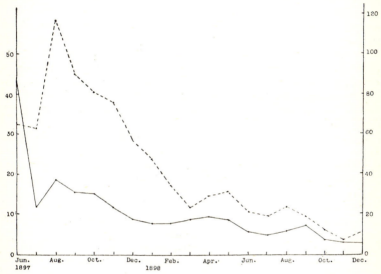

FIG. 47.—Decline in frequency, etc., of after-shocks of the Assam earthquake.

sionally, though less frequently, attain the dimensions of those disturbed by destructive earthquakes, for instance, 176,000 sq. miles on Feb. 1, 349,000 on Apr. 18, 200,000 on May 7, 332,000 in October, and 287,000 on Nov. 28.

In a final brief, but valuable, table, Montessus gives the following details for each month from June 1897 to Dec. 1898; the number of centres in action, the maximum disturbed area, the average disturbed area, the number of earthquakes, and the mean daily frequency. In *Fig.* 47, the continuous line (scale on left-hand side) represents the monthly variation in mean daily frequency, and the broken-line (scale on right-hand side) those in the number of epicentres in action. It is important to notice that the daily frequency refers, not to the shocks observed at any one station, but to the number of shocks that were actually recorded. It will be seen that, after the first month, the two curves on the whole rise and fall together. Yet, except during the first month, the number of shocks originating in each centre is least when the mean daily frequency and the number of centres in action are greatest[*].

294. The records analysed by Montessus close with the year 1898. After this date, it would seem that the observation of after-shocks was discontinued, except at Shillong, where the records of the pendulum seismograph have been kept for more than thirty years. Those for the intervals 1903-1908 July and 1909 July-1931 are considered in the present section[†].

In many of these records, the predominant movement of the ground is clearly defined. The most frequent lines of motion are about north-south, east-west and N. 145° E.-S. 145° W. Now, the centres at and near Gauhati lie nearly north of Shillong, the centre near Tura almost due west, and that near Goalpara about S. 145° W. That is to say, the after-shock centres that were most frequently in action during 1897 and 1898 retained their predominance for thirty years and more.

The decline in frequency of the after-shocks follows the usual law. It will be sufficient to illustrate this decline by giving the annual numbers of earthquakes registered at Shillong. Oldham gives the times of 486 shocks in 1898. During the years 1903 to 1907, the annual numbers were 85, 78, 67, 76 and 80. From 1910 to 1930, the annual numbers were 20, 23, 18, 15, 8, 17, 15, 12, 15, 9, 11, 8, 15, 11, 6, 7, 9, 3, 4, 4 and 25, the increase during the last year being due to after-shocks of the Dhubri earthquake of July 3.

If the annual numbers of earthquakes in both series follow the law $xy = $ constant, where y is the number of earthquakes recorded during the year the middle of which is x years from the middle of 1897, then the equation is $xy = 594$ for the interval 1898-1907, and $xy = 239$ for the interval 1910-1929. Thus, a distinct break occurs after the year 1907.

At about the same time, there is a reversal of epoch in several periods. In the two intervals 1903-1907 and 1910-1929, the epochs of the annual period are Feb. and Aug.; those of the diurnal period about midnight and noon; and those of the lunar monthly period fall at the times of full and new moon.

Thus, the Shillong earthquakes ceased to be after-shocks of the earthquake of 1897 after about ten years; the next year or two

---

*Montessus de Ballore, **2**, pp. 15-23, 30-39; Oldham, **3**, pp. 124-128; **4**, pp. 1-102; **5**, p. 140.

†Davison, C., " On the earthquakes recorded by the pendulum seismograph at Shillong (Assam) from 1903 to 1931," *India Geol. Surv. Rec.,* vol. 69, 1936, pp. 184-202.

formed a transitional interval; but, from 1909 onwards, the crust-movements in Assam resumed their original form and may in course of time lead up to another great destructive earthquake.

X. BIBLIOGRAPHY

1 LUTTNAM-JOHNSON, H. " The earthquake in Assam." *Journ. Soc. Arts,* vol. 46, 1898, pp. 473-493.

2 MONTESSUS DS BALLORE, F. DE. " The seismic phenomena in British India, and their connection with its geology." *India Geol. Surv. Mem.,* vol. 35, 1904, pp. 1-42.

3 OLDHAM, R. D. " Report on the great earthquake of 12th June 1897." *India Geol. Surv. Mem.,* vol. 29, 1899, pp. i-xxx, 1-379.

4 OLDHAM, R. D. " List of after-shocks of the great earthquake of 12 June 1897." *India Geol. Surv. Mem.,* vol. 30, 1900, pp. 1-102.

5 OLDHAM, R. D. " On tidal periodicity in the earthquakes of Assam." *Bengal Asiat. Soc. Journ.,* vol. 71, 1902, pp. 139-152.

6 OLDHAM, R. D. " The Cutch (Kachh) earthquake of 16th June 1819 with a revision of the great earthquake of 12th June 1897." *India Geol. Surv. Mem.,* vol. 46, 1928, pp. 1-47.

CHAPTER XI

ALASKA EARTHQUAKE : 1899 Sep 10

1. INTRODUCTION

295. On 1899 Sep. 11, it was known in seismological observatories all over the world that a violent earthquake had occurred in some distant region on the previous evening. From the records at several stations, it was clear that the origin of the earthquake must have been in or near Alaska*, and this determination was soon verified by the arrival of meagre despatches from the central area.

There for a time the matter rested. The earthquake was evidently one of the first magnitude, or it would not at that time have been recorded in such distant regions. The damage to property, however, was insignificant, simply because there was little property to destroy. Nor was there any loss of life, for the country is almost uninhabited. So far as we know, there were only eight persons within the central region. Indeed, nearly six years elapsed before it became known that the earthquake presented phenomena of unusual interest. Fortunately, most of them left traces that were quite distinct in 1905, though others presented features that were not recognised until a year or two later.

The main earthquake series lasted from 1899 Sep. 3 to Sep. 29. It included at least four world-shaking earthquakes, one on Sep. 3, two on Sep. 10, and one on Sep. 23, as well as great earthquakes on Sep. 15, 17, 26 and 29 and hundreds of minor shocks. The area disturbed was the southern part of Alaska and especially that district in which the average trend of the coast is nearly east and west (*Fig.* 48). The region surrounding Yakutat Bay is that in which the severest shaking and the more remarkable phenomena were manifested.

296. Yakutat Bay is a deep indentation in the otherwise almost unbroken stretch of coast-line between Cross Sound and Controller Bay. Its form will be seen from the map in *Fig.* 49. On the west side, the bay is bordered by a low foreland of glacial gravels. On the east side, the foreland forms the coast for about

---

*Milne, *Brit. Ass. Rep.,* 1900, pp. 82-83.

half its length, while the northern half of the bay is bounded by a straight and precipitous shore and the land behind rises abruptly to heights of 3,000 or 4,000 ft. Towards the north, Yakutat Bay merges into a narrow arm called Disenchantment Bay, which is a true fiord bounded on both sides by steep mountains. It reaches from Point Latouche to the Hubbard glacier, its head being thus an ice-wall from 4 to 5 miles long. At its north end, the inlet turns abruptly backwards and is afterwards known as Russell Fiord. The shores of the northwest arm are straight and moun-

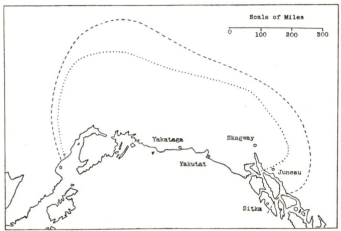

Fig. 48.—Map of Alaskan earthquake of Sep. 3 and 10 (Tarr and Martin).

tainous, but, in the south arm and at the head of the bay, they are irregular and mountainous. From the angle between the south and northwest arms, a large fiord, known as Nunatak Fiord, extends eastwards as far as Nunatak Glacier. The length of the inlet from the ocean to the head of Russell Fiord is 70 or 75 miles.

297. To the north of Yakutat Bay, the country is occupied by lofty mountain ranges, such as the Chugach Mountains (6,000 to 10,000 ft.), the St. Elias Range (with culminating peaks of 18,000 and 19,500 ft.) and the Fairweather Range. From these mountains, extensive glaciers descend towards the sea, some of which, such as the Galiano, Atrevida, Hubbard, Nunatak and Hidden Glaciers, will be referred to in a later section*.

II. INVESTIGATION OF THE EARTHQUAKE

298. In the summer of 1905, a party of geologists were sent by the U.S. Geological Survey to study the mineral resources of

*Tarr, etc., **2**, pp. 12-14.

Yakutat Bay. The party was under the direction of Prof. R. S. Tarr, with Mr. L. Martin as physiographic assistant. Very early in their work, they noticed dead mussels and barnacles adhering to the cliffs, far above the reach of the present tides. If the barnacles had died many years ago, they would have lost their hold on the rock, and indeed many of them had fallen on the ledges below. It was evident that, not long before, there must have been a considerable rise of the land, and the observers at once, and as it proved rightly, connected the uplift with the earthquakes of 1899. In 1906, Prof. Tarr again visited the district, intending to study the glaciers farther to the west, but was unable to cross them owing to their great advance and the unusually crevassed condition of their surfaces. Further observations were made by Tarr and Martin in 1909 on the effects of the earthquake on the glaciers, and again in 1910 by Martin alone.

During the three summer months (June to Sep.) of 1905, every part of the 150 miles of coast, except a few miles between Hubbard and Turner Glaciers, was carefully examined and more than one hundred measurements of the changes of level were made. The results of their observations are given in a valuable joint report published by the U.S. Geological Survey.

iii. Preparation for the Earthquake

299. With one possible exception (on Aug. 27), the first earthquake occurred on Sep. 3 at 3.3 p.m. (Yakutat mean local time) or 0.22 a.m. on Sep. 4 (G.M.T.). The earthquake was felt at about 30 places, all of which lie within the area bounded by the dotted line in *Fig.* 48. The land-area shaken contained not less than 170,000 sq. miles, so that, as the epicentre was probably near the coast, the total disturbed area must have been not less than 300,000 sq. miles and perhaps much more. In other words, as regards the disturbed area, the earthquake belongs to the same class as the Mino-Owari earthquake of 1891 and the California earthquake of 1906. The shock was strong enough to be recorded in the observatories of Europe and other distant places. At Yakataga (100 miles west of Yakutat), tree-tops snapped and the ocean beach was raised 3 ft. The tide was at half-ebb and receded to low water in 20 min., not returning high for 36 hours. During the next 6 hours, 48 after-shocks were observed. There is some uncertainty as to the position of the epicentre, but, as there was uplift of the coast and probably faulting at Yakataga, and, as no seawaves were reported in Disenchantment Bay or Russell Fiord on that day, it is probable that it was not far from Yakataga. This place, moreover, is close to the centre of the area known to have been disturbed by the earthquake.

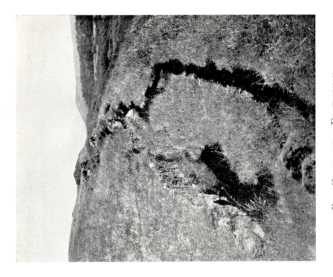

B. CALIFORNIA EARTHQUAKE.

Fault-trace near Olema, showing the ridge phase (Lawson).

A. ASSAM EARTHQUAKE.

Inglis Monument at Chhatak (Oldham).

PLATE V.

[*To face page* 160.

A. ASSAM EARTHQUAKE.
Sand-vent at Rowmari (Oldham).

B. ASSAM EARTHQUAKE.
Landslips near Cherrapunji (Oldham).

PLATE VI.   [*To face page* 161.

300. During the next week, many after-shocks were felt near Yakutat Bay. Then, on Sep. 10, came two great earthquakes, one about 8 a.m. and the other at 12.22 p.m. (local time) or about 5 p.m. and 9.20 p.m. (G.M.T.), both of them world-shaking earthquakes, the second being much the stronger. On the same day, about 50 minor shocks were felt. Both of the great earthquakes originated in or near Yakutat Bay, but it is probable that the uplift occurred with the later shock, as the earlier one was not accompanied by any seawave.

301. The first shock, at about 8 a.m., lasted about 1½ min. at Disenchantment Bay. It was so violent that men were unable to stand, and the lower alder brush shook and bent like reeds in a gale of wind. Besides this place and Yakutat village, the shock was felt at Upper Alsek River, Skagway, Upper Yukon River, Copper River delta, Juneau, Chugach Mountains and Valdez. As the last place is 250 miles from Yakutat Bay, the disturbed area must have contained at least 200,000 sq. miles. It was probably very much larger*.

IV. Nature and Effects of the Shock

302. During the first half of Sep. 1899, eight men were camped on the moraine-covered margin of Hubbard Glacier, near the point where Disenchantment Bay merges into Russell Fiord and not more than six miles from the point where the greatest uplift occurred. The shock is said to have lasted 2½ or 3 min., and, while it lasted, it was impossible to stand, the ground waved up and down like the swells of the sea, only with much more energy, and was broken along jagged cracks. The dam of a small lake behind was broken, and a flood washed down on the camp, burying part of it beneath rocky debris. Soon afterwards, a great seawave, about 20 ft. high, was seen advancing towards the shore, and was preceded by great geysers shooting upwards, some of them several feet across and 30 or 40 ft. high. A second wave, 20 or 30 ft. high, followed. Avalanches fell down the mountain slopes with a deafening roar. The Hubbard Glacier, which has a front five miles across, was broken and great quantities of ice were discharged into the fiord. Many dead fishes, probably killed by the shock, were thrown up on the shore†.

V. Disturbed Area

303. The broken-line on the map (*Fig.* 48) bounds all the places, with two exceptions, at which the shock is known to have

---

*Martin, **1**, pp. 346-357; Tarr, etc., **2**, pp. 69-78.
†Martin, **1**, p. 359; Tarr, etc., **2**, pp. 15-17.

been felt. Of these places, Cook Inlet is 410 miles, and Birch Creek district and Homer are 430 miles, from Yakutat Bay. The land-area disturbed contains 216,000 sq. miles, so that the total area cannot be less than 432,000 sq. miles. But even this amount, great as it is, must be too small, for the shock was felt at two isolated places to the west, which are respectively 670 and 730 miles from Yakutat Bay. Thus, if the boundary of the disturbed area is regarded as a circle of 700 miles radius, the total area shaken by the earthquake must amount to about $1\frac{1}{2}$ million sq. miles. In other words, if this estimate is correct, the earthquake must rank, as regards disturbed area, with such great earthquakes as those of Lisbon in 1755, Assam in 1897, Kangra in 1905, and Kansu (China) in 1920*.

VI. EVIDENCES OF CHANGE OF LEVEL

304. In most earthquakes that have been accompanied by changes of level, the district chiefly affected has been an inland one. The changes observed have therefore been relative only, except in some recent earthquakes when repeated precise levellings have been made and compared with those of an earlier date. In Alaska, however, most of the measurements are referred to sea-level and are therefore absolute. Moreover, the country is so deeply indented by Yakutat Bay that the field of observation may be regarded as areal rather than linear. In most parts of the bay, the shores have been uplifted, in a few depressed, while in others no movement whatever could with certainty be detected.

Both in area and vertical amount, uplifts are far the more important of the movements. The evidences of recent uplift follow three lines—physiographical, biological and human.

305. *Physiographical Evidence of Uplift.*—At first sight, this is the most striking evidence of the uplifts. Before the earthquake, there had been a prolonged interval of rest, during which the sea had in various places cut back cliffs, planed rock-benches at their feet, and deposited some of the material in extensive beaches. The benches vary in width from 2 to 40 ft. In many places, they are now elevated from 10 to 40 ft. In 1905, the sea had not cut an appreciable cliff or rock-bench anywhere.

At the bases of the cliffs behind may be seen the caves and chasms that had been worn in them before the uplift occurred (*Plate* 9A). In 1905, chasms were just beginning to be cut at the new sea-level.

The beaches are best preserved at the places where they were most uplifted. They are not unlike ordinary beaches at low tide,

---

*Tarr, etc., **2**, pp. 126-129.

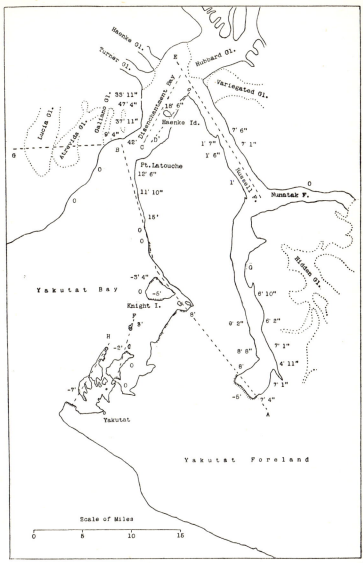

FIG. 49.—Changes of level along the coasts of Yakutat Bay (Tarr and Martin).

except for the wave-worn scarps in front and the young shrubs
that have taken root in the sand (*Plate* 8A).

While the cliffs were being worn back and the rock-benches
planed away, the streams flowing into Yakutat Bay were building
up their deltas. Many of these deltas are now laid bare above the
sea and gullies are being formed in them by the streams, while the
seaward slopes are being cut back by the waves into low cliffs from
5 to 25 ft. in height.

306. In Russell Fiord, a small island before the earthquake
was connected by a sand-spit with the mainland at low tide. The
spit is now so much uplifted that the highest tides cannot cover
it. To the north of Haenke Island, there used to be two submerged reefs that were never visible before the earthquake. They
are now bare at low tide. Again, in the cove to the southeast of
Knight Island, four small islets have appeared. It is said that all
four were submerged at high tide before 1899. Now, two of them
are exposed at all states of the tide and the others between half
and low tides. On Haenke Island, there used to be only two land-
ing-places before the earthquake. Now, there are many, the island
having been uplifted 17 to 19 ft.*.

307. *Biological Evidence of Uplift.*—In measuring the
amount of uplift, the biological evidence is even of greater service
than the phenomena described above. On approaching the coast
in a boat, the white shells of dead barnacles were a striking feature
in 1905. Many of the barnacles were still firmly attached to the
rocks, the valves being often held together by the organic tissue.
In places, they are far more abundant than the living forms at the
present sea-level. Moreover, few of the latter are more than $\frac{3}{8}$ in.
in diameter, and they contrast strongly with the giant dead
barnacles, many of which are $1\frac{1}{2}$ in. across. Dead mussels were
even more abundant and almost as widely distributed as the
barnacles. They resembled, and were indeed at first mistaken for,
clusters of blue flowers attached to ledges 18 ft. or more above the
present sea-level. They were often found adhering to the rocks by
the hair-like byssus, and the preservation of so delicate a structure
until 1905 is another indication of the recency of the movement.
Besides barnacles and mussels, limpets were occasionally found
attached to uplifted ledges of rock in 1905. In certain parts of the
west side of Disenchantment Bay, there were also seen what looked
from a distance like broad horizontal bands of whitewashed rock.
They proved to be the bleached remains of a pink bryozoan that
grows in tidal pools and below the sea-level.

308. One curious result of the uplift is the mixture in one

---

*Tarr, etc., **2**, pp. 18-22.

spot of land and sea organisms. The remains of barnacles, mussels and bryozoans now rest in places that have been invaded by the willow and alder, the wild geranium and other land plants. The scattered condition of the flowering annuals and perennials and the grasses indicates the recency of the uplift, which is clearly proved by the woody shrubs, such as the willow and alder. These are without exception small, and, of all that were cut down in 1905, none showed more than five annual rings and most had only three or four. " Evidently ", as Tarr and Martin remark, " these shore-lines had been open for occupation by land-plants for only four or five years. The earthquake was in the autumn six years before "*.

309. *Human Evidence as to the Uplift in* 1899.—There is also other evidence tending to connect the uplifts with the earthquakes of 1899. Prof. I. C. Russell visited Disenchantment Bay and Russell Fiord in 1890 and 1891, and observed none of the shore-lines that were so clear in 1905. He landed with difficulty on Haenke Island, now accessible at many places. In 1895, the Canadian surveyors of the Alaskan Boundary Commission took a number of photographs in Yakutat Bay. One shows Cape Enchantment as an island. In 1905, it was a peninsula joined to the mainland by a bar that is covered only by the highest tides. Three months before the earthquake, Prof. G. K. Gilbert landed upon beaches that have since been raised 15 ft. or more, and, though one of the chief authorities on abandoned shore-lines, saw no signs whatever of the uplift. Moreover, the Alaskan natives definitely stated that the uplifts occurred with the earthquakes of Sep. 1899, and their evidence, when it could be tested, was never found to be untrue or exaggerated. Thus, it would seem almost certain that the changes of level took place on 1899 Sep. 10, and chiefly, if not entirely, with the second great shock, as this was the only earthquake followed by seawaves†.

310. *Evidences of Submergence.*—These were far less numerous and less conspicuous than those of elevation. In most of them, trees were killed by sand being piled up round their bases, by waves washing away their foundations, or by the submergence of their roots in salt water (*Plate* 8B). It is important to notice that all the areas of submergence consist of unconsolidated deposits. In some cases, it is, of course, possible that the submergence might be due to a settling of the deposits during the shaking, but it is probable that the submergence was due to a real downward movement of the crust because (i) these places are in narrow belts close to, and on

---

*Tarr, etc., **2**, pp. 22-24, 29.
†Tarr, etc., **2**, pp. 25-27.

the downthrow side of known fault-zones, and (ii) because trees equally close to the shore and in equally unconsolidated gravels, but away from fault-lines, show no evidence of submergence*.

311. *Coasts showing little or no movement.*—There are large areas, covering 50 miles or more of the coast of Yakutat Bay and its branches, where little or no change of level has occurred, or where the uplift, if it took place, was too small to be proved. In some cases, dead barnacles were seen on a stretch of coast on which there were also living barnacles at equal heights above the present sea-level. It is possible that there may have been an uplift of a foot or less, so that some barnacles were killed, while others were kept alive by an occasional splash of salt water. On the map (*Fig.* 49), such areas are marked as having undergone no movement unless there was conclusive proof of either elevation or submergence†.

VII. Dislocations of the Crust

312. *Vertical Displacements of the Ground.* — In measuring the uplift, the most useful evidence was that provided by the dead barnacles. The vertical distance between the highest living barnacle and the highest dead barnacle attached to the rock was taken to measure the uplift. In reality, the amount may in places have been slightly greater, for the highest living barnacles may have owed their preservation to occasional splashes of salt water, while the highest dead barnacles in 1899 may have lost their hold by 1905. The effect of the double error may be to lessen the actual uplift by from 6 to 12 in. Fully four-fifths of the estimates of uplift were made by means of barnacles. The remainder depended on the rise of mussels and other similar forms. On the raised beaches, a few measurements were made of the vertical distance between two parallel lines of driftwood, but, as a rule, these were checked by barnacle measurements in the neighbourhood.

Along the four miles of coast to the south of the Turner Glacier, where the greatest uplifts occurred, there were no living barnacles or any other marine forms clinging to the rocks at the present sea-level, though abundant dead barnacles were collected on the raised beaches and uplifted rock headlands. In such cases, the vertical distance was measured between the present high-tide mark and the top of the zone of abundant dead barnacles.

313. In the case of submergence, the measurements are probably less exact. They were usually made on the vertical distance between the base of the lowest dead tree in place and that of the

---

*Tarr, etc., **2**, pp. 27-28.
†Tarr, etc , **2**, p. 28.

highest tree or shrub that had been or was being killed by the deposition of sand and gravel around it.

314. From observations made along the coast in both directions for a hundred miles or more from Yakutat Bay, it appears that, with two possible exceptions (at Cape Spencer and Yakataga), the changes of level were confined to the bay and its branches. The evidence, of course, does not extend beyond the neighbourhood of the coast. With regard to the snow-covered mountainous tract to the north, we have, and can have, no information whatever.

The total length of the shores of Yakutat Bay and its branches is about 150 miles. The measurements made in 1905 (more than 100 in number) show that for about 50 miles there was either no change or a very small change of level. In *Fig.* 49, these parts of the coast are indicated by ciphers, measurements of elevation are given in feet and inches, while the depressed portions of the coast-line are indicated by shading.

315. The map shows at once how variable are the changes of level both in direction and amount.

(i) There are considerable stretches of coast along which changes of elevation are either very small or do not exist. Such, as a whole, are the foreland and neighbouring islands, the west shore of Yakutat Bay from opposite Point Latouche southwards, part of the west side of Knight Island, and most of the coast from Knight Island to within 4 or 5 miles of Point Latouche. Along the southwest coast of the main branch of Russell Fiord, the uplift is 2 ft. or less. On the coasts of Nunatak Fiord, the level on both sides seems unchanged.

(ii) The areas of depression are much smaller. Here and there along the coast from Yakutat to Knight Island, in a short length of coast to the north of Knight Island, and at the southern end of the south branch of Russell Fiord, the land has been lowered by amounts of as much as 7 or 8 ft.

(iii) The areas of elevation are far more extensive and the amounts in some parts extraordinary. Near Knight Island, the uplift of the mainland coast ranges from 5 to $12\frac{1}{2}$ ft. At Point Latouche, the shores are raised 11 to 12 ft., and about 7 or 8 ft. between that point and Haenke Island. On the island itself, the coast has been elevated by from 17 to 19 ft. The most remarkable uplift of all is that of the west coast of Disenchantment Bay between Turner and Black Glaciers. Here, the amount of rise ranges from 37 ft. to the greatest ever recorded in any earthquake, of 47 ft. 4 in. The northeast shore of the main branch of Russell Fiord has undergone a nearly uniform elevation of about 7 ft., rising in one place to 9 ft., while both shores of the southern branch, except the south coast, have been raised by amounts varying from 3 to 10 ft.

316. A remarkable feature of these changes of elevation is their rapid variation in amount over short distances of the coast. For instance, at one point on the west coast of Disenchantment Bay, the amount of uplift was 42 ft., about a mile to the west it is 30 ft., and about a quarter of a mile farther it is 9 ft. On the east side of the same bay, the uplift is 17 ft. 1 in., close to the north end of the peninsula; in the small island (Osier Island) close to the north of it, there is no evidence of any change of level. In the main portion of Russell Fiord, which is about 1½ miles wide, the elevation is slightly more than 7 ft. along the east coast, and at no point on the opposite shore more than 2 ft. Lastly, at the southern end of the south branch of the same fiord, the change of level varies suddenly from an uplift of 7 ft. 4 in. to a depression of 5 ft.*

317. *Evidence of Faulting.* — Such sudden variations in the changes of level must be due either to faulting or folding or warping. Minor faults, as will be seen, occur in many parts of the Yakutat Bay region, but no great faults were detected such as would account for the abrupt variations. Nevertheless, it can hardly be doubted that the variations must be attributed to faulting rather than to folding. Tarr and Martin mention four points that are opposed to the latter explanation. (i) The lines of deformation extend in too many directions; (ii) the zones of gradation between areas of different degrees of deformation are very narrow, while the intervening areas of uplift are broad; (iii) minor faulting occurs in parts of the central region; and (iv) profound faulting is implied by the occurrence of the great earthquakes.

318. The straight broken-lines in *Fig.* 49 represent the courses of the faults that are inferred from the variations in vertical displacement. One of the most remarkable of these faults is that marked A. At its southeastern end, it crosses the head of Russell Fiord just where the uplift changes to depression, and where also there is a change in geological structure; it also passes through three other areas in which uplift gives place rapidly to depression or to no change of level. To the east of this line, there is a straight mountain front with truncated spurs reaching out nearly to the fault-line. Moreover, the four small islands in Eleanor Cove (to the east of Knight Island) lie just where the fault is believed to pass, and the longer axes of these islands are parallel to the fault-line.

319. Another fault B runs along the east shore of Yakutat Bay, where the mountain front is straight and steep and is scarred by numerous avalanches. If this line is continued across Yakutat Bay, it meets the opposite side just to the west of the short line of

*Tarr, etc., **2**, pp. 30-32.

coast in which the uplift changes rapidly from 30 ft. to 9 ft. It is uncertain whether the fault B is connected with the fault A, which it intersects at a low angle, but not many faults more than 30 miles in length are straighter than the two considered as one.

320. The great uplift of more than 47 ft. on the west side of Disenchantment Bay, the somewhat smaller uplift of 17 to 19 ft. on Haenke Island and on the shore of the peninsula to the north of it, and the still smaller uplift of 7 to 9 ft. along most of the east side of Disenchantment Bay are explained by the existence of two faults C and D, one on either side of Haenke Island. A fifth fault E must follow the course of the main portion of Russell Fiord, for the northeast shore consists of crystalline rocks elevated from 7 to 9 ft., while the southwest shore is formed of unmetamorphosed rocks that were in no place uplifted by more than 1 ft. 10 in. In addition to these five faults, the evidence for which is distinct, Tarr and Martin attribute other displacements to three minor faults. Two of them, F and H, lie in the archipelago between Knight Island and Yakutat village. Their existence seems to be implied by the linear arrangement of uplifted and depressed areas in the midst of a region which otherwise shows but little sign of displacement. The course of the remaining fault-line G is somewhat doubtful. It seems to extend from a point on the west side of Yakutat Bay to a short distance west of Lucia Glacier.

321. *Minor Faults.* — Besides these great lines of inferred faulting, there are a series of visible minor faults in several places. The finest series occurs on a hill close to the lower end of Nunatak Glacier. The hill is 1,450 ft. in height and is composed of steeply dipping gneisses, schists and slates, with a general northwest strike parallel to the main axis of the St. Elias Range. The southern summit of the hill was found to be broken by a series of small parallel faults, the scarps of which divide the hill-top and side into a series of parallel steps with a trend of N. 40° W. There are scores of such faults, the number along any transverse line ranging from 20 to 40. In length, they vary from a few feet to several hundred yards. The scarps are usually vertical, and vary in height from an inch or less to a few feet, one of them nearly 8 ft., the average being a foot or less. Measurements of the faults were made in 1906. Along one line, 26 faults have their upthrow on the southwest side with a total upthrow of $30\frac{1}{2}$ ft., while 3 have their upthrow on the northeast, the total amount being 12 ft.

322. There is, of course, no proof of the connexion of these minor faults with the great faults inferred above, but there can be little doubt that they were formed during the earthquakes of 1899. In 1905, the edges of the scarps were still sharp and the talus-slopes at their bases were either small or absent. They could hardly

have been exposed for more than six years, for weathering takes place rapidly in these regions. In 1909 and 1910, the weathering of the scarps was more advanced, and some of the smaller scarps were already mantled by talus-slopes*.

VIII. SEISMIC SEAWAVES

323. As the earthquake ceased, three great seawaves, at intervals of five minutes, swept over the whole shore of Yakutat Bay. At the village of Yakutat, the water rose 15 ft., from low tide to a foot above the highest tide point. " The bay itself was full of whirlpools that were whirling trees, lumber and driftwood around and around so fast that the eye could hardly follow them."

The waves varied in height and destructiveness throughout the bay, and the traces left by them in some parts persisted for at least six years. At Logan Beach, on the east side of Yakutat Bay, the beach and the land behind it were wrecked by the waves. In 1905, the new beach was littered with trunks and limbs of trees, the beach that was raised in 1899 was strewn with similar debris, and an older raised beach, on which mature trees were growing up to 1899, presented a tangle of uprooted, broken and shattered trunks. All vegetation was killed up to a height of 40 ft. above the sea-level, and the receding wave scattered the debris in confusion along the lower stretches of the coast (*Plate* 8B). One of the trees broken by the waves was 75 years old.

On the west side of the bay, near the spot where the coast was uplifted 42 ft., the waves were also destructive. They were at least 30 ft. in height and swept inland a quarter of a mile. Part of a cottonwood grove was uprooted, and the dead trunks were piled in confusion along its edges.

At the entrance to Disenchantment Bay and at Cape Stoss, the waves came from the north. As they swept into the outer Yakutat Bay, they decreased rapidly in height and power, and, outside the bay, were seldom observed. Small water-waves, which may have been connected with the earthquake, were seen at Valdez, near Skagway, and on the Yukon, on a branch of the Kuskokwim, and on the Koyukuk. No movements were registered on the nearest mareographs at St. Michael (Alaska) and San Francisco.

Thus, it is clear that the origin of the seawaves lay in Disenchantment Bay, in which the greatest uplifts of the coast occurred, and that the insignificance of the waves outside was due to the narrowness of the inner bay, the width of which in no part exceeded 5 miles†.

---

*Tarr, etc., **2**, pp. 33-45.
†Tarr, etc., **2**, pp. 16, 46-48, 79.

IX. Landslips

324. The tracks of avalanches were unusually numerous in the Yakutat Bay region, and were especially prominent in the forest-covered districts. Not that the slopes are steeper there than elsewhere, nor that the conditions of the rock formation are more favourable. They are most abundant near the main lines of inferred faulting, that is, along the mountain front near Knight Island, on the east side of outer Yakutat Bay, and from there northwards along the mountainous face of the bay as far as Point Latouche. Here, the mountains are seamed by innumerable landslides, by which thousands of trees and perhaps millions of tons of rock were carried down. According to the natives, the aspect of the mountain face in this part was entirely changed in 1899.

Far outside this region, landslips in great number occurred, especially near Yakataga and Kayak—it was probably near the former place that the epicentre of the first great earthquake lay—in the Chugach Mountains, in the Upper Copper River valley, in the Wrangell Mountains, near the head-waters of White River and the upper Alsek River, and in the district round Birch Creek, Atlin and Berners Bay*.

X. Effects of the Earthquakes on Glaciers

325. Except in their magnitude, the phenomena of the Alaska earthquakes that are described above do not differ materially from those of other earthquakes. Some effects of the earthquakes, namely, those on glaciers, seem, however, to be unique.

326. *Shattering of Glaciers.*—The shattering of glaciers and the discharge of icebergs were the first and most evident effects of the earthquake. Not only in Disenchantment Bay, but even 150 miles to the east in Glacier Bay, this shattering occurred. The well-known Muir Glacier in that bay suffered more than most glaciers. Formerly, this glacier presented a vertical front at least 200 ft. in height, from which huge bergs were detached at intervals. In 1907, according to Klotz and Morse, the front had become sloping, its shape was entirely changed, and one of the two arms into which it had become divided seemed to be nearly dead. Since 1894, and probably since 1899, the total retreat of the Muir Glacier was 8½ miles and that of the Grand Pacific Glacier 8 miles. It is not quite certain whether this retreat was entirely due to the earthquakes, but there is no doubt that the icebergs shed from its front so clogged the inlet as to render it inaccessible to steamships until 1907.

327. *Advance of the Yakutat Bay Glaciers.*—To the north of

---

*Tarr, etc., **2**, pp. 48-51.

Yakutat Bay lie the St. Elias and Fairweather Ranges, with one exception the region of heaviest precipitation in North America. In the country lying around the bay, the total annual fall ranges as high as 149 and 190 in. Among the mountains beyond, it is probably greater, and above 2,000 or 3,000 ft. practically all of it falls as snow. If an excess of a few inches of snow-fall for a few years is enough to cause a notable advance of the glaciers in normal times, it is not difficult to realise the effect of the vast avalanches of snow that must have been thrown down by the earthquakes into the head-reservoirs of the Yakutat Bay glaciers (see art. 145).

At the time of the earthquakes, and even until 1905, the recession of the glaciers after the last advance was still in progress*. In that year, the surfaces of the glaciers visited were smooth, almost free from crevasses, and could be traversed easily for miles.

Ten months later, in June 1906, when Tarr revisited the district, the appearance of some of the smaller glaciers was entirely changed. The surface of Variegated Glacier (10 miles in length) was smooth and almost unbroken in 1905. In the following year, the glacier for at least 6 or 7 miles upwards was a wilderness of crevasses and its surface was quite impassable. The front of the glacier, stagnant in 1905, had advanced and its surface was from 100 to 200 ft. higher. Similar changes had occurred in Haenke Glacier (6 or 7 miles long), except that its front had made a greater advance. Atrevida Glacier (8 miles long) was easily crossed in 1890 and was apparently in the same condition in 1905. In June 1906, it was quite changed, its surface was a labyrinth of crevasses. The ice had also advanced by several hundred yards on the west side. Other glaciers, however, such as Hubbard, Turner, Nunatak and Hidden Glaciers, among the largest of the district, had undergone little, if any, material change.

328. In 1909, the glaciers were again visited. Those that were advancing in 1906 had become stagnant and their surfaces had so far healed that to cross them was possible, though less easy than in 1905. The turn of the larger glaciers had, however, come. Hidden Glacier (16 or 17 miles in length) had pushed forward 2 miles in the interval. Its advance, once rapid, had begun to subside, though its surface was still roughened by the partially healed system of crevasses. Hubbard Glacier was also advancing, but only slightly, and in the following year it had become stagnant like the others. Lucia Glacier (17 or 18 miles long) was advancing in 1909, and its surface was so broken that it could not be crossed, though it could be traversed in 1906 and again in 1911. Between

---

*Galiano Glacier, which is only 2 or 3 miles in length, had begun to advance before 1905.

the summer of 1909 and 1910, Nunatak Glacier (20 miles in length) had advanced between 700 and 1,000 ft. In 1910, the longest glaciers of the district showed no signs of any change.

Thus, the shortest glaciers were the first to advance, and afterwards in turn those of greater length. The phenomena were otherwise similar in all the glaciers. Though moving slowly before 1899, they advanced with a spasmodic rush, and by several hundred yards in ten months or less. At the same time, they increased in thickness. Their surfaces, formerly smooth and practically un-fissured, were rapidly transformed into a wilderness of ice pinnacles and crevasses. Then, after a few months of such conditions, the advance of the glaciers ceased and their broken surfaces were healed*.

XI. After-Shocks

329. Of the slighter shocks that must have been incessant for some days at Yakutat village and in Disenchantment Bay, no record has been kept. There were, however, several of greater promin-ence at various places, such as those of Sep. 17, 7.15 and 7.30 p.m., felt at Yakutat, and on the same day at 8 p.m. at Skagway (160 miles to the east-southeast). On Sep. 17, a shock felt at Skagway, though not at Yakutat, was recorded in many parts of the world. Strong shocks were also felt near the delta of the Copper River (220 miles west-northwest of Skagway) on Sep. 23 and 26 and were recorded at many distant stations. With the earthquake felt at the same place on Sep. 29, the great series of Alaskan movements may be said to have definitely closed†.

XII. Origin of the Earthquakes

330. We may now summarise the nature of the displacements that gave rise to the series of earthquakes. The principal move-ments occurred within less than one month. The origin of the first great shock, on Sep. 3, is doubtful. The movements that cause the other shocks up to noon on Sep. 10 were probably at some depth. They do not appear to have caused any surface disloca-tions. The greater part, if not all, of the uplift occurred with the great earthquake of Sep. 10 along several main lines of fracture and secondary faults. These faults divide up the crust into at least three distinct blocks, the known sides of which are roughly parallel. The first block is bounded on three sides by the faults A, B, C and E (*Fig.* 49) and extends an unknown distance towards the southeast. The second block is bounded towards the east and

---

*Tarr, etc., **2**, pp. 51-61.
†Tarr, etc., **2**, pp. 84-101.

south by the faults C and G, and extends an unknown distance towards the west. The third block includes the northeast shore of the main portion of Russell Fiord and extends an unknown distance towards the northeast.

All of these blocks were uplifted with respect to the level of the sea. Their elevation was, however, accompanied by other movements. On the west side of the fault or faults, A, B, there was a noticeable depression. In many places, and probably in more than were actually seen, were a number of minor faults, due apparently to local adjustments in the tilted blocks. There can be little doubt that some of the differences in the amount of uplift should be attributed to these small differential adjustments.

XIII. BIBLIOGRAPHY

1 MARTIN, L. " Alaskan earthquakes of 1899." *Amer. Geol. Soc. Bull.*, vol. 21, 1910, pp. 339-406.
2 TARR, R. S., and MARTIN, L. " The earthquakes at Yakutat Bay, Alaska, in September, 1899." *U.S. Geol. Surv.*, Prof. Paper no. 69, 1912, pp. 1-135.

CHAPTER XII

CALIFORNIA EARTHQUAKE : 1906 Apr. 18

I. INTRODUCTION

331. Though well entitled to rank among the great earthquakes of the world, the California earthquake of 1906 was by no means of unusual strength. In San Francisco, not more than 390 lives were lost, or about one-tenth per cent. of the population at the time, and the total area disturbed contained probably about 373,000 sq. miles. The most remarkable feature of the earthquake was the displacement of the crust along an old fracture, known as the San Andreas rift, that runs from Cape Mendocino to the Colorado Desert, a total length of more than 600 miles.

II. THE SAN ANDREAS RIFT

332. The course of this great rift is represented by the broken-line in *Fig.* 50. Three submarine portions lie between Shelter Cove and Point Arena (72 miles in length), Fort Ross and Bodega Head (13 miles), and Bolinas Lagoon and Mussel Rock (about 19 miles). In the two latter sections, there can be little doubt as to the continuity of the fault. In the longer northern section, there is less direct evidence of continuity, except in the trend of the neighbouring isoseismal lines.

If the rift is drawn on a small scale map, say, one on 15 miles to the inch, it appears as a nearly even line with its convexity towards the Pacific. From Point Arena to Fort Ross, a distance of 43 miles, its course is so nearly a straight line bearing S. 37° E. that at no place is it more than ¾ mile from the chord joining the extreme points. From Point Arena to the south end of Carissa Plain (about 360 miles), its general trend is S. 40° E., the fault being at most 15 miles from the line joining these places. South of the Carissa Plain, its direction changes gradually from S. 40° E., until, after a course of about 40 miles to the south edge of the Mohave Desert, it becomes 65° or 70° E. of S. When, however, the rift is plotted on a larger scale, say, 2 miles to the inch, it is seen that its course is no longer a smooth uniform line, but is rather a succession of slightly curved arcs facing, it may be, in opposite directions.

333. From Humboldt County to near San Francisco, the rift

lies almost entirely on the southwest side of the coastal ranges.
From Bodega Head to Bolinas Lagoon, it occupies a marked
depression, about three-fifths of
which lies below the sea-level in
Tomales and Bodega Bays. South
of Mussel Rock, where it joins the
San Francisco peninsula, the rift
first crosses a rolling upland and
then follows the rectilinear San
Andreas valley, from which it takes
its name. From this point to the
southern end, the relation of the
rift to the adjoining mountain-
ranges changes no less than seven
times, beginning on the northeast flank of the Santa Cruz
range in the San Francisco
peninsula and ending in the
Colorado Desert on the southern
flank of the San Bernardino
range.

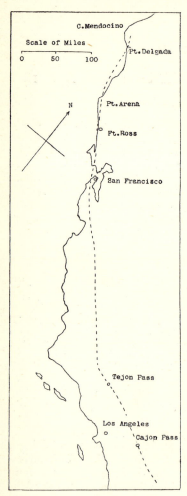

FIG. 50.—Course of the San Andreas Rift (Lawson).

334. The whole course of the
rift is marked by features due
rather to dislocation than to erosion, such as the depressions that
form Tomales and Bodega Bays
and the San Andreas and Crystal
Springs Lakes. Minor, but still
characteristic, features are the
long lines of straight cliffs or the
occurrence of ponds or lakes in
straight rows. In the northern
section of the rift, in which rain-
fall is abundant and erosion effi-
cient, the marks of dislocation soon
disappear. In 1921, only 15
years after the earthquake, Prof.
Bailey Willis followed the course
of the rift during a journey by
aeroplane from San Francisco to
Los Angeles and back. At first,
there were but few signs of displacement to be seen. Farther
south, the rift could be traced by the linear arrangement, sometimes for 25 miles, of numerous landslide scars and small ponds.
When it enters the arid country, the rift becomes more distinct and

A. ASSAM EARTHQUAKE.
Landslips in Mahadeo Valley, Garo Hills (Oldham).

B. ALASKA EARTHQUAKE.
Submerged coast on the east shore of Khantaak Island (Tarr and
Martin).

PLATE VII.   [*To face page* 176.

A. ALASKA EARTHQUAKE.
Raised beach on west side of Disenchantment Bay (Tarr and Martin).

B. ALASKA EARTHQUAKE.
Forest on east shore of Yakutat Bay destroyed to a height of 40ft.
above the present sea-level by the seawave (Tarr and Martin).

PLATE VIII. [To face page 177.

continuous. From an altitude of 12,000 ft., it could be seen like a large empty irrigation canal, stretching for 10 miles to the south until it was lost in the desert haze.

335. In the southern Coast Ranges, the displacements dwarf all similar events of historic times. For miles at a stretch, the ground on one side or other of the fault-line has sunk, giving rise to basins and to cliffs from 300 to 400 ft. in height.

336. The section of the rift from the southern border of the Mohave Desert to Cajon Pass has recently been surveyed by Mr. L. F. Noble. Across this area, the rift can be traced as a continuous chain of trough-like depressions and ridges, the line followed by them being so straight that it can be seen for 25 miles or more. Many of the features of the rift in this region are so fresh—perhaps dating from 1857—that they are almost unmodified by erosion. They change in form abruptly from place to place along the fault. Within half a mile, for instance, a scarp may give place to a ridge and the ridge to a trough, or a scarp facing in one direction may die out and change to a scarp facing in the opposite direction. The features differ greatly in size, from trenches a few feet wide and a foot or two deep to others 100 ft. deep and many hundred feet wide. In general, the older features are on a much larger scale than those of recent age.

Some recent changes afford clear evidence of horizontal movement along the fault. At a place about 3 miles southeast of Cajon Pass, four deep ravines descend the steep slope of the San Bernandino range and stop abruptly on the northeast side of the fault. The lower parts of the ravines reappear on the southwest side, but at points 150 ft. to the northwest of their former lines.

As a rule, the zone that borders the main fault is a mosaic of elongated blocks, trending parallel to the fault. The prevailing structure is a sort of slicing, that seems to be the result of horizontal shearing along the fault. Some of the blocks are prisms of granite a mile long and $\frac{1}{4}$ mile wide. Strips or ribbons of Tertiary rocks also occur, one of which is 12 miles long and usually less than 100 yd. wide.

At few places along the fault are the rocks on opposite sides the same. In one portion 50 miles long, for instance, the fault is bordered continuously on the south by a series of pre-Cambrian schists, while on the north side the rocks are either Mesozoic granites or pre-Cambrian gneisses. Facts such as these illustrate how great have been the aggregate movements along the fault in past times*.

---

*Gilbert, **14**, p. 103; Lawson, **18**, pp. 2-3, 48-52; Noble, **21**, pp. 415-428; Willis, **29**, pp. 136-139.

iii. Seismic History of the District

337. Several previous earthquakes of great interest are briefly described in the report of the State Commission. Of these, the earthquakes of 1857, 1865 and 1890 seem to have been connected with different parts of the San Andreas rift, and that of 1868 with a parallel rift on the eastern side of San Francisco Bay.

338. *Earthquake of 1857 Jan. 9.*—The principal earthquake occurred at 8.13 a.m., but it was preceded by at least four shocks, the first of which, at 11.20 p.m. on Jan. 8, was strong enough to damage all the houses in Santa Barbara. The shock was felt from Fort Yuma to Sacramento, so that its disturbed area was probably not less than that of the earthquake of 1906. The most interesting feature of the earthquake was its origin along the southern half of the San Andreas rift. In 1906, the displacement occurred along the northern half, from near Cape Mendocino to San Juan, a distance of 270 miles. In 1857, the displacement extended from Cholame Valley southeastward to the San Bernardino Valley, a distance of about 225 miles. Thus, a portion of the fault about 100 miles in length, from San Juan to Cholame Valley, was not perceptibly displaced at the surface during either earthquake.

As in 1906, the area of destruction covered a band clinging to the line of the rift. Houses were damaged at San Diego, Los Angeles, Fort Tejon (where one life was lost), Santa Barbara, Visalia and Monterey, the distance between the first and last places being 380 miles. At Fort Tejon, the shock was strong enough to break off some large trees close to the ground and to tear up others by the roots*.

339. *Earthquake of 1865 Oct. 8.*—The earthquake occurred at 0.45 p.m. In San Francisco, there was a violent shock lasting for about 5 sec., followed after a very brief interval by a much stronger shock lasting for 10 sec. or more. At Santa Cruz, the shock was apparently more violent than elsewhere, every brick building in the town being reported as ruined, and in San Jose, Petaluma and San Francisco many houses were damaged. The disturbed area must have been comparatively small, for the shock does not seem to have been felt at Eureka, Visalia, Los Angeles or Santa Barbara. The records of the earthquake are too scanty to furnish details, but, as far as they go, they seem to show that the epicentre lay in the Santa Cruz Mountains, between San Jose and Santa Cruz, and that the earthquake was due to a small movement along the San Andreas rift, probably not far from the southern end of the portion displaced in 1906. It is worthy of notice that aftershocks were felt at San Jose, Santa Clara and Santa Cruz†.

---

*Lawson, **18**, pp. 449-451.
†Lawson, **18**, pp. 448-449.

340. *Earthquake of* 1890 *Apr.* 24.—This is the only other earthquake before 1906 that can be definitely referred to a movement along the San Andreas rift. At San Juan, at the southern end of the fault-trace of 1906, a fissure was opened in the line of the rift. The railway bridge at Chittenden was displaced, as also in 1906*.

341. *Earthquake of* 1868 *Oct.* 21.—Though it had no close connexion with the San Andreas rift, the fault of 1868 is of much

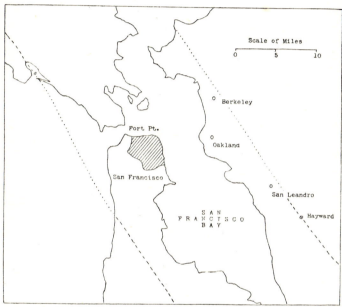

Fig. 51.—Course of the Hayward Rift (Lawson).

interest, and, indirectly, it may have affected the occurrence of the great earthquake nearly forty years later.

The earthquake was due to a movement along the base of the Berkeley Hills on the east side of San Francisco Bay. These hills present a remarkably even, straight front, that is no doubt a degraded fault-scarp. Along the base of this scarp, a crack, known as the Hayward rift, opened at about 7.50 a.m. on 1868 Oct. 21. Its position is represented by the broken-line on the right of *Fig.* 51, with its inferred continuation towards the northwest dotted. It has been determined at intervals along a nearly straight line running in the direction of S. 37° E. for about 20 miles from San

---

*Lawson, **18**, p. 449.

Leandro. It is thus parallel to the San Andreas rift and about $18\frac{1}{2}$ miles from it on the northeast side. The amount of horizontal displacement, if any, was much less than that at the San Andreas rift in 1906 and its direction is not known. The vertical movement was also small and seems, though this is not quite certain, to have been a downthrow on the southwest side. The fault-trace was usually a mere crack, but in places, especially on the lower ground, was an open fissure. As in the earthquake of 1906, auxiliary branching cracks were associated with the main fault. In some places, the fault lay at the base of a hillside, in others high up the slope, in at least one low hill it passed near the top through a saddle-like depression.

The greatest intensity of the shock was along and near the crack, especially at Hayward (intensity 10), where nearly every house was thrown off its foundations.

As in 1906, the part of San Francisco that suffered most was an area of about 200 acres of " made land." A few fires broke out after the earthquake, but there was no want of water and they were soon extinguished.

The number of lives lost during the earthquake was 5, and about 25 more from secondary causes. The value of the property destroyed was about £73,000. Though isoseismal lines cannot be drawn, owing to the rarity of records, it is clear that the area of damage and the disturbed area were much smaller than in 1906. There is no evidence that the shock was felt to the north of Chico or to the south of Monterey. As the distance between these places is about 220 miles, the disturbed area cannot have exceeded 22,000 sq. miles*.

IV. INVESTIGATION OF THE EARTHQUAKE

342. On Apr. 21, the Governor of the State of California nominated a committee of eight scientific men, known as the State Earthquake Investigation Commission. Of this body, Prof. A. C. Lawson was appointed chairman, the other members being Messrs. G. K. Gilbert, H. F. Reid, J. C. Branner, A. O. Leuschner, G. Davidson, C. Burkhalter and W. W. Campbell. The work was divided among three committees, the tasks of which were : (i) to trace the fault-rift and measure displacements along its course, (ii) to collect records of the time of occurrence, and (iii) to study the seismograms obtained all over the world. The work of the first committee was helped by many volunteer observers, the whole fault-trace being divided into seven sections. By the end of the year, the materials were nearly all collected, and the results of the discussions fill two quarto volumes — the first edited by

*Lawson, **18**, pp. 434-448.

Prof. Lawson, the second written by Prof. Reid—and a folio of maps and plates.

343. As soon as the news of the earthquake reached Japan, the Imperial Government sent a small commission to California, consisting of Profs. F. Omori (director), T. Nakamura and T. Sano. Prof. Omori spent about 80 days in California, and, on his return to Japan, wrote a few notes, but the complete report of the commission remains unwritten.

v. Loss of Life and Property

344. No estimate seems to have been made of the total loss of life and damage to property. There can be little doubt, however, that, for so great an earthquake, the losses were comparatively small. San Francisco is the only large city in the immediate neighbourhood of the rift, and here the intensity of the shock does not seem to have risen above the degree 9 of the Rossi-Forel scale. In the city itself, the number of lives lost was about 390. The damage was greatest in the low-lying business district, much of which was built on land reclaimed from the bay. To the south of the city, the water-mains were broken by the fault-movement, and thus the fires that broke out in several places spread until they were checked by blowing up rows of buildings. The number of houses destroyed in San Francisco is estimated at 28,188, and their value at about 22 million pounds. The area of the burned district was 4·1 sq. miles, or slightly more than half the corresponding area in Tokyo after the Kwanto earthquake of 1923, and the total loss of property is estimated at between 73 and 104 million pounds, or less than one-fifth of the amount lost in Tokyo in 1923[*].

vi. Intensity of the Shock

345. *Isoseismal Lines.*—The isoseismals shown in *Fig.* 52 are reproduced in part from those drawn by the State Commission. The scale of intensity used is a simplified form of the Rossi-Forel scale. For the highest or tenth degree, the tests are: " Great disasters; overturning of rocks; fissures in surface of earth; mountain slides "; but, in practice, fissures in the ground were adopted as the main or only test. The isoseismal 10 thus enclosed a narrow band, in no place more than a few miles in width, along the axis of which runs the great fault-line. So narrow is the band that it is impossible to depict the course of the isoseismal 10 apart from the broken-line that represents the fault-trace in *Fig.* 52. A portion of it, that in which it traverses the San Francisco peninsula, and the corresponding parts of the isoseismal 9 are shown on a larger scale in *Fig.* 53.

*Omori, **23**, p. 19.

For the sake of clearness, the isoseismals 9 and 7 are also omitted in *Fig.* 52. Thus, the curves reproduced correspond to intensities 2 to 6 and 8, the first of which may be regarded as the boundary of the disturbed area, and the last as that of the area within which notable damage occurred to buildings.

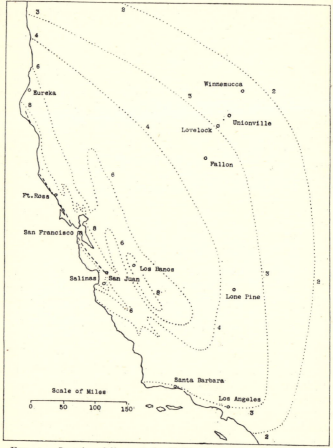

FIG. 52.—Isoseismal lines of the California earthquake (Lawson).

The area of damage clings very closely to the line of the San Andreas fault. It is remarkable for its great length (350 miles) along that line from northwest to southeast. In no part is its boundary more than 50 miles from the fault. Its total land-area is about 5,140 sq. miles, or, including the detached portion near Los Banos, 6,300 sq. miles.

346. Though the isoseismal lines cannot be regarded otherwise than as approximately drawn, they nevertheless throw welcome light on the origin of the earthquake. For instance, the arrangement of the lines along the coastal territory between Point Arena and Shelter Cove indicates that the submarine course of the fault-line lies but a few miles off the shore. It is therefore probable that the fault-line in Humboldt County to the north is continuous with that extending southeastward from near Point Arena.

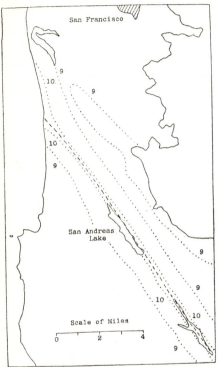

Again, as they approach the coast north of Eureka, the isoseismal lines converge towards one another. It may be inferred from this that the displacement along the fault ends on the mainland and is not prolonged beneath the sea to the north. A similar, but rather more marked closing of the isoseismal lines also occurs at the south end of the disturbed area, suggesting that here the depth of the displacement was less than at the northern end.

Fig. 53.—Isoseismal lines in the San Francisco peninsula (Lawson).

Lastly, on the southwest side of the fault, the areas enclosed by the isoseismals, so far as it was possible to trace them, are much less than those on the northeast side. It would seem that the intensity diminished more rapidly on the former side than on the latter. It is possible that this fact may imply that, of the crustal blocks on both sides of the fault, the southwest block was the more passive during the movement that caused the earthquake. But the less intensity on the southwest side may also be due to the nature of the underlying rocks, for, on that side of the fault, there are extensive areas of granitic rocks at the surface, while, on the other side, these rocks are deeply buried beneath sedimentary formations.

347. *Disturbed Area.* — It is difficult to determine with precision the boundary of the disturbed area. In the country lying to the east of the Sierra Nevada, settlements are few and far between, many of them contain but few inhabitants, and, of these, the great majority were asleep when the earthquake began.

The area extends from Coos Bay, Oregon, on the north, to Los Angeles, on the south, a distance of about 730 miles. Lawson considers that the disturbed area extends as far east as Winnemucca, but, in this town, the shock was not felt, though a hanging lamp was seen to swing. If, however, we may take the isoseismal 2 so drawn as the boundary of the disturbed area, the land-area shaken would be about 175,000 sq. miles, and the total disturbed area, if we may assume that the sea-bed was similarly affected, would contain about 373,000 sq. miles*.

348. *Relation of Intensity to Site.*—Many examples have been given in the preceding pages that show the relation between the intensity of the shock and the nature of the rock on which it was observed. In no earthquake, perhaps, are the examples of this relation so striking as in the California earthquake of 1906. For instance, the town of Petaluma is built partly on rock, partly on the alluvium of the tidal marshes of San Francisco Bay, and is 14 miles from the San Andreas fault. Nearly all the chimneys built on alluvial land were damaged. On the hill-slopes underlain by rock, about half the chimneys were injured. Moreover, four small areas, all lying on alluvium, are indicated as areas of exceptionally severe destruction, while a belt, in which there was practically no damage, crosses the part underlain by rock.

349. A high intensity is associated as a rule with the alluvium of the valley bottoms. Of this relation, an excellent illustration is afforded by the valley of the Salinas River. This river falls into Monterey Bay. Along the flood-plain tract of the valley and along the beach of Monterey Bay, the intensity of the shock was 9. This intensity was observed for several miles above the town of Salinas, and there were extensive fissures in the alluvium as far as Gonzales. The shock was of intensity 8 up to the valley as far as Chualar, of intensity 7 at King City (45 miles above Salinas), 6 near San Ardo (65 miles), and 5 at Paso Robles (99 miles). As will be seen from the map in *Fig.* 54, the isoseismal lines were almost parallel to the river, the intensity diminishing rapidly in the transverse direction.

350. *Variation of Intensity in San Francisco.* — Mr. H. O. Wood made a very careful study of the distribution of damage in San Francisco, and, though the main results of his inquiry are not new, the evidence that he collected was so detailed that it may be useful to give a summary of his conclusions.

---

*Lawson, **18**, pp. 160. 321, 323, 330-346 ; Omori, **23**, p. 8.

The city of San Francisco occupies the northern end of the peninsula. It lies entirely to the east of the San Andreas rift, the southwestern corner being less than a mile from it, and the northeastern corner more than 9 miles. On the east side, rocky ridges stretch out into the bay, and between them are valleys occupied by alluvium. Formerly, the floors of these valleys near their

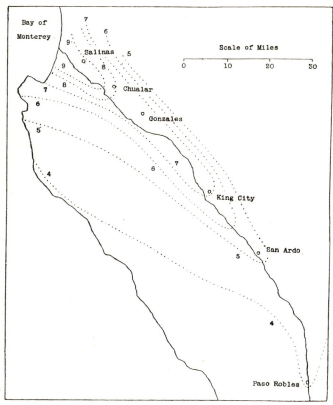

Fig. 54.—Isoseismal lines in the Salinas Valley (Lawson).

mouths were tidal marshes and creeks, now converted into " made land." The hills are composed of firm rock—sandstone, chert, etc. —often cropping out at the surface, and elsewhere covered with a thin coating of soil.

On the whole, the intensity of the shock decreased from southwest to northeast, but there were many marked variations of intensity that were clearly connected with changes in the nature of the ground. The areas of lowest intensity—with occasional fall of chimneys, etc.—are comparatively small and occur mainly in the central and southeastern parts. They are always those in which the hard rock is either exposed at the surface or is covered with a very thin mantle of soil. A slightly higher intensity—marked by general, but not universal, fall of chimneys and the fissuring of walls—prevails in the northeastern quarter of the city, usually on the flanks of hills where the hard rock is exposed or where the covering of soil is thin. A higher degree of intensity—brickwork badly cracked, with occasional collapse—is attained on the flanks of hills that face the Pacific, and in the low lands of the valleys and the portions of the water front where the sand and alluvial deposits are thick.

The highest intensity reached in San Francisco was found as a rule only in areas of small extent, situated either on " made land " filling a small ravine or lagoon or on loose sand or earth. There were, however, two large areas of exceptional destruction, both of " made land," one at the northeast corner of the peninsula, the other on the shore about a mile to the south. In these, masonry blocks of good construction were shattered and tubular cast-iron columns were broken off near their bases. The ground was thrown into waves and open fissures were formed, especially near the wharves. Buildings on the water-side slid seawards, in some places by as much as 2 ft. The shock caused the materials of the " made land " to settle down so that the surface of the whole district was lowered by amounts ranging from a few inches to as much as 3ft.*

VII. Position of the Epicentre

351. The position of the epicentre was determined approximately by Omori from an examination of the seismogram obtained at the Lick Observatory. From the duration of the preliminary tremors and from the direction of the first movement, he estimated that the epicentre must be 80 or 90 miles N.N.W. from Mount Hamilton, or in lat. 38° 15′ N., long. 123° W., that is, near Tomales Bay.

352. Prof. H. F. Reid has made similar estimates for the beginning of the movement and the beginning of the violent shock, from the records at San Francisco, Berkeley, Mount Hamilton and Ukiah. Taking the velocity near the epicentre as 7·2 km. per sec., he found that, for the beginning of the shock, the time was 5h. 11m. 58s.±3s., and the position of the epicentre lat. 37° 49′ N.±12′, long. 121° 36′ W.±16′. For the beginning of the violent motion, the corresponding results are 5h. 12m. 28s.±2s., and lat.

---

*Lawson, **18**, pp. 220-242, 335-346.

38° 3′ N.±4′, long. 122° 48′ W.±5′, this latter point lying between Olema and the southern end of Tomales Bay. As Reid remarks, the violence of the shock in this district was probably not exceeded elsewhere, and the displacements along the fault-line were the largest known*.

VIII. Nature of the Shock

353. *Nature of the Earthquake-Motion.*—Within the central area, the nature of the shock as a rule closely resembled that felt at Berkeley. Here, the feeble motion began at 5h. 12m. 6s., a.m., and the last sensible tremor ended at 5h. 13m. 11s., giving a total duration of 65 sec. The shock consisted of two parts, the first of which lasted about 30 sec. This was followed by a comparative lull for about 10 sec., after which the vibrations continued with renewed vigour, reaching a greater intensity than before and subsiding after about 25 sec.

According to some careful observers, the duration was even greater than that given above. In San Francisco, Prof. G. Davidson timed the first movement at 5h. 12m. 0s., a.m.; hard shocks were felt until 5h. 13m. 0s., then a slight decrease in strength until 5h. 13m. 30s., the motion ceasing at 5h. 14m. 30s., giving a total duration of $2\frac{1}{2}$ min. At the Naval Observatory, Mare Island, according to the director, Prof. T. J. J. See, the preliminary tremors lasted a little more than a minute, the violent shocks about 40 sec., and the final tremors about $1\frac{1}{2}$ min., the total duration being $3\frac{1}{2}$ min.

354. The pause near the middle of the movement was a characteristic feature of the shock at places in the destructive zone or nearly as far as the isoseismal 7, and the second maximum was usually considered as the stronger. Beyond the isoseismal 7, only one maximum as a rule was observed.

355. Few observations seem to have been made on the range or the acceleration of the motion. In San Francisco, according to Omori, the range or double amplitude of the principal vibrations was about 4 in. or 10 cm. and the complete period of each vibration about 1 sec. From this, it follows that the maximum acceleration was about 2,000 mm. per sec. per sec., a value about equal to that which Omori afterwards obtained for the Messina earthquake of 1908 at Messina, but less than half the value (4,300 mm. per sec. per sec.) found at several places in the central area of the Mino-Owari earthquake of 1891.

356. *Direction of the Shock.*—The report of the State Commission reproduces seismograph records at eight places in the States of California and Nevada. They show how complicated the

---

*Omori, **23**, pp. 9-10; Reid, **26**, pp. 7-11.

movement was in its early stages. The strongest vibrations seem to have taken place along more definite lines, and the average directions obtained by Omori from numerous overturned bodies at each of 11 places differ little, in all probability, from the true values. The average directions given by Omori are: (i) San Francisco N. 76° E., San Jose N. 81° E., Chittenden N. 38° E., Watsonville N.E., Santa Rosa and Tomales N., Point Reyes Station (east side of

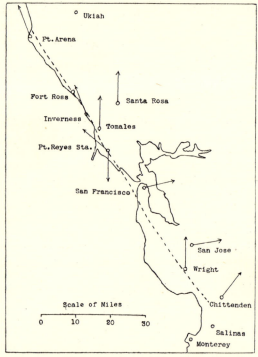

FIG. 55.—Mean direction of the shock (Omori).

fault), S.; (ii) Point Arena N.N.W., Inverness N.W., Point Reyes Station (west side of fault), W.N.W., Wright N.; the first group of places being on the east side of the fault, and the second group on the west side. These mean directions are represented in *Fig.* 55. The mean general direction of the fault is N. 37° W. Thus, on the whole, the motion on each side was directed away from the fault.

In the town of San Mateo, which lies about 1 mile west of San Francisco Bay and about 3 miles northeast of the San Andreas fault, Mr. R. Anderson made a detailed study of the directions of fall in more than one thousand houses. He found that there were two dominant directions of fall, namely, S.W. and N.W. The percentages of fall in these two directions are given in the following table:—

	S.W.-N.E.	N.W.-S.E.
Movement of houses on their foundations	31	27
Fall of chimneys	43	33
Movement of dishes	47	42
Movement of furniture	49	30
Spilling of liquids	51	34

357. *Visible Waves.*—These were observed at more than 20 places, from Freshwater and Ferndale in Humboldt County to San Lucas in Monterey County, the distance between them being about 360 miles. Many of the places lie within the isoseismal 9 and on alluvial ground. It is clear, from the descriptions given, that the waves resembled undulations in water. The estimates of their size may be exaggerated, but several observers agree in stating that they were 2 or 3 ft. in height. At San Jose, many persons saw waves in the ground more than a foot in height, and, according to one careful estimate, about 60 ft. from crest to crest. Near the same place, waves were seen travelling from the south, but, about the middle of the shock, they were met by others, the whole surface resembled hillocks or cross seas, and the tree-tops waved wildly.

358. *Observations at Sea.*—The seaquake was felt on ships at sea from near Cape Mendocino to San Francisco Bay. The sensations were those usually experienced, as if the ship had run aground or had struck on rocks, as if the anchor-chain were running out of the hawser-pipe, and, even at a point 145 miles due west of Point Reyes, as if the ship had struck the bottom lightly and then appeared to drag over soft ground. In San Francisco Bay, the vibrations lasted about 30 sec., with a heavy jar about the middle, the shock being so strong that loosely piled books and papers were shaken down from a table. Farther north, in the harbour of Eureka, a vessel was hurled several times against the wharf, throwing down piles of timber and shingles*.

IX. SEISMIC SEICHES, ETC.

359. The agitation of smooth surfaces of water was noticed at several places near the boundary of the disturbed area. For instance, at Fallon (240 miles from the fault-line) and Lovelock (280 miles), men working on the irrigation canals saw the water ripple and splash lightly against the sides as if by low waves or by tilting

*Lawson, **18**, pp. 166-167, 175, 183, 205, 209, 212, 354, 356, 371-373, 377-381; Omori, **23**, pp. 7-9, 17, 19; Reid, **26**, pp. 3-4; Taber, **28**, pp. 274-275.

of the bed. They felt no shock themselves, though a few others near the same places noticed a slight movement.

360. The swinging of hanging lamps to distances of 300 miles and more from the fault was frequently observed. Near Unionsville (300 miles), a hanging lamp was seen to swing, though no shock was felt. At Winnemucca (340 miles), one observer, who was awake, noticed a hanging lamp with glass prisms sway about 3 in. and it continued swinging for some time. At Eureka (370 miles), a slight shock was felt, that made hanging objects swing. These places lie close to, but within, the boundary of the disturbed area, as drawn on the map in *Fig.* 52. Farther south, hanging lamps were seen to sway at Lone Pine (140 miles from the southern portion of the fault) and Bishop (150 miles)*.

x. DISLOCATIONS OF THE CRUST

361. The general course of the San Andreas fault has been described above. The perceptible movement in 1906 was confined to the northern half from near San Juan to near Point Delgada, the total distance being about 270 miles. Throughout the whole of this portion, the plane of the fault, wherever it could be seen, was practically vertical, and the crust on the southwest side, relatively to that on the other, was displaced to the northwest. From San Juan to San Francisco, the surface movement seems to have been entirely horizontal; at any rate, there is no certain evidence of vertical displacement. North of the Golden Gate, however, there was a small uplift of the southwest side with respect to the other, by an amount ranging from a few inches to 3 ft.

362. *Appearance of the Fault.*—When the movement was entirely horizontal, the surface manifestation was not usually a simple crack, but rather a disturbed zone several feet wide. In most places, the surface formed a ridge from 3 to 10 ft. wide and from a few inches to 1½ ft. high, as if it had been raised by a gigantic mole creeping underground. Both width and height of the zone varied with the extent of the displacement. In other parts, and as a rule for short distances only, it appeared as a shallow trench, with ragged vertical sides from 2 to 6 ft. apart. In a third type, the ground is neither elevated nor depressed, but is traversed by a system of cracks roughly parallel to one another and inclined to the general direction of the fault at an angle of about 45°. These types are called by Gilbert the ridge phase, the trench phase and the échelon phase.

The various appearances of the fault trace are represented in the accompanying illustrations. *Plate* 5B shows the trace at a

---

*Lawson, **18**, pp. 321-323.

point one mile northeast of Olema. In this region, the ridge
phase predominates. *Plate* 10A illustrates the trench phase at
a place west of Olema, and *Plate* 10B a similar trench 1½
miles south of the same place, but occupied by ponds.
The fault touches both ponds, and is seen crossing the space
between them. *Fig.* 56 represents the ground plan of one
series of secondary oblique cracks
near Point Arena, as drawn by
Omori. The broken-lines indicate the
directions of the shear-cracks. In
this example, the angle between the
cracks and the main fault line was 42°.
In eleven other examples measured by
Omori, the angle ranged from 35° to
47°, the average of all twelve being
40°.

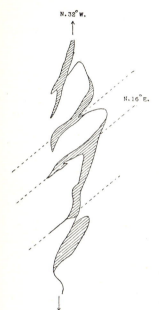

FIG. 56.—Ground-plan of shear-cracks near Point Arenas (Omori).

363. *Horizontal Displacements.*—
Wherever a fence, road, line of trees,
bridge or other structure was crossed by
the fault, the separated parts were offset
(*Plates* 9B and 11B). The measured
amount of displacement is very variable,
ranging from a foot or less to 21 ft. For
instance, near Fort Ross, offsets of 8 ft.,
12 ft., 15 ft. and 12 ft. were measured.
Near the head of the Bolinas Lagoon,
the following were noted: 10 ft., 7 ft.
8 in., more than 12 ft., 13½ft., 15 ft.,
11 ft., 15½ ft., 16 ft. and 15 ft. Such
differences are probably due to several
causes, of which two seem to be
more important than the others.

(i) The displacement was not always confined to one sharp
line, but might be distributed over a zone of auxiliary cracks that
took up part of the displacement. For instance, at one point in the
San Francisco peninsula, a total offset of 10 ft. was distributed over
ten different cracks. Many of these cracks no doubt escaped observation in some places, and others perhaps existed that, owing to
the yielding nature of the soil, did not form ruptures on the surface.
(ii) There is evidence, again, of such drag in the soil for a considerable distance on both sides of the fault. Fences, formerly straight,
have been bent into a slight curve for distances of 200 or 300 yd.
from the fracture. Thus, it would seem probable that the highest
figures obtained for the surface displacements must have been less,
rather than greater, than the shift in the firm rocks below. In the

Idu (Japan) earthquake of 1930, the displacement at the surface along the Tanna fault was much less than that in the tunnel at a depth of more than 500 ft. (art. 470).

In the middle half of the fault trace, extending from Point Arena to Crystal Springs Lake, the greatest offsets measured were usually 15 or 16 ft., and this may be taken as the amount of horizontal displacement along the fault for this section. In the southern quarter, from Crystal Springs Lake to San Juan, the greatest offset was about 8 ft. In the northern quarter, from Point Arena to Point Delgada, the displacement along the fault is unknown*.

364. *Vertical Displacements.*—With regard to vertical movements of the crust, two kinds of evidence were available, that of small fresh scarps formed along the fault, and that of small changes in the relative level of land and sea. Of these, the evidence of the fault scarps was the more valuable. One such scarp, about 3 ft. in height, that occurred near the head of Pine Gulch Creek, is shown in *Plate* 11A.

The scarps were entirely confined to the region north of the Golden Gate. They were not, however, continuous features, but ran, often for distances of hundreds of yards, along the fault, with intervals in which no abrupt scarp could be detected. Usually, they faced northeast, but, in a few cases for short distances, in the opposite direction. Near Fort Ross, for instance, along a portion of the fault less than 1½ miles in length, there were twelve stretches of scarp from 125 to 1,000 ft. long. Of these, eight, with a total length of 2,250 ft., faced northeast; while four, with a total length of 750 ft., faced southwest.

365. The second kind of evidence is less conclusive. The records of the tide-gauge at Fort Point in the Golden Gate showed no change of level from before to after the earthquake. At Bolinas Lagoon near the centre of which the fault is less than ¼ mile from the west shore and ¾ mile from the east, there may have been some change of level. From an examination of the lagoon made in the autumn of 1906, Gilbert concluded that, in the larger section of the lagoon to the east of the fault, there was a general subsidence of about a foot. On the west side of the fault, there may have been a slight local elevation, but the evidence for the change is not free from doubt†.

366. *Re-Triangulation of the District.* — Previous accurate surveys of part of the region traversed by the San Andreas fault were made by the U.S. Coast and Geodetic Survey in 1851-65 and

---

*Lawson, **18**, pp. 147-151; Omori, **23**, pp. 11-12; Taber, **28**, p. 272.
†Lawson, **18**, pp. 80-91, 147-151.

A. California Earthquake.
Offset of road near Wright (Lawson).

B. Alaska Earthquake.
Elevated sea-cave on the east shore of Disenchantment Bay (Tarr and
Martin).

PLATE IX.

B. CALIFORNIA EARTHQUAKE.
Fault-trace near Olema, with ponds (Lawson).

A. CALIFORNIA EARTHQUAKE.
Fault-trace near Olema, showing the trench phase
(Lawson).

PLATE X.

[*To face page* 193.

1874-92. After the earthquake, a new triangulation was carried out, extending from Mount Toro and Santa Ana on the south to Ross Mountain and near Fort Ross on the north. The length of the region covered is 170 miles, its greatest width is 50 miles, and its area not less than 4,000 sq. miles. It includes 51 old triangulation points, of which 11 were primary points, and 10 others of secondary degree of accuracy in a detached area near Point Arena. The results obtained from the different surveys are given by Messrs. J. F. Hayford and A. L. Baldwin in a paper published in the Report of the State Commission (vol. 1, pp. 114-145).

The displacements of all 61 points have been calculated on the supposition that the two easternmost points, Mount Diablo and Mocho, remained unmoved during the earthquake of 1906. Mount Diablo is 27 miles from San Francisco in a direction a little north of east. Mocho is 51 miles E.S.E. of San Francisco. They are regarded as clearly beyond the region of appreciable permanent displacements by the earthquake of 1906.

All that can be asserted about the movements measured is that they occurred at some time or times between 1866 and the close of 1906. It is unknown, also, whether the displacements were accomplished suddenly or were spread over some months or even years. According to Hayford and Baldwin, part of the movements occurred in or about 1868 and part later, and they are referred by them to the earthquakes of 1868 and 1906. In the former year, they consider, an area of about 1,000 sq. miles was permanently displaced about 5·2 ft. in the direction N. 11° W.

367. During the earthquake of 1906, the crust-movements were remarkable for their regularity of distribution. The amount of relative displacement of the two sides of the fault, as detected by the triangulation, shows, indeed, no variation along the fault trace from Point Arena to San Juan, with the exception of a district near Colma, where the relative displacements were unusually small. The principal conclusions formed by Hayford and Baldwin from the survey are as follows :—

(i) Points on opposite sides of the fault moved in opposite directions, those on the northeast side to the southeast and those on the southwest side to the northwest.

(ii) The displacements of all points were approximately parallel to the fault.

(iii) The displacements on each side diminished as the distance from the fault increased.

(iv) For points on opposite sides of the fault and at the same distance from it, the displacements on the southwest side were on the average about twice those on the northeast side.

For instance, taking only points the displacements of which can be estimated with accuracy, on the northeast side, 10 points at an average distance of 0·9 mile from the fault had an average displacement of 5·1 ft.; 3 points at an average distance of 2·6 miles were displaced 2·8 ft.; one point 4·0 miles was displaced 1·9 ft. On the southwest side, 12 points at an average distance of 1·2 miles suffered an average displacement of 9·7 ft., 7 points at 3·6 miles one of 7·8 ft., and one point at 23 miles (Farallon Point Lighthouse) of 5·8 ft.

368. Let us imagine a straight line to have been drawn before the earthquake on the surface at right angles to the fault trace. After the earthquake, the line would be broken, the two ends would be separated by the shift along the fault, and the two portions would become slightly, almost imperceptibly, curved. That on the northeast side would be concave towards the southeast, and that on the southwest side towards the northwest.

369. It should be mentioned that Prof. Lawson suggests a different explanation of the earlier movement brought to light by Messrs. Hayford and Baldwin. He would regard it, not as evidence of a sudden movement in 1868, but as the expression of a slow creep due to the gradually increasing strain in the earth's crust that culminated in the great slip of 1906. Moreover, the last of the four conclusions given above depends on the stability of the Diablo-Mocho base-line. If this line were itself distorted during the earthquake, it is possible that the absolute movements on the two sides of the fault may in reality have been nearly equal to one another*.

XI. Seismic Seawave

370. To the west of San Francisco, from Bolinas Bay to Mussel Rock, the course of the San Andreas fault is submarine. On land, there is no evidence of vertical displacement to the south of Mussel Rock; but, to the north of Bolinas Bay, there was a relative uplift of the west side of the fault amounting to one or two feet. The absence of any periodic wave recorded by the tide-gauge at Fort Point, on the south side of the Golden Gate, indicates that the vertical displacement, if any, along the submarine portion of the fault must have been very small.

While, however, there was no periodic wave recorded, there was a slight depression, of little more than 4 in. in the water-level soon after the earthquake. The mareogram shows a blurring of the pencil-mark, due to the direct action of the shock. The depression of the water-level occurred about 9 min. later. It immediately began to recover, and the record shows that the surface rose without any minor oscillations to the normal level within 7

---

*Lawson, **18**, pp. 114-145.

min., and that it was not followed by a complementary rise of the water.

The Fort Point station lies about $7\frac{1}{4}$ miles from the fault-line on the east side, and it is estimated that the wave would take about 9 min. or little more to traverse this distance. Thus, it seems probable that the depression of the water-level was caused by a slight drop of the sea-bed along the fault at the time of the earthquake*.

XII. MISCELLANEOUS EFFECTS OF THE EARTHQUAKE

371. *Landslides.*—Among the Coast Ranges and along the sea-coast, three types of landslides occurred, known as earth-avalanches, earth-slumps and earth-flows. Of these, earth-slumps were of frequent, the others of exceptional, occurrence.

Earth-avalanches are masses of dry earth and rock that have fallen from cliffs or slid down precipitous slopes. They are distinguished from the other forms of landslides not only in the material but in the absence of water. They were found along the sides of steep cañons within the zone of great intensity, and especially along high and steep sea-cliffs, such as those of Humboldt County between Cape Mendocino and Point Delgada. Along many miles of this coast, there was a general slipping of rock and earth into the sea, and farther south, between Shelter Cove and Point Arena, where the cliffs are not so high, there was a general shedding of material from their surface, so that the sea was muddy for many days after the earthquake. Inland, some of the most remarkable avalanches fell from the steep walls of a cañon near Chittenden and close to the line of fault. On Deer Creek, in the Santa Cruz Mountains, an extensive avalanche slid down half a mile, carrying with it a number of redwood trees, from 3 to 6 ft. in diameter and about 200 ft. in height. The avalanche covered an area of 10 acres to a depth of from 30 to 60 ft.

372. The formation of earth-slumps is closely connected with the climate of the region. Along the slopes of the Coast Ranges, the solid rock is covered with a mantle of soil and decomposed rock that accumulates more rapidly than the rain can remove it. During the dry summer, the surface layer shrinks and cracks to a considerable depth, permitting the ready access of the early winter rains, which add to its weight and render it fluid or plastic. With a severe earthquake, like that of 1906, the movement of the earth-slump is started, leaving a horseshoe-shaped scarp overlooking the sunken area. As the mass moves down, it encounters the resistance of more stable portions of the slopes below and is thus crowded upon

*Lawson, **18**, pp. 369-371 ; Omori, **23**, pp. 8-9.

itself. The largest earth-slump occurred along the coast a short distance to the south of Cape Fortunas. In May 1906, it projected like a new cape into the ocean. In the direction of its movement, the length of the earth-slump was nearly a mile, its width varied from one-quarter to one-half a mile, and it stretched one-quarter of a mile into the ocean. The surface of the slump was very irregular, not unlike that of a much-crevassed glacier. It seems to have flowed like a partially plastic mass, expanding as it descended, though its total descent vertically was less than 500 ft. The whole mass had probably been on the point of sliding when it was set in motion by the earthquake.

373. Earth-flows are a special form of earth-slumps, containing more water and being therefore more mobile. They were mainly due to the rush of water expelled from the ground by the compressive action of the shock. As a rule, they originated in valleys or gullies, but occasionally also on hillsides. Once started, they crept down the slopes like lava-streams and formed a fan or tongue of debris on the ground below. One of the most remarkable earth-flows occurred on a hillside about 9 miles south of San Francisco. At the moment of the earthquake, there was a sudden outflow of sand and water that became mixed with the loam on the slope. The whole mass flowed down a shallow valley, covering a distance of 900 yd. in 3 min. As the average width of the flow was 100 ft., while its thickness varied from 13 ft. at the top to 3 ft. at the bottom, the total volume of compacted wet sand must have been about 89,000 c.yd.*

374. *Fissures.*—Secondary fissures, unconnected with the rift, occurred both on hill slopes and in the alluvial beds of valleys. On the hillsides, they were usually associated with landslides, actual or incipient. Outside the zone of the rift, fissures were common in valleys. They were usually parallel or nearly parallel to the nearest portion of the stream trench, along which they ran for several hundred feet, in some cases for several hundred yards. They were arranged in linear series, the cracks either overlapping *en échelon,* or grouped as parallel fissures in bands a few hundred feet in width.

In the alluvial floors of many streams, superficial earth-movements occurred, called earth-lurches by Lawson. They vary from the opening of a mere crack, with a slight movement of the ground on one or both sides, to a violent and complicated deformation of the surface. Cracks and fissures cut the soil into strips or prisms that lurch towards the stream-trench. Earth-lurches differ from the landslides described above in their occurrence on level ground.

---

*Lawson, **18**, pp. 384-401.

They were caused directly by the horizontal jerk of the earthquake. Lurching of soft ground also occurred on the tidal mud-flats of Tomales Bay and on the " made land " of San Francisco. In such places, as there was no trench, the movement caused a ridging of the surface with compensating depressions elsewhere*.

375. *Effects on Underground Water.*—In the alluvium of river-valleys, one of the most common phenomena was the expulsion of water from apertures that suddenly appeared in the level ground. The water was thrown as jets to a height of several feet, in some cases, it is said, to as much as 20 ft., and continued rising for several minutes after the earthquake. The vents so made were very numerous; in some parts they occurred closely grouped together, in others there were only a few to the acre or they were quite isolated. For weeks or months afterwards, they could be recognised in the form of craterlets, usually funnel-shaped, and were rimmed by fine sand evidently brought up from some depth. They varied in diameter from 1 ft. to about 10 ft.†

376. *Effects on Trees.* — In a belt extending for about a quarter of a mile on either side of the San Andreas rift, many white oaks (*Quercus lobata*) were either uprooted or had large branches 2 ft. across broken off by the force of the shock. Some trees more than 6 ft. in diameter were overturned. At one spot, a live oak (*Quercus agrifolia*), growing within a few feet of the rift, was split down the trunk but remained standing. At another, 2 miles southwest of the fault, redwood trees (*Sequoia sempervirens*) had their tops broken off at 75 or 100 ft. above the ground‡.

XIII. AFTER-SHOCKS

377. *Distribution in Space.*—A list of the after-shocks felt or recorded has been compiled by Prof. A. O. Leuschner. It is, however, regarded as nearly complete for Berkeley only, where several observers endeavoured to record every shock. The numbers of after-shocks in excess of 20 at different places are as follows: Berkeley 115, San Francisco 107, Los Gatos 67, Scott's Valley 60, Mile Rocks 42, Oakland 34, Mount Hamilton 31, Salinas 29, Ferndale 28, Eureka 26, Napa 22. Of these places, Eureka and Ferndale are close to the northern end of the fault-trace, Los Gatos and Mount Hamilton a short distance to the north, and Salinas a few miles to the south, of its southern end, Berkeley, San Francisco, Oakland and Napa are near the central region.

378. *Periodicity of After-Shocks.*—As few of the shocks were recorded by instruments, it is useless to consider the existence of

---

*Lawson, **18**, pp. 401-402.
†Lawson, **18**, pp. 402-409.
‡Taber, **28**, pp. 272-273.

a diurnal period.   The effects of changes of activity throughout the day apply much less strongly to a period so short as that of 42 min. During the interval Apr. 18-23, there is evidence in the Berkeley record (36 after-shocks) of the 42-min. period, with its maximum at 18 min., that is, coinciding roughly with the return-movements, and an amplitude of ·62*.

XIV.   LATER SEISMIC HISTORY OF THE DISTRICT

379.   Since 1906, several earthquakes, a few of semi-destructive intensity, have occurred that were probably due to movements along the San Andreas rift.   One of the strongest of recent earthquakes (intensity 8-9, Rossi-Forel scale) was that of 1911 July 1 in Central California, but its epicentre lay several miles to the north-east of the fault.

Three slight earthquakes, on 1912 Sep. 12, 1913 Oct. 25 and 1914 Jan. 23, have been attributed to centres along the fault, the first a short distance to the north of Santa Cruz, the second north-west of Berkeley, and the third near San Bruno.   On 1914 Nov. 8, a shock of intensity 8 originated in a centre close to the small town of Laurel and near the crest of the Santa Cruz range.   On 1916 Oct. 22, an earthquake of intensity 7 or slightly more disturbed an area of about 27,000 sq. miles, with its epicentre at or near the Tejon Pass.   On 1923 July 22, a movement, again in the southern half of the fault, may have given rise to an earthquake of intensity about 8 in the neighbourhood of the San Bernardino valley.   On 1923 Sep. 19, an earthquake of intensity 6 occurred, with its epicentral area on the San Andreas rift, close to the village of Corralitos or about 13 miles east of Santa Cruz.   In the slight earthquake (intensity 3) 1925 Feb. 10, the innermost isoseismal encloses a small area on both sides of the rift, the epicentre being about ¾ mile north of the north end of Crystal Springs Lake in the San Francisco peninsula.   On 1926 July 25, an earthquake of intensity 6-7 originated in a centre about halfway between Idria and Panoche.

380.   One of the most interesting, as well as one of the strongest, successors of the earthquake of 1906 occurred on 1927 Aug. 20.   At the nearest points on land, its intensity was 8.   The epicentre was clearly submarine, about 33 miles W.N.W. of Eureka, and close to the northerly continuation of the San Andreas rift beyond Point Delgada†.

---

*Lawson, **18**, pp. 410-433.

†Beal, **3**, pp. 215-219; Branner, **5**, pp. 51-60; Byerly, **7**, pp. 203-206; **8**, pp. 213-217; Davis, **9**, pp. 25-28; **10**, pp. 5-13; Laughlin, etc., **17**, pp. 105-106; Macelwane, **19**, pp. 109-112; Macelwane, etc., **20**, pp. 15-19.

xv. Bibliography

1 Austin, M. "The Temblor : a personal narrative." *The California Earth-quake of* 1906 (1907), pp. 339-361.

2 Baratta, M. "La catastrofe sismica di S. Francisco." *Riv. d'Ital.,* Oct. 1906, pp. 594-601.

3 Beal, C. H. "Earthquake in the Santa Cruz Mountains, California, November 8, 1914." *Amer. Seis. Soc. Bull.,* vol. 4, 1914, pp. 215-219.

4 Beal, C. H. "The earthquake in the Imperial Valley, California, June 22, 1915." *Amer. Seis. Soc. Bull.,* vol. 5, 1915, pp. 130-149.

5 Branner, J. C. "Geology and the earthquake." *The California Earth-quake of* 1906 (1907), pp. 63-78.

6 Branner, J. C. "The Tejon Pass earthquake of Oct. 22, 1916." *Amer. Seis. Soc. Bull.,* vol. 7, 1917, pp. 51-60.

7 Byerly, P. "The Idria (California) earthquake of July 25, 1926." *Amer. Seis. Soc. Bull.,* vol. 17, 1927, pp. 203-206.

8 Byerly, P. "The Eureka (California) earthquake of August 20, 1927." *Amer. Seis. Soc. Bull.,* vol. 17, 1927, pp. 213-217.

9 Davis, E. F. "Notes on the San Bruno earthquake of January 23, 1914." *Amer. Seis. Soc. Bull.,* vol. 4, 1914, pp. 25-28.

10 Davis, E. F. "Central California earthquake of November 8, 1914." *Amer. Seis. Soc. Bull.,* vol. 5, 1915, pp. 5-13.

11 Derleth, C. "The destructive extent of the California earthquake of 1906 : its effects upon structures and structural materials, within the earth-quake belt." *The California Earthquake of* 1906 (1907), pp. 79-212.

12 Evans, J. W. "An earthquake model." *Geol. Soc. Quart. Journ.,* vol. 66, 1910, pp. 346-351.

13 Fairbanks, H. W. "The great earthquake rift of California." *The Cali-fornia Earthquake of* 1906 (1907), pp. 319-338.

14 Gilbert, G. K. "The investigation of the San Francisco earthquake." *Popular Science Monthly,* 1906, pp. 97-115 ; *The California Earthquake of* 1906 (1907), pp. 213-256.

15 Holden, E. S. *List of recorded earthquakes in California, Lower Cali-fornia, Oregon and Washington Territory,* 1887, 78 pp.

16 Jordan, D. S. "The earthquake rift of April, 1906." *The California Earthquake of* 1906 (1907), pp. 1-62.

17 Laughlin, H. R., Arnold, R., and Kew, W. S. W. "Southern Cali-fornia earthquake of July 22, 1923." *Amer. Seis. Soc. Bull.,* vol. 13, 1923, pp. 105-106.

18 Lawson, A. C. (edit.). "The California Earthquake of April 18, 1906." *Report of the State Earthquake Investigation Commission,* vol. 1, 1908, 451 pp. ; vol. 2, 1910, 192 pp.

19 Macelwane, J. B. "The Corralitos earthquake, September 19, 1923." *Amer. Seis. Soc. Bull.,* vol. 13, 1923, pp. 109-112.

20 Macelwane, J. C., and Ripetti, W. C. "The Crystal Springs, California, earthquake of February 10, 1925." *Amer. Seis. Soc. Bull,* vol. 17, 1927, pp. 15-19.

21 Noble, L. F. "The San Andreas Rift and some other active faults in the desert region of south-eastern California." *Washington, Carnegie Inst. Yearbook,* vol. 25, 1925-26, pp. 415-428.

22 Oldham, R. D. "The geological interpretation of the earth-movements associated with the Californian earthquake of April 18th, 1906." *Geol. Soc. Quart. Journ.,* vol. 65, 1909, pp. 1-20.

23 Omori, F. "Preliminary note on the cause of the San Francisco earth-quake of April 18, 1906." *Imp. Earthq. Inv. Com. Bull.,* vol. 1, 1907, pp. 7-25 ; *The California Earthquake of* 1906 (1907), pp. 281-318.

24 Omori, F. "Preliminary note on the seismographic observations of the San Francisco earthquake of April 18, 1906." *Imp. Earthq. Inv. Com. Bull.,* vol. 1, 1907, pp. 26-43.

25 OMORI, F. "Note on the San Francisco earthquake of April 18, 1906." *Imp. Earthq. Inv. Com. Publ.,* no. 21, appendix II.

26 REID, H. F. "The California Earthquake of April 18, 1906." *Report of the State Earthquake Investigation Commission,* vol. 2, 1910, *The Mechanics of the Earthquake,* 192 pp.

27 RICCÒ, A. "Terremoto di San Francisco al 18 aprile 1906." *Catania Acc. Gioen. di Sci. Nat. Boll.,* 1906, 5 pp.

28 TABER, S. "Local effects of the California earthquake of 1906." *California Earthquake of* 1906 (1907), pp. 257-280.

29 WILLIS, B. "Aerial observation of earthquake rifts." *Amer. Seis. Soc. Bull.,* vol. 11, 1921, pp. 136-139; *Science,* vol. 54, 1921, pp. 266-268.

CHAPTER XIII

MESSINA EARTHQUAKE : 1908 Dec. 28

I. INTRODUCTION

381. The Calabrian earthquakes of 1783 and their successors up to Oct. 1907 have been described in Chapter II. Little more than a year after the last date, on 1908 Dec. 28, a great earthquake destroyed Messina and Reggio and many towns and villages along the coasts of Sicily and Calabria. Not many earthquakes have been more carefully studied. Prof. G. Mercalli visited the central area in the following April and wrote a brief but useful report. Prof. F. Omori, at the request of the Japanese Government, spent more than two months in the central district, and, on his return, published a preliminary report on the earthquake; the complete report, unfortunately, has never been written. Prof. M. Baratta, the historian of Italian earthquakes, paid two visits to the stricken area, and his very valuable report is the fullest account that we possess of the earthquake. Prof. G. Platania investigated the important seawaves. The records published by the Central Office of Meteorology and Geodynamics contain a complete list of the after-shocks.

The whole area of the Straits was re-surveyed by the R. Instituto Idrografico in the early months of 1909 and, beginning early in March, a new series of precise levellings was carried out along the south coast of Calabria and in the neighbourhood of Messina.

II. EARLY EARTHQUAKES OF THE MESSINA ZONE

382. At least six prominent earthquakes have been assigned by Mercalli to the Messina zone.

The first occurred on 1509 Feb. 25. It caused much damage to buildings at Reggio and Messina. On 1599 June 8, a very strong earthquake resulted in the collapse of houses in the same cities and their surrounding districts. On 1780 Mar. 28, an earthquake ruined some buildings in Messina, and, on Apr. 9, a violent earthquake visited both Messina and Reggio. One of the most interesting earthquakes of the zone was the fourth principal earthquake of the 1783 series (art. 77). Lastly, during the night of 1876 Sep.

13-14, an earthquake caused slight damage to buildings in Reggio, though not in Messina*.

After the earthquake of 1907 Oct. 23, shocks of slight to strong intensity visited different centres of the Calabro-Messinese area. On 1908 Dec. 20 or 21, a slight shock was felt at Reggio, on Dec. 25, others still slighter occurred in the same place, while two more are said to have been felt there during the night of Dec. 27-28. With the possible exception of these slight shocks, there seems to have been no warning of the great movement of the Reggio-Messina zone on Dec. 28. This was registered at the observatory of Messina at 5h. 20m. 27s. (4h. 20m. 27s., a.m., G.M.T.).

III.   Loss of Life and Property

383.   No precise estimate of the loss of life due to the Messina earthquake has ever been made. The early total of 100,000, given by both Omori and Rizzo, is now regarded as excessive. Outside the cities of Messina and Reggio, our information seems to be definite. In the province of Messina, excluding the city itself, 2,398 persons were killed; in the province of Reggio outside the city, 10,874; and, in the district round Monteleone, 10; making a total of 13,282. In some towns and villages, the losses were un-usually heavy, as is shown by such death-rates as 43·7 at Cannitello, 33·1 at Faro Superiore, 30·8 at Salice, 25·2 at Gallina, 23·9 at Gallico Superiore, and 21·0 per cent. at Pace.

384.   It is for the two principal cities that our knowledge is most defective. For the Messina district, the figures given by the Minister of Agriculture are: buried 27,523, died of wounds 325, presumed killed under the ruins 32,477. Thus, allowing 2,398 for the surrounding villages, we have 57,927 left for the city. Baratta still considers this number as excessive and that it should be reduced by the number of " presumed killed," leaving a total for Messina of 25,450.

According to an estimate of P. De Nava, the number of killed in the city of Reggio lay between 30 and 40 per cent. of the popula-tion of 27,158, that is, between 8,147 and 10,863.

Thus, if we take the lower estimates for the two principal cities, the total number of persons killed by the earthquake would be 46,869; if we take the higher, it would be 82,035.

385.   The area of great destruction, within which many houses in every town were ruined, is represented by the outer of the two dotted lines in *Fig.* 57. In the area enclosed by the inner dotted

---

*Eredia, **8**, pp. 481-496; Martinelli, **12**, pp. 305-326; Mercalli, **17**, pp. 42-43.

line, the destruction was complete or nearly so, and the death-rate much higher than elsewhere.   It includes the three important towns of Messina, Reggio Calabria and Villa San Giovanni.

In Messina, 98 per cent. of the houses were ruined.   The enor‧mity of the destruction there, wrote Omori, " is really beyond one's imagination.   All the buildings in the city were, with a very few exceptions, considerably cracked or absolutely reduced to masses of ruin, which looked like hills of *debris;* even those houses, whose

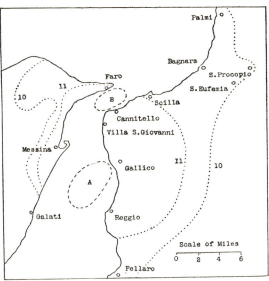

FIG. 57.—Meizoseismal area of the Messina
earthquake (Baratta).

perimetral walls were not overthrown, had their roofs and floors knocked down from top to bottom, so that the inside was filled with *debris;* it being not rare that 15 or more dead bodies were found buried one upon the other in the space of a single small room at the ground floor ".

386.   The principal causes of these disasters, apart from the nature of the site, have been pointed out by Mercalli, Omori and others : (i) the walls of the houses were too high or too thin for their height; (ii) many of them were built of river-pebbles or of brick bound with poor cement; (iii) roofs and floors were badly connected with the main walls and often fell while the walls were left stand-ing; (iv) towers and lofty buildings were built close to low houses and, by their fall, destroyed the latter; and (v) the streets were so

narrow that some of them were completely blocked by masses of
stone 16 ft. in height.

387. The material damage was estimated by Baratta to
amount to 240 million lire at Messina, 47 million at Reggio, and 263
million elsewhere, or altogether 550 million lire or about 22 million
pounds*.

IV. INTENSITY OF THE SHOCK

388.   Maps showing one or more isoseismal lines have been
drawn by Baratta, Mercalli, Omori and Riccò. Baratta's maps of
the central area and of the boundary of the disturbed area are reproduced in *Figs.* 57 and 58.

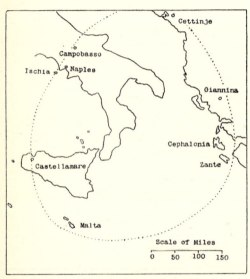

The outer of the
two dotted lines in
Fig. 57 represents an
isoseismal of in-
tensity 10 (Mercalli
scale), and the in-
ner line one that may
be regarded as of
intensity 11. From
the dimensions of
fallen bodies, Omori
estimated the maxi-
mum acceleration at
Messina to be 2,000
mm. per sec. per sec.,
or about the same as
that at San Fran-
cisco during the Cali-
fornia earthquake of
1906.

FIG. 58.—Disturbed area of the Messina
earthquake (Baratta).

The inner curve in
Baratta's map en-
closes about 130 sq.
miles. All the other isoseismals are irregular in form, except the
boundary of the disturbed area, which, as will be seen from *Fig.* 58, is
unsymmetrical with respect to the epicentre. This curve is about 500
miles long and 430 miles wide and contains about 170,000 sq. miles,
an area much greater than that of any other known Calabrian earthquake, probably because the boundary in this case is an isoseismal
of low intensity†.

---

*Baratta, **3**, pp. 234-253; Mercalli, **17**, pp. 4, 28-29; Omori, **19**, pp. 39-40.
†Baratta, **3**, pp. 214-215, 230; Lacroix, **10**, pp. 207-209; Mercalli, **17**, p. 31;
Omori, **19**, pp. 38-39.

v. Position of the Epicentres

389. From the form and position of the meizoseismal area, it is clear that the focus lay beneath the sea. Further light is thrown on its position by a study of the directions of the shock at places along and near the coast. These directions, as plotted by Baratta, converge within two small areas indicated by the broken-lines in *Fig.* 57. Both areas are submarine, one lying between Gallico and Reggio and the other at the northern entrance to the Strait between Faro and Canitello.

vi. Nature of the Shock

390. At Messina, the first phase of the movement, according to Prof. G. B. Rizzo, was sussultory and lasted from 2 to 3 sec. It was succeeded by an undulatory motion in the N.W.-S.E. direction, that lasted 7-8 sec. and threw down pieces of plaster and bricks from partition walls. Then, after an interval of about a second, there followed very violent undulations in the N.E.-S.W. direction, of about 15 sec. duration, by which the city was destroyed. At Palmi, the first part of the shock was undulatory and lasted for 6 or 7 sec., then, after a pause of a second, the movement was renewed, at first sussultory and ending with a violent rotatory motion.

Outside the area of destruction, and even as far as Lecce (206 miles from Messina), the double nature of the shock was distinct. At Potenza (170 miles), the first part was undulatory and lasted 6 sec., and was followed by a pause of about 5 sec., and then by stronger undulations lasting 20 sec.

391. Within the meizoseismal area, the mean duration of the shock was 34 sec. in Calabria and 30 sec. in Sicily. Outside it, the mean duration was 34 sec. in the Eolian Islands, 36 on the eastern slope of Calabria, 38 in the Calabrian plain, and 40 sec. in the district round Monteleone. In the whole disturbed area, the average of 78 estimates was 30 sec.

392. Baratta measured the direction of the shock at 34 places. They intersect, as already mentioned, within the two areas, A and B (*Fig.* 57). Most of the movable objects fell during the early undulations. It would appear, then, that there were two foci, that the southern focus was the earlier in action and that the impulse in the northern focus was much the stronger. The distance between the centres of the two areas is about 7·8 miles*.

vii. Warping of the Crust

393. At many points along the coast, the ground subsided by small amounts. At Messina, the harbour causeway sank in parts

---

*Baratta, **3**, pp. 267-304; Mercalli, **17**, pp. 4-9.

into the sea, so that waggons were found immersed three-fourths in water. The road along the coast was broken into strips parallel to its length and several yards wide and partially submerged (*Plate* 12A). Of these strips, two were lowered by about 2 ft. 3 in., and two others by less amounts. Soundings made after the earthquake in the harbour revealed, however, no notable changes since 1903. The bathymetric lines follow the same courses at both epochs, except in the creek on the east side of the harbour, where a slight lowering has certainly occurred.

At Reggio, the coast was lowered about 3 ft. so that the steps of the ferryboat landing stage were brought under water, while some yards of the coast disappeared. Soundings made in the harbour in the following February, when compared with others made five months before, reveal subsidences here and there of as much as 3 ft. Allowing for errors in sounding, the director of the R. Hydrographic Institute, P. Marzolo, concludes that, with the earthquake of 1908, a slight sinking probably occurred in the harbour.

394. During the first three months of 1909, soundings were repeated over the whole area of the Strait. When compared with those made in 1876-77, it is seen that the general course of the bathymetric curves at the two epochs is the same. There are neither abrupt nor gradual variations of depth perceptible. The slight differences that exist may, according to Marzolo, be attributed to errors in sounding that can hardly be avoided, especially when they are made in a sea with strong currents. The only exception occurs just outside the north entrance to the Strait. Here, the curves of 200 and 300 metres are farther apart on both coasts than they were twenty years before, and the curve of 400 metres near the Calabrian coast no longer exists. Either there has been a gradual elevation of the sea-bed in this district, or—and Marzolo considers this alternative the more probable—materials have been conveyed by currents and deposited over the spot.

395. More decisive in their results are the repeated series of precise levellings begun early in March 1909. They were made, in Sicily, from Messina by Castanea to Gesso, and, in Calabria, all along the coast from Giaio Tauro to Melito di Porto Salvo. Along the former route, the previous levels were made in 1908, and, along the latter, in 1906-08 (*Fig.* 59).

Assuming the height of Giaio Tauro to be unchanged, there appears to be at first a very slight elevation of the coast as far as Bagnara, but at no point by more than one-fifth of an inch. The general subsidence becomes noticeable at and near Favazzina, where the ground is lowered from 2·3 to 4·9 in. At Scilla, the subsidence amounts to 7·2 in., at Ponte Bavere to 11·3 in., at Villa San Giovanni to 16·7 in. From there, it increases, though not regularly, to 21·3 in. at Reggio, reaching its maximum 22·9 in. at a point two miles south of that city, and then decreasing to 18·9 in. at San Gregorio, 15·4 in. at Pellaro, and, still more rapidly within the next six miles, to 2·8 in. at Saline, after which the change is one of

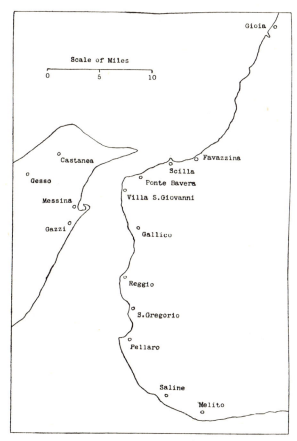

FIG. 59.—Subsidence of the coasts of the Straits of Messina (R. Com).

elevation, with respect at any rate to Gioia Tauro, of as much as 5·0 in. at the end of the route at Melito di Porto Salvo.

396.   In Sicily, the level of Paracarro, 8·3 miles west of Messina, was assumed to be unchanged.   At the next station (Fontana delle Catenella), there was apparently an elevation of less than one-tenth of an inch.   With this possible exception, the

change was invariably one of depression and the amounts were even greater than those on the Calabrian coast, such as 24·4 in. at Messina, and 26.9 in. and 28.0 in. at places within two miles of the harbour. Thus, on land, at any rate, the movement seems to have been one of warping*.

VIII. RUPTURE OF DEEP-SEA CABLES

397. That actual movements of the sea-bed occurred with the earthquake seems to be shown by the rupture of at least two telegraph cables.

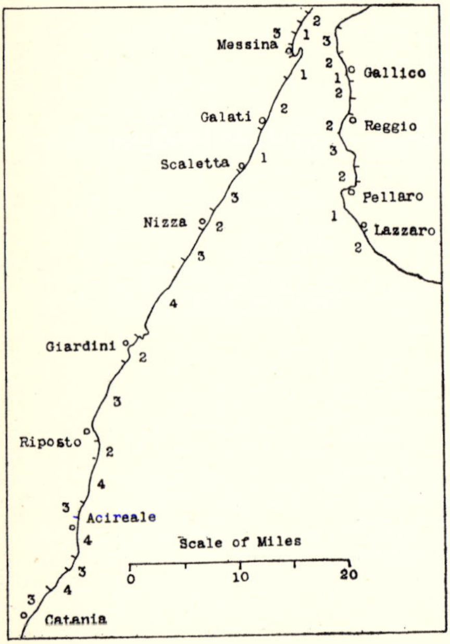

FIG. 60.—Height of sea-waves in the Straits of Messina (Baratta).

The cable crossing the Strait between Gazzi and Gallico was laid down in 1904 and was interrupted for the first time in coincidence with the earthquake at a point 2 miles from Gallico and at a depth of 250 fathoms.

T h e   Milazzo-Lipari cable was laid down in 1881. Between 1888 and 1892, it was interrupted four times, during and after the eruption of Vulcano. At the time of the Calabrian earthquake of 1905 Sep. 8, it was broken at a point 6½ miles east of the south end of Vulcano at a depth of 625 fathoms. At the time of the Messina earthquake, it was ruptured again at the same spot†.

IX. SEISMIC SEAWAVES

398. About 5 to 18 min. after the earthquake, seawaves flowed in over the coasts of the central area, especially on both sides of the Strait, in Sicily also along the whole of the east coast, along

---

*Loperfido, **11**, pp. 131-156; Marzolo, **16**, pp. 113-115; Mercalli, **17**, pp. 38-40.
   †Baratta, **3**, pp. 360-362; Platania, **22**, pp. 434-439, 456-458.

B. CALIFORNIA EARTHQUAKE.

Displacement of fence by the movement along the San
Andreas fault (Gilbert).

A. CALIFORNIA EARTHQUAKE.

Fault-scarp near head of Pine Gulch Creek
(Lawson).

PLATE XI.   [*To face page* 208.

B. Messina Earthquake.
Transport of block of concrete by seawave (Omori).

A. Messina Earthquake.
Subsidence of quay at Messina (Baratta).

PLATE XII.   [*To face page* 209.

the north coast to Brolo, and along the south coast to near Litata, and in Calabria as far as Scilla on the west coast and near Bianco on the east. The principal area visited is shown in *Fig.* 60, in which an attempt is made to represent their force and magnitude according to a scale devised by Baratta. The scale contains seven degrees, of which only the first five apply to the area illustrated, namely: 1. the waves very strong with great damage; 2. very strong with moderate damage; 3. very strong with slight damage; 4. strong but without damage; and 5. moderate. It will be seen that the effects were most serious on the Sicilian coast about $2\frac{1}{2}$ miles north of Messina, to the south of Messina harbour, and between Galati and Scaletta, and, on the Calabrian coast, near Gallico and between Pellaro and Lazzaro.

Nearly all the observers who noticed the first movements of the sea agree that the initial phase was a retreat from the shore, followed by three large waves, of which the second was usually the greatest, and by many others lasting for several hours.

399. Many measurements of the height of the waves were made by Platania and others, mostly from remains left by them on walls and trees. Along the Sicilian coast of the Strait, the height reached was $2\frac{1}{2}$ ft. at Torre del Faro, 10 ft. at Messina, 26 ft. at Galati and Scaletta, 30 ft. at Nizza, 38 ft. (the maximum) at San Alessio, 31 ft. at Giardini, falling to 20 ft. at Riposto, 12 ft. at Acireale and $6\frac{1}{2}$ ft. at Catania. Along the Calabrian coast, the greatest heights recorded were 18 ft. at Gallico, 32 ft. at Reggio, 43 ft. (the maximum) at Pellaro and 22 ft. at Lazzaro.

400. On both sides of the Strait, many buildings were swept away by the waves. In Sicily, 79 people were drowned, and, on the Calabrian coast, more than 141.

Two examples of the work done by the seawaves may be given. A concrete block that formed part of a pier at Reggio, though it weighed about 15 tons, was carried to a distance of 22 yd. (*Plate* 12B). Close to Pellaro, the river Fiumerella was crossed by a railway bridge, consisting of a single iron girder 48 yd. long and parallel to the sea coast. The bridge was carried away by the waves into the river and turned through an angle of 55*.

x. After-Shocks

401. The great earthquake, that occurred at 5.20 a.m., put out of action nearly all seismographs within 200 miles of the origin. The first after-shock was, however, recorded at Mileto at 5.36 and

---

*Baratta, **3**, pp. 360-362, 335-374; Mercalli, **17**, pp. 36-38; Omori, **19**, pp. 41-43; Platania, **22**, pp. 369-458.

at Catania at 5.44. On Dec. 28, 138 shocks were recorded at Mileto, of which 28 were of intensity 5 (Mercalli scale). At Messina, 87 shocks were felt during the last four days of 1908, and, during successive months, 93, 20, 123, 90, 75, 82, 96, 76, 46, 48, 51 and 62. Of these 949 shocks, 53 were strong and 5 ruinous. The strongest of all the after-shocks occurred on 1909 July 1 and caused fresh damage to buildings in Messina with the loss of several lives*.

402. *Periodicity of After-Shocks.*—Taking all the after-shocks during the first three months of 1909, the maximum epoch of the diurnal period occurred at midnight and the amplitude was ·49. From April to December, the period is indefinite. In 1910, the maximum epoch was at 10 a.m. and the amplitude ·20.

403. For the 42-minute period, the maximum epoch during the interval Dec. 28, 6.0 a.m. to Jan. 2, 5.0 a.m. occurred at 15 min. after the return-waves with an amplitude of ·36. During the interval Jan. 2-12, the number of shocks is small, but the analysis seems to point to a reversal of epoch. After Jan. 12, there is no trace of the period.

BIBLIOGRAPHY

1 AGAMENNONE, G. "Le repliche del disastroso terremoto Calabro-Messinese del 28 dicembre 1908." *Riv. di Astr.,* anno 6, 1912, 6 pp.

2 ANGOT, A. "Sur le tremblement de terre due 28 décembre 1908." *Paris Acad. Sci. C.R.,* vol. 148, 1909, pp. 62-63.

3 BARATTA, M. "La Catastrofe Sismica Calabro Messine (28 dicembre 1908)", 1910, 426 pp.

4 BLASERNA, P., etc. "Relazione della Commissione Reale incaricata di designare le zone piu atatte per la riconstruzione degli abitati colpiti dal terremoto del 28 dicembre 1908 o da altri precedenti " (1909).

5 CIRERE, R. "Sur le tremblement de terre du 28 décembre 1908." *Paris Acad. Sci. C.R.,* vol. 148, 1909, p. 64.

6 COMAS SOLA, J. "Le tremblement de terre du 28 décembre 1908, enregistré à l'Observatoire Fabra (Barcelone)." *Paris Acad. Sci. C.R.,* vol. 148, 1909, pp. 202-203.

7 EGINITIS, D. "Sur les tremblements de terre du 28 décembre 1908 et du 23 janvier 1909." *Paris Acad. Sci. C.R.,* vol. 148, 1909, pp. 739-740.

8 EREDIA, F. "Contributo allo studio dei terremoti messinese." *Ital. Soc. Sism. Boll.,* vol. 13, 1908-09, pp. 481-496.

9 HOBBS, W. H. "The Messina earthquake." *Amer. Geogr. Soc. Bull.,* vol. 61, 1909, pp. 409-422.

10 LACROIX, A. "Resumé de quelques observations de M. A. Riccò sur le tremblement de terre de Sicile et de Calabre du 28 décembre 1908." *Paris Acad. Sci. C.R.,* vol. 148, 1909, pp. 207-209.

11 LOPERFIDO, A. "Livellazione geometrica di precisione eseguita dall'Istituto geografico militare sulla costa orientale della Sicilia, da Messina a Castanea, a Gesso ed a Faro Peloro e sulla costa occidentale della Calabria da Gioia Tauro a Melito di Porto Salvo, per incarico del Ministro di agricoltura, industria e commercio." *Rel. della Com. R., etc.,* 1909, pp. 131-161.

*Agamennone, 1; Baratta, 3, pp. 318-326; Martinelli, 14, 15.

12 MARTINELLI, G. " Fenomeni sismici calabro-siculi precedenti il terremoto del 28 dicembre 1908." *Ital. Soc. Sism. Boll.*, vol. 13, 1908-09, pp. 305-326.

13 MARTINELLI, G. " Osservazioni preliminari sul terremoto Calabro-Messinese del 28 dicembre 1908." *Ital. Meteor. Soc. Boll.*, vol. 28, 1909, 11 pp.

14 MARTINELLI, G. " Notizie sui terremoti osservati in Italia durante l'anno 1908." *Ital. Soc. Sism. Boll.*, vol. 15, 1911, appendix, pp. 550-639.

15 MARTINELLI, G. " Notizie sui terremoti osservati in Italia durante l'anno 1909." *Ital. Soc. Sism. Bol.*, vol. 16, 1912, appendix, pp. 1-618.

16 MARZOLO, P. " Sui risultati degli scandagli eseguiti nello stretto di Messina, da alcune R. Navi e Torpediniere, nel 1° trimestre 1909." *Rel. della Comm. R., etc.*, 1909, pp. 113-115.

17 MERCALLI, G. " Contributo allo studio del terremoto Calabro-Messinese del 28 dicembre 1908 " (1909).

18 ODDONE, E. " Calcolo provvisorio della profondita dell'ipocentro del terremoto Calabro-Siculo del 28 dicembre 1908." *R. Acc. Linc. Proc.*, vol. 18, 1909, pp. 186-192.

19 OMORI, F. " Preliminary report on the Messina-Reggio earthquake of Dec. 28, 1908." *Imp. Earthq. Inv. Com. Bull.*, vol. 3, 1909, pp. 37-45.

20 OMORI, F. " Note on the recent sea-level variation at the Italian and Austrian mareograph stations, and on the cause of the Messina-Reggio earthquake of 1908." *Imp. Earthq. Inv. Com. Bull,* vol. 5, 1913, pp. 87-100.

21 PERRET, F. A. " Preliminary report on the Messina earthquake of December 28, 1908." *Amer. Journ. Sci.*, vol. 27, 1909, pp. 321-334.

22 PLATANIA, G. " Il maremoto dello Stretto di Messina del 28 dicembre 1908." *Ital. Soc. Sism. Boll.*, vol. 13, 1908-09, pp. 369-458.

23 TACCONI, E. " Nota degli scandagli nello Stretto di Messina : Esame sommario dei materiali estratti." *Rel. della Com. R., etc.*, 1909, pp. 122-129.

24 TARAMELLI, T. " Sull' esame dei saggi di fondo nello stretto di Messina ottenuti cogli scandagli eseguiti dalla R. Marina nel 1° trimestre 1909." *Rel. della Com. R., etc.*, 1909, pp. 117-121.

CHAPTER XIV

TANGO EARTHQUAKE : 1927 Mar. 7

1. Introduction

405. The Japanese islands have been divided by Omori into three well-marked seismic zones. The outer zone borders the eastern or convex margin, the inner zone clings to the western or concave margin, while between them lies the inland zone. From the year 416 to the beginning of the present century, there were 221 destructive earthquakes in Japan, of which 47 occurred in the outer, and 17 in the inner, zone. Ten of them were of unusual violence, and, of these, 7 originated in the outer zone and 3 inland. Within the same interval, the Pacific coast was swept by 23 great seawaves and the Japan Sea coast by only 5 small ones.

The same inequality marks the earthquakes of less violence. Taking only shocks that disturbed a land-area of more than 25,000 sq. miles, Omori found that, from 1885 to 1905, there were 257 such earthquakes in Japan. Of these, 146 originated in the outer zone and only 9 in the inner*.

406. Within four years after the great Kwanto earthquake of 1923, Japan was visited by two destructive earthquakes, both of them with epicentres near the Japan Sea coast, one in the province of Tazima in 1925, the other in that of Tango in 1927†. It is remarkable that both provinces have within historic times been almost free from earthquakes. In Sekiya's great catalogue of 1898 earthquakes from 416 to 1864, the province of Tazima is never mentioned as having been shaken by an earthquake, while for the province of Tango there are only two entries, in 1662 and 1854, and those of earthquakes with origins elsewhere‡.

This comparative immunity seems to point, not only to an intimate relation between the Tazima and Tango earthquakes, but to some real connexion of both with the great Kwanto earthquake of 1923. Imamura has given other examples of the transference of activity from the outer to the inner zone. For instance, the Nemuro earthquake of 1894 Mar. 22, near the east coast of Hokkaido, was followed on Oct. 22 by an earthquake in the pro-

---

*Imp. Earthq. Inv. Com. Bull., vol. 1, 1907, pp. 114-123.
†The province of Tango lies about 250 miles due west of Tokyo. It is bounded on the west by the province of Tazima. (Fig. 61.)
‡Tokyo Imp. Univ. Coll. Sci. Journ., vol. 11, 1899, pp. 315-388.

vince of Ugo on the west coast of the Main Island. Again, the great submarine Sanriku earthquake of 1896 June 15, off the northeast coast of the Main Island was succeeded on Aug. 31 by an earthquake on the opposite coast of Ugo province*.

407. *The Tazima Earthquake of* 1925. — This destructive earthquake occurred on May 23 at 11h. 10m. 49s., a.m. (2h. 10m. 49s., a.m., G.M.T.). Its epicentre, represented by the black spot on the left side of *Fig.* 61, lies near Tai and in the Tuiyama Cove,

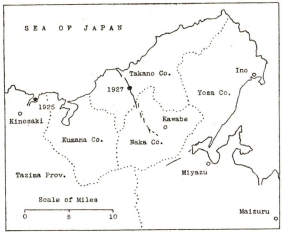

FIG. 61.—Map of the central counties of the Tango earthquake.

in lat. 35° 38·7′ N., long. 134° 50·5′ E. The meizoseismal area was small, 12½ miles long from north to south and 10 miles wide; but, as the epicentre was submarine, the length of the area may have been as much as 25 miles. The damage to property is represented by the following figures—2,180 houses burned, 1,295 collapsed, 773 half-collapsed and 3,200 damaged, or altogether 7,514 houses ruined or in part destroyed, representing a total loss of from 10 to 13 million pounds. The number of persons killed was 428, and of wounded 834. Most of the destruction occurred in the villages surrounding Tuiyama Cove, where the percentage of burned and collapsed houses reached 82 at Kinosaki, 86 at Kei and 99 at Tai. A second centre of destruction occurred at Toyooka, about 7 miles south of the epicentre, where by reason of the earthy soil on which it was built, 90 per cent. of the houses were either ruined or burned. As in most Japanese earthquakes, the actual death-rate was low, the highest figure reached being 8·0 per cent at Kinosaki, 1·4 at Tai, and 0·8 per cent. at Toyooka.

*Imamura, **3**, pp. 95-96.

408. An interesting feature of the earthquake is the formation of two faults on the top of Hachiganaru Hill, a hill 758 ft. in height on the north side of the valley of Tai. The faults start from the shore and run in a south-westerly direction for a length of about 1 mile, the greatest distance between them being about ¼ mile. At the top of the steep slope, the western fault gives rise to landslides and finally resolves itself into a number of clefts, the width of which varies between 8 and 12 in. The horizontal movement along this side is small, the west side being shifted towards the south but by somewhat less than 2½ in. On the eastern fault, the vertical displacement ranges from 2 ft. to 2 ft. 7½ in., in some places reaching as much as 3 ft. 4 in.

409. Soon after the Tango earthquake of 1927, a series of precise levellings was carried out over part of the area of the Tazima earthquake, from Ebara through Toyooka to Kumihama, then turning to the east, and thus omitting the meizoseismal area of the earthquake. Comparing the heights of the bench-marks with those made during the previous survey in 1888, the ground shows a depression ranging from 7·8 in. at Ebara, through 18·4 in. at Toyooka, to 6·8 in. at Kumihama. About the same time, the Hydrographic Survey of the Imperial Japanese Navy carried out a fresh series of soundings in the sea bordering the epicentral zone, but no change of depth of more than a foot was detected since the last survey in 1892.

410. The after-shocks were recorded at Toyooka, 7 miles south of the epicentre, the numbers observed being 23 in the latter half of May 23, and 31, 32, 65, 36, 20, 17, 5 and 7 during the remaining days in May, the number recorded from May 23-31 being 236, and from June 1-17, 122, a total of 358 in 26 days*.

II. Loss of Life and Property

411. The numbers of persons killed and injured and of houses destroyed or burned are given in the following Table:

County	No. of persons		No. of houses				
	killed	injured	collapsed	half-collapsed	burned	half-burned	total
Takano	799	1,100	3,133	2,077	1,378	54	6,642
Naka	1,635	1,338	3,080	2,811	2,771	36	8,698
Yosa	551	637	3,763	3,380	810	25	7,978
Kumana	6	61	476	1,271	2	—	1,749
Other counties	26	149	181	282	—	—	463
Total	3,017	3,285	10,633	9,821	4,961	115	25,530

*Imamura, 3, pp. 71-107; Koto, 10, pp. 1-75; Yamasaki, 46, pp. 109-113.

In the four central counties, the death-rate was only 2·3 per cent. The rate of 24·5 per cent. at Mineyama is probably the highest for any recent Japanese earthquake. At Itiba the rate was 11·9, at Simazu 8·2, at Gô 6·4, at Yamada 6·3 and at Amino 5·1.

The total number of houses entirely destroyed was 15,594 or 58 per cent. of the whole number in the four central counties. The places that suffered most were those lying close to the fault-lines. At Mineyama, about 80 per cent. of the houses collapsed, and most of the rest were burned*.

III. Investigation of the Earthquake

412. As soon as the news of the earthquake reached the Earthquake Institute, the staff and assistants were sent to the central district.

Under the direction of Prof. A. Imamura, sensitive portable tromometers of improved types were erected at three places surrounding the epicentre, at Maizuru and Kinosaki (*Fig.* 61) on Mar. 11 and at Ine on Mar. 12. Here they remained until Dec. 22, when the seismograph at Ine was removed to Kobe on Jan. 21, while a fourth instrument was added on the same day at Taiza. After 1928 June 24, the observations at Kinosaki were discontinued, but they were carried on at the other three stations until the beginning of Aug. 1928. The records of the after-shocks were placed under the care of Prof. N. Nasu, who has published several reports on them of the greatest interest. In addition to the four seismographs, two Ishimoto tiltmeters were erected under the guidance of Prof. M. Ishimoto, one at Miyazu on Mar. 11, the other at Kawabe on May 26.

The geology of the central district was studied by Prof. H. Tsuya, while Profs. N. Yamasaki and F. Tada traced the courses of the remarkable faults and measured the displacements along them. Prof. T. Taniguchi investigated the causes that led to the collapse of so many houses in the district. Valuable studies of the earthquake were also made by other Japanese men of science, among which should be mentioned especially those by Prof. S. Nakamura, by Messrs. K. Watanabe and H. Sato, members of the Imperial Geological Survey of Japan, and lastly by the veteran Prof. B. Koto, the author of the well-known memoir on the cause of the Mino-Owari earthquake of 1891. The reports of the last-named writer are illustrated by very numerous photographs of the faults of both the Tazima and Tango earthquakes.

In no other earthquake have the movements of the crust been studied so exhaustively as in the Tango earthquake. After several

*Imamura, 2, p. 185.

earthquakes since 1897, new series of levellings and trigonometrical measurements have been repeated once and the results compared with those last made in the same districts. After the Tango earthquake, they were repeated no less than five times by the Land Survey Department of the Imperial Japanese Army and the results, as worked out in valuable memoirs by Prof. C. Tsuboi, have thrown new and welcome light on our knowledge of the mechanism of a great earthquake. In addition to this work on land, the task of sounding the sea-bed bordering both the Tazima and Tango pro-

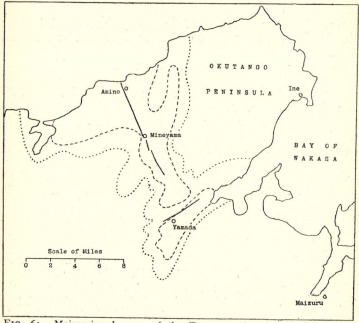

FIG. 62.—Meizoseismal areas of the Tango earthquake (Yamasaki and Tada).

vinces was entrusted to the Hydrographic Department of the Imperial Japanese Navy.

IV. INTENSITY OF THE SHOCK

413. The area most severely shaken is well-known as one of the centres of the silk textile industry in Japan, the largest towns in it being Amino and Mineyama, with populations of 5,836 and 4,585, while close to it, on the shore of the bay of the same name, lies Miyazu with 12,401 inhabitants. The meizoseismal area is

represented in *Fig.* 62, in which the broken-line bounds the district in which 10 per cent. or more of the houses were thrown down or burned, and the dotted line that in which 1 to 9 per cent. were so destroyed. Both lines cling rather closely to the two remarkable faults indicated by thick lines on the map, that will be described in the next section. Within about a mile of these faults, about 90 per cent. of the houses were destroyed and the maximum acceleration of the vibrations, according to Imamura, was as high as $\frac{2}{5}$ or

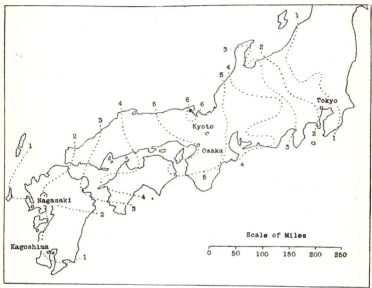

FIG. 63.—Isoseismal lines of the Tango earthquake (Watanabe and Sato).

$\frac{1}{2}$ of that due to gravity, or from 3,760 to 4,700 mm. per sec. per sec. Similar values for the maximum acceleration from the dimensions of fallen tombstones, are given by Nakamura, such as 4,230 mm. per sec. per sec. at Mineyama and 3,290 mm. per sec. per sec. at Kaya. Such figures show that the intensity of the Tango earthquake did not differ materially from that of the Mino-Owari earthquake of 1891 or the Kwanto earthquake of 1923.

414. The isoseismal lines for the whole disturbed area, as traced by Watanabe and Sato, are given in *Fig.* 63, the scale of intensity which is that adopted by the Central Meteorological Observatory of Japan, being: 6. violent, 5. strong, 4. strong (rather weak), 3. weak (rather strong), 2. weak, and 1. slight. The area within the isoseismal 6 is estimated as not more than 4 sq. miles.

The isoseismal 4 includes about 21,600 sq. miles, the isoseismal 2 about 36,900, and the isoseismal 1 or boundary of the disturbed area about 58,500 sq. miles. The shock was felt, but very slightly, at Tokyo, about 250 miles from the epicentre, so that the total area disturbed may have contained nearly or quite 200,000 sq. miles*.

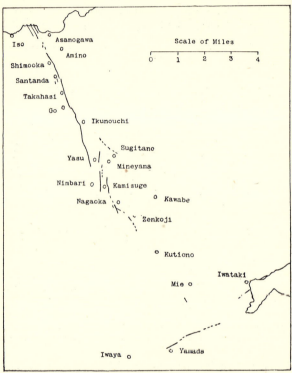

Fig. 64.—Map of the Gomura and Yamada faults (Yamasaki and Tada).

v. The Earthquake Faults

415. At the time of the earthquake, two remarkable faults were produced along old lines of dislocation. They have been called the Gomura and Yamada faults after the villages, Go and Yamada, near which they are well developed. The Gomura fault

---

*Nakamura, *Earthq. Res. Inst. Bull.,* vol. 4, 1928, p. 179; **18**, pp. 443-446; Omori, *Imp. Earthq. Inv. Com. Publ.,* no. 4, 1900, pp. 15-16; Suda, *Kobe Imp. Mar. Obs. Mem.,* vol. 1, 1924, *Table* vi; Watanabe, etc., **45**, *Fig.* 2; Yamasaki, etc., **48**, *pl.* 17.

is about 11·2 miles long, and runs along the west boundary of the Oku-Tango peninsula with a general trend from N. 20° W., to S. 20° E. Relatively to the other, the west side is, as a rule, up-lifted and shifted to the south, the maximum amounts of displace-ment being 2 ft. 4½ in. and 9 ft. 2½ in., respectively. The Yamada fault is about 4¼ miles long and runs along the southern scarp of the Oku-Tango peninsula in a direction nearly at right angles to the other, from S. 55° W. to N. 55° E., the north side being raised relatively and shifted to the east through amounts that range as high as 2 ft. 3½ in. and 2 ft. 7½ in., respectively. The courses of the faults are shown in *Fig.* 64.

416. The faults cross both valleys and hill-spurs, but they vary in appearance with the nature of the ground they traverse. In mulberry fields, the soil may look as if it had been turned over by the plough or as enlarged mole-tracks. In soft muddy rice-fields, the surface may be gently warped. On hard ground, such as roads, they take the form of rifts showing vertical and horizontal displacements. On mountain slopes, again, they are often concealed under rock avalanches or they form sharp clefts, sometimes in a zone 20 yd. wide, cutting deep into the ground, and usually arranged *en échelon.*

417. *Gomura Fault.*—The Gomura fault starts from the coast between Iso and Asamogawa and runs in a general S. 30° E. direction to near the village of Mie. The total length of its course on land is 11·2 miles. The fault is not continuous. It consists of a system of nearly parallel rifts (*Fig.* 64) so arranged that each follows the one to the north on its east side. Except in the northern part lying to the west of Lake Asamo, the crust on the west side of the fault has, relatively to that on the other, been dis-placed to the south. The greatest horizontal displacement measured is 9 ft. 2½ in. between the villages of Takahasi and Go. The west side has also been raised, relatively, with the exception again of its northern portion, and it was near the village of Go that one of the greatest vertical displacements (of 27·2 in.) was observed.

As already mentioned, the Gomura fault belongs to an old line of dislocation. Yamasaki and Tada have remarked that this fracture is a fault-scarp still clearly traceable, that it forms the south-western boundary of a rift-valley running along the neck of the Oku-Tango peninsula, and that it consists of a series of step-faults along each of which the new faults or rifts have been formed. In the neighbourhood of this fault, the epicentres of the after-shocks lie on the west side, and, from a knowledge of the depths of their foci, Imamura estimates the dip of the fault to be 70° to the south-west. At one spot near the centre of the fault, where the rift runs across mountain-spurs and valleys, Tada was able to measure the inclination of the fault as 60°-80° to the southwest. He proved also that the fault is a reversed one.

418. That the crust on the west side of the fault was raised with reference to the sea-level seems clear from the uplift of the coast described in a later section. The soundings carried out by the Hydrographic Department also show, according to Terada and Higasi, that the uplift along the fault is continued into the sea-bed and that the difference of elevation on the two sides of the fault is indeed greater under water than anywhere on land. A distinct

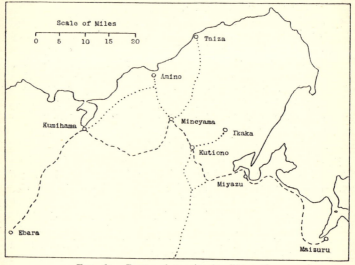

Fig. 65.—Route of precise levellings (Imamura).

submarine extension of the fault is, again, implied by the distribution of the after-shock epicentres. Some of these have been traced along or near the continuation of the fault to a point 18½ miles from the coast (*Fig.* 64), so that the total length of the Gomura fault must be very nearly 30 miles.

419. Yamasaki and Tada have assigned the names of neighbouring villages to the several rifts of the Gomura fault. The Takahasi, the most important and continuous of the series, runs from the shore in the direction of S. 30° E. to Santanda, after which it turns gradually to S. 15° E. until it reaches Yasu, its total length being 5·5 miles. The relative horizontal displacement of the west side is 12·6 in. to the north in the neighbourhood of the coast. After passing Lake Asamo, the displacement is everywhere to the south, 33·1 in. near Shimooka,

increasing to 110·6 in. near Go, and gradually decreasing to 28·3 in. near Yasu. The relative vertical displacement of the west side is 14·2 in. downward at the northern end. Elsewhere the displacement is upward, 19·7 in. near Shimooka, increasing to 27·2 in. near Go, and then decreasing gradually to 7·1 in. at Yasu. Two minor faults also run from the shore parallel to and on either side of the main fault and some hundreds of yards from it. A remarkable and unusual feature of this rift is the occurrence of slickensides on the granite surface of the fault-plane at two places near the villages of Ikunosuchi and Iwatani. At the former place, the strike of the fault is S. 19° E. and its dip 80° to the west. The striations rise towards the southern end, showing that the crust on the west side slipped upward in the southerly direction, in other words, that the fault there is a reversed one.

420. The other rifts are of less importance and interest. The Nimbari rift trends S. 8° W., its length is 1·5 miles, and the greatest horizontal and vertical displacements are 61·8 and 19·7 in., respectively. The Nagaoka rift is discontinuous and can be traced only on the plains. It runs in the direction S. 30° E. for 2·3 miles, with maximum horizontal and vertical displacements of 27·2 and 27·6 in. The Mie rift is the shortest of the series, its length is only 0·2 mile, its direction S. 60° E., and the greatest horizontal and vertical displacements are 11·8 and 15·7 in. The rift has disturbed and fissured the surface of paddy fields, but otherwise it is comparatively inconspicuous. The fifth and last, the Sugitani, rift is isolated from the other four, and is indistinct and discontinuous. Its trend is S. 66° E., its length only 0·6 mile, the maximum vertical displacement being 15·7 in. without any horizontal shift*.

421. *Yamada Fault.*—The Yamada fault runs along an old fault-scarp on the southern side of the Oku-Tango peninsula. Its course is shown in *Fig.* 64. The general trend of the fault is in the direction N. 55° E. and its total length, so far as it makes any change in the surface-features, is 4·7 miles. The distribution of the after-shock epicentres shows, however, that it probably extends farther in both directions, so that its total length may be about 18 miles. In all parts, the crust on the north side has been elevated relatively and shifted to the east. The maximum horizontal and vertical displacements, of 31·5 and 27·6 in., were measured near the village of Yamada, in which nearly all the houses are crushed into pieces. The fault here crosses a highway and cultivated land and forms a remarkable flexure instead of a steep rift. Farther to the east, on the hill Shiroyama, large cracks were formed in granite.

*Nasu, **22**, p. 51 ; Terada, etc., **32**, pp. 296-299 ; Yamasaki, etc., **48**, pp. 167-174.

At this point, Nakamura measured a displacement of about 4 in. horizontally and 18 in. vertically*.

VI. HORIZONTAL DISPLACEMENTS OF THE GROUND

422. Soon after the earthquake, the revision of the trigonometrical survey was carried out for all the primary and secondary triangulation points in the central area and surrounding region. The last survey before the earthquake was made in Dec. 1884 to

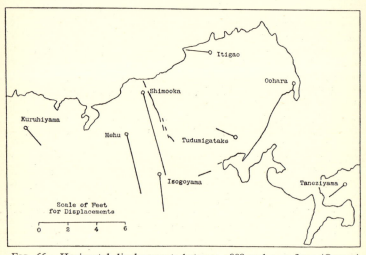

FIG. 66.—Horizontal displacements between 1888 and 1927 June (Omura).

Oct. 1888, and the dates of the new surveys are as follows :—

    I.   1927 May-June.
    II.   1927 Aug.-Sep.
    III. 1927 Oct.-Nov.
    IV. 1928 Apr.-Sep.

In the last survey, the revision included several new triangulation points of the first and second orders as well as those of the third order, the total number of points of the first, second and third orders of which the displacements were measured being 6, 41 and 226. In calculating these displacements, it was necessary to assume that the positions of two of the points were unchanged. As there is evidence that the Kasagatayama and Hyonoyama points were but slightly, if at all, affected by the earthquake, they were taken as

*Nakamura, **18**, pp. 434-437; Watanabe, etc., **45**, pp. 8-10; Yamasaki, etc., **48**, pp. 167-175.

fixed points. Both lie to the south of the area illustrated in *Figs.*
66, 68 and 69*.

423. The displacements of 8 triangulation points during the
interval between 1884-88 and the first re-survey ending in June
1927 are given in *Fig.* 66. It will be seen that the three stations
on the west side of the Gomura fault are displaced towards the south

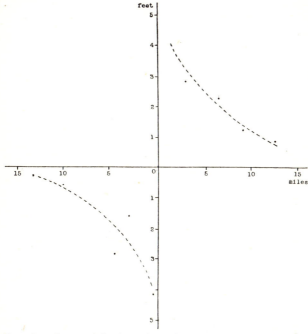

FIG. 67.--Curve of horizontal displacements between 1888 and
1927 June (Imamura and Kishinouye).

along lines that are nearly parallel to the fault, Shimooka by 67·3
in., Mehu by 43·7 in., and Isogoyama by 29·9 in. On the east side
of the fault, the displacements are usually towards the fault, at
Itigao by 20·1 in., Tudumigatake by 17·3 in., and Taneziyama by
16·4 in. It is clear, also, from this map, that the displacement on
the whole decreased with increasing distance from the fault. The
rate of decline is represented by Imamura and Kishinouye by the
curves in *Fig.* 67. In drawing them, they selected those stations

*Imamura, **4**, pp. 116-119; Imamura, etc., **5**, pp. 35-41; **6**, pp. 112-113;
Omura, **24**, p. 223; **27**, pp. 185-191; Tsuboi, **39**, pp. 190-203, 338-345.

that lie on or near the straight line drawn at right angles to the fault at the point where the observed displacement was greatest. The interval taken was that between 1884-88 and Aug. 1927, the close of the second re-survey. In *Fig.* 67, the distances from the fault are taken as abscissæ and the displacements parallel to the fault as ordinates, the stations used, from west to east, being Kinosaki, Nyon, Isosunayama, Shimooka, Yosizawa, Itigao, Taiko-

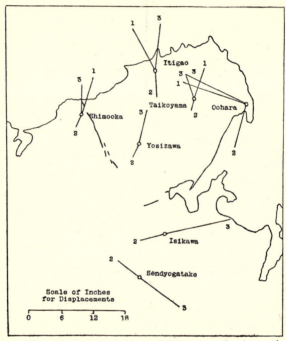

Fig. 68.—Horizontal displacements in successive intervals between 1927 May and 1928 Sep.

yama and Oohara. The curve has two branches and, when these are produced to meet the axis of y, the intercept between their points of intersection corresponds to the displacement along the fault and agrees roughly with the amount actually measured.

424. During the intervals between successive re-surveys, the horizontal displacement, like the vertical, varied considerably in direction. Maps of the displacements for the three intervals are given by Imamura and Tsuboi. They show no uniformity of direction on either side of the Gomura fault. During the first interval, for instance, the displacements at stations so near one another as

Taikoyama and Oohara were nearly at right angles. During the second, at Isikawa and Yuragatake, they were nearly opposite. The directions for the three intervals at the more important stations are represented in *Fig.* 68. It will be seen that, at several places, the direction from the second interval to the third is almost exactly

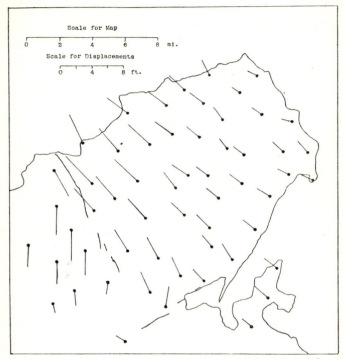

FIG. 69.—Horizontal displacements between 1888 and 1928 Sep. (Tsuboi).

reversed. The average of the angles betwen these directions at the 15 stations given is, indeed, 178°.

425. Compared with the diversity of successive intervals, it is interesting to notice the uniformity of the displacements between 1888 and the fourth survey in 1928. These are represented in *Fig.* 69. In this map, the displacements at 56 stations are shown, the revision for those of the third order having been carried out in the last survey*. It is clear from the map that, within an interval of

---

*The complete map, showing the displacements of stations of the third order, closely resembles that given in *Fig.* 68, but also covers a larger area.

a year and a half after the earthquake, the whole mass of the Oku-Tango peninsula was displaced in a nearly northwest direction with but very slight deformation of its parts. On the west side of the Gomura fault, the directions of displacement are also nearly uniform, but in the opposite direction. Close to this fault are two triangulation points, Shimooka and Yosizawa, on the west and east sides of the fault respectively. The total displacement at Shimooka was 50·1 in. in the direction S. 25° E., that at Yosizawa was 43·1 in. in the direction of N. 43° W. The component of the relative movement at the two places parallel to the fault was thus 91·3 in.*

VII. Vertical Displacements of the Ground

426. A line of precise levels was carried out in 1888, nearly forty years before the earthquake. The route then followed is represented by the broken-line in *Fig.* 69. It starts from Ebara, passes through Kumihama, Mineyama, Kutiono, Miyazu and ends at Maizuru, the route being 61 miles in length and including 48 bench-marks at nearly equal distances apart. The dates of the five repetitions of levelling along this line are as follows :—

I.   1927 Apr. 12-June 16.
II. 1927 June 1-July 31.
III. 1928 Mar. 3-Apr. 20.
IV. 1929 Aug. 7-Oct. 10.
V.   1930 June 17-Sep. 21.

After the earthquake, several new routes of precise levellings were added to cover the district with greater uniformity. They are represented by the dotted lines in *Fig.* 69. The lines runs from Kumihama to Amino (11·2 miles), Mineyama to Amino (6·2 miles), Mineyama to Taiza (9·9 miles), Kutiono to Ikaka (5·0 miles), and Kutiono to Hukutiyama (27·3 miles), the latter station being outside the map to the south of Kutiono. The total length of the new routes is about 60 miles, and the number of new bench-marks is 51.

427. The results of these surveys have been studied by Tsuboi in an admirable series of papers, the principal conclusions of which are given in the present section.

As the heights of both Ebara and Maizuru were changed, the variations in the heights of the bench-marks were expressed relatively to one of them. The Kutiono bench-mark (no. 1,232), which is common to several routes, was adopted as the standard. The instruments employed (the Zeiss Level No. III.) were so accurate that it was possible to estimate the difference of heights of bench-marks within 0·05 mm., so that the closing error is less than 3 mm. (0·12 in.).

---

*Imamura, **4**, *Figs.* 51, 53 and 55; Tsuboi, **39**, *Figs,* 31-33; **43**, *pl.*

428. The first diagrams (*Figs.* 70-72) represent the vertical displacements of the bench-marks along the old route from Ebara to Maizuru. In each of them, the distance of any bench-mark measured along the route from Ebara is taken as the abscissa and the vertical displacement as ordinate. The distances between successive bench-marks being nearly constant, they have, for simplicity,

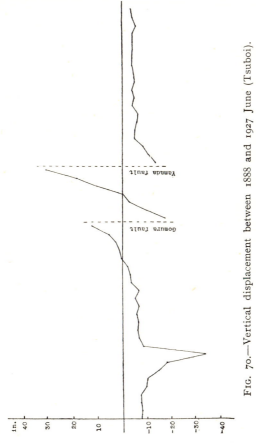

FIG. 70.—Vertical displacement between 1888 and 1927 June (Tsuboi).

been taken as equal. *Fig.* 70 represents the variation in height between 1888 and the first series of levels in 1927. Though most of the displacements were no doubt produced at the time of the earthquake, they must include some changes due to the secular deformation of the crust, others also that may have been produced by the Tazima earthquake of 1925. The first depression at the sixth

bench-mark from Ebara occurs indeed at Toyooka and may be connected with that earthquake. Farther on, the route crosses both
the Gomura and Yamada faults, at each of which there is a sudden
fall, of 31·3 in. at the former and 44·8 in. at the latter. Between
the two faults, there is a rapid increase upwards in the vertical dis-

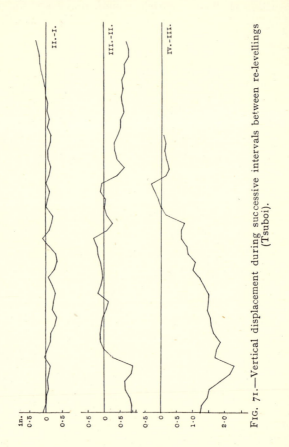

FIG. 71.—Vertical displacement during successive intervals between re-levellings (Tsuboi).

placements, due to the northward tilting by as much as 20″ of the
block bounded by the two faults.

429. The vertical displacements during successive intervals
between the re-levellings are represented in *Fig.* 71. These curves,
it will be seen, bear no close resemblance to the curve in *Fig.* 70,
and indeed the displacements in some sections occur in opposite
directions. On the other hand, the curve representing the total

change from the first to the fourth re-levelling (*Fig.* 72) corresponds in its general features with the curve in *Fig.* 70.

430. The route from Ebara to Maizuru varies greatly in direction. Certain sections of them, however, are approximately straight, and the displacements along two of these sections are represented during successive intervals in *Figs.* 73 and 74. Displacements in the first interval are denoted by small circles, those in the second by small black spots, and those in the third by crosses. In each figure, it will be seen, the points are distributed, not on a continuous curve, but on a number of segments of straight lines.

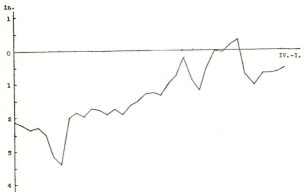

FIG. 72.—Total vertical displacement between the first and fourth re-levellings, 1927 Apr. to 1929 Oct. (Tsuboi).

Moreover, the ends of these segments lie practically on the ordinate of the same bench-mark. As Tsuboi suggests, the explanation of these peculiarities seems to be that the crust of the Tango district is not a continuous mass, but is made up of a number of separate blocks, each of which moved with comparative ease after the earthquake and on the whole as a rigid body. By connecting the various limiting bench-marks, it is possible to mark out approximately the boundaries of the crust-blocks, as shown in *Fig.* 75. The faults of the district are traced in *Fig.* 76, and a comparison of the maps show how closely the two series of lines agree and thus that the geological faults continued to be active after, as well as during, the great earthquake. Two other points of some interest are evident from *Figs.* 73 and 74. One is that the displacements of some blocks occur in opposite directions in successive intervals. The other, as will be seen from *Fig.* 74, that two blocks may be subjected to a common tilting during the first interval but as separate units during the second.

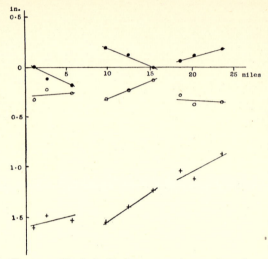

FIG. 73.—Vertical displacements in section from
Kumihama to near Mineyama (Tsuboi).

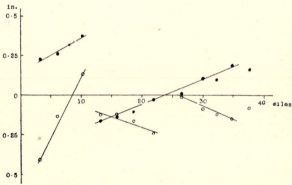

FIG. 74.—Vertical displacements in section from Mineyama
to near Miyazu (Tsuboi).

431. The varying differences between the heights of the bench-marks on either side of an active fault-line also throw light on the rates at which the faults are growing. The most interesting are those relating to the Gomura and Yamada faults. These are given in the following table:

Gomura Fault			in.
1927 Apr. 24-1927 June 5	...	... ...	0·22
,, June 5-1928 Mar. 9	. .	... ...	0·39
1928 Mar. 9-1929 Sep. 2	...	... ...	0·01
Yamada Fault			
1927 Apr. 23-1927 June 5	...	... ...	0·07
,, June 5-1928 Mar. 13	...	... ...	0·48
1928 Mar. 13-1929 Sep. 11	...	... ...	0·45

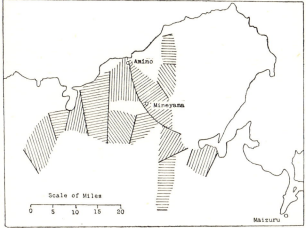

FIG. 75.—Boundaries of crust-blocks in the Tango district (Tsuboi).

Thus, during the first two intervals, the rate of displacement along Yamada fault was nearly constant. It was maintained, though at less rate, until two and a half years after the earthquake. On the other hand, the rate of growth of the Gomura fault was at first more rapid, but, during the last interval of a year and a half, it was almost inappreciable*.

VIII. UPLIFT OF THE COAST

432. A remarkable, and also very unusual, precursor of the earthquake was a temporary change in the sea-level observed at

---

*Tsuboi, **38**, pp. 71-83; **39**, pp. 153-220, 338-345; **41**, pp. 234-237.

several points along the coast. At Mitu (about 3½ miles northeast of the Gomura fault), very low water occurred at 4 p.m., the time of the earthquake being 6.27 p.m. The surface fell about 5 ft. below mean sea-level and the bed of the harbour was in part laid bare. This lasted until the earthquake took place, after which the port was gradually filled, but not so rapidly as to cause waves on the shore. High water occurred two hours after the earthquake and was about 2 ft. higher than usual. By the next morning, the sea returned to its usual level. At Sioe (2½ miles southwest of the Gomura fault), fishermen noticed a slight rise of the water (of about 6 in.) less than half an hour before the earthquake. When the

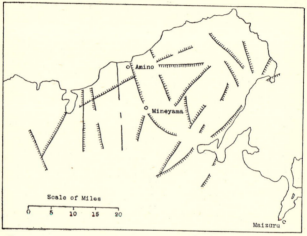

FIG. 76.—Map of the faults in the Tango district (Tsuboi).

shock occurred, the water retired rapidly from the harbour, and to such an extent that the base of a rock near its entrance was laid bare, though usually about 35 ft. below the sea-level. Afterwards, the water returned gradually into the harbour, but did not reach its former level.

433. That there was also a more or less permanent elevation of the coast is clear from observations made after the earthquake. Nakamura visited the coast on Mar. 17 and 18 and made several measurements of its uplift. The previous sea-level was then well marked by bands of living shell-fish and sea-weeds left bare by the retreat of the sea. The difference between the heights of high and low tide is usually small on the Japan Sea coast, and thus the amount of uplift can be measured with some approach to accuracy.

The elevation took place chiefly on the west side of the Gomura fault to the neighbourhood of Tuiyama Cove (*Fig. 77*). The east side was also slightly elevated, but as much as 5·5 in. at Asamogawa, but at Kohama (1 mile east of the latter place) no change could be detected.   To the west of the fault, the uplifts measured were greater, such as 18·9 in. at a point west of Iso, 17·7 in. at Sioe, 23·6 in. at Hamadume, 14·6 in. at Hakoisi and 9·1 in. at Hodokuri.   At Minatomiya, no sensible change in sea-level could be detected.   The western boundary of the elevated tract must therefore lie between Hodokuri and Minatomiya, where the coast is a sandy beach. Thus, the total length of coast uplifted must have been about 5 miles*.

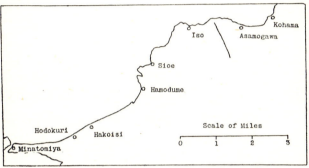

FIG. 77.—Uplift of the coast in the Tango district.

IX.   DEFORMATION OF THE OCEAN-BED

434.   During the months of May to August 1927, the Hydrographical Office of the Imperial Japanese Navy carried out extensive surveys of the sea-bed from some miles west of the Tazima earthquake-zone round the Oku-Tango peninsula.   The results of the soundings are given in a valuable series of charts and profiles, in which the soundings made during the previous survey, in 1892, are added for comparison.   The maps show at once that there was no sign of any such conspicuous change as occurred in Sagami Bay with the Kwanto earthquake of 1923.   As some deformations of the sea-bed were, however, suspected, each sounding on the old survey was compared by Terada and Higasi with the mean of four new soundings in its neighbourhood.   This comparison enabled them to draw curves of equal vertical displacement of 1, 2 and 3 metres, with the following results:

---

*Nakamura, **18**, pp. 438-440, 448-449.   Imamura (**2**, pp. 179-180) gives the greatest elevation as 31.5in.   According to Watanabe and Sato (**45**, p. 11), the permanent rise was roughly measured on Mar. 17 and found to be 31.5in. at Sioe and about 39.4in. at Iso.

(i) The discontinuity observed on land on the two sides of the Gomura fault extends under the sea to a considerable distance, the difference being decidedly greater under sea than on land.

(ii) A conspicuous zone of depression of more than 2 fathoms encircles the whole coast-line at a distance of from two-thirds of a mile to two miles from it, which, beyond, is succeeded by a broader zone of upheaval.

(iii) The northeast side of the Oku-Tango peninsula has undergone a general upheaval, a continuation of the general upward movement of the peninsula as shown by its coast erosion terraces[*].

x. Seismic Seawaves

435. Soon after the earthquake, seawaves were observed at Taiza, Sioe, Tuiyama and other places, but at all of them they were small and harmless. At Taiza, the level of the water immediately after the earthquake was lowered 4 ft. 3 in. and rocks in the harbour, usually covered by 3 or 4 ft. of water, appeared above the surface. After a minute or two, the sea returned rising as much as it had previously fallen, after which the oscillations rapidly decreased. The movements of the sea before and after the earthquake at Mitu and Sioe have been referred to already[†].

xi. After-Shocks

436. The principal earthquake occurred on Mar. 7 at 6.28 p.m. and the first after-shock was recorded at Maizuru on Mar. 11 at 10.12 p.m. During this interval, many after-shocks were felt, 83 during the remainder of Mar. 7, 153 on Mar. 8. After the second day, they decreased gradually in frequency. By the end of the month, 899 after-shocks had occurred, of which 413 were strong enough to be felt. From 1927 Mar. 11 to the end of July 1928, the total number of shocks recorded was 1,327.

Nine of these shocks were rather strong and disturbed a large area, especially that on Apr. 1. Their times of occurrence and the position of their epicentres are as follows :

Mar. 7,	6.44 p.m.	Yamada fault.
,,	7.46 p.m.	,,
,,	10.24 p.m.	Off the coast near Asamogawa.
Mar. 8,	0.35 a.m.	Yamada fault.
,,	0.48 a.m.	Off the coast near Asamogawa.
,,	9.18 a.m.	Yamada fault.
,,	11.42 p.m.	Off the coast near Asamogawa.
Mar. 11,	7.36 a.m.	Gomura fault.
Apr. 1,	6.29 a.m.	Near Miyazu.

---

*Terada, etc., **32**, pp. 296-299; Yonemura, **49**, pp. 227-230.
†Imamura, **2**, p. 180.

For our knowledge of the after-shocks of the Tango earthquake, we are indebted chiefly to Nasu, who has studied them in a very valuable series of memoirs*.

437. *Types of After-Shocks.*—With a very few exceptions, the seismograms of after-shocks, according to Imamura, fall into two well-marked classes, which he calls types A and B.

In seismograms of type A, the initial phase is comparatively large, the ratio of the amplitude of $\overline{S}$ to that of $\overline{P}$ ranging from 1·5 to 4·0. The principal portion consists of an isolated wave with a period of 0·5 sec., a series of quick waves (of period 0·12 sec.) being superposed on it and following it for a few seconds. Two or three long waves (probably surface waves), each with a period of $2\frac{1}{2}$ to 3 sec., occupy the first half of the whole movement. The shocks corresponding to this type are distributed on or near the Yamada fault. Their foci seem to be very shallow, the deepest being not more than 5 miles from the surface.

In seismograms of type B, the initial phase is comparatively small, the ratio of the amplitude of $\overline{S}$ to that of $\overline{P}$ being from 10 to 30. The principal portion consists of waves of quick periods as in type A, but the slow waves are lacking. The shocks corresponding to this type belong to the Gomura fault, the epicentres lying usually to the west of the fault. Their foci are less shallow than those of the other type and are in some cases as much as $12\frac{1}{2}$ miles in depth†.

438. *Determination of the Foci of After-Shocks.*—When the origins of earthquakes are not very distant, say, less than 1,000 km. (or 621 miles), Omori showed‡ that the distance of the origin (Δ km.) could be determined from the duration of the preliminary tremor (t sec.) by means of the formula

$$\Delta = 7\cdot42\ t.$$

If the durations of the preliminary tremor are known at three stations, the distances given by this formula determine the position of the epicentre and the depth of the focus.

439. After using Omori's formula for some time, Nasu found that the results for the Tango after-shocks were not quite satisfactory and replaced the above formula by

$$\Delta = 8\cdot41\ t.$$

The value of the coefficient is not, however, constant. It varies slightly with the focal depth, and may range from 7·8 to 9·3 for

---

*Nasu, **19**, pp. 245-331; **20**, pp. 133-152; **21**, pp. 378-381; **22**, pp. 29-129; **23**, pp. 164-166; Watanabe, etc., **45**, pp. 2-3.
†Imamura, **2**, pp. 180-181.
‡*Imp. Earthq. Inv. Com. Bull.,* vol. 9, 1918, pp. 33-40.

depths not greater than 10 km., but the average value 8·4, holds for all depths up to 20 km. When the shocks are very slight, the seismograms may not determine with sufficient accuracy the durations of the prelimary tremors, but, in his valuable tables of after-

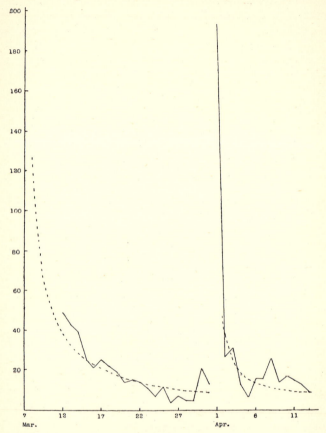

FIG. 78.—Decline in frequency of after-shocks of the Tango earthquake (Nasu).

shocks up to Aug. 1928, Nasu has calculated the depths of as many as 477 after-shocks.

440. *Decline in Frequency.*—The continuous line in *Fig.* 78 represents the daily frequency of after-shocks from Mar. 12 to Apr. 13. Its most remarkable feature is the rapid increase after the strong shock of Apr. 1. If y is the number of after-shocks occurring during a day x days after Mar. 7, Nasu found that the value of

y for any day from Mar. 7 to Mar. 29 was given by the equation

$$y = \frac{218}{x + 0\cdot 7}$$

After Apr. 1, it was necessary to add another term and the formula became

$$y = \frac{218}{x + 0\cdot 7} + \frac{34}{x - 25 + 0\cdot 16}$$

The broken-lines in *Fig.* 78 represent these two curves.

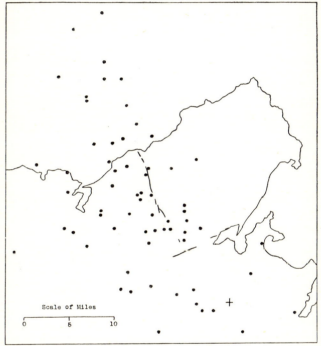

FIG. 79.—Distribution of epicentres of after-shocks of the Tango earthquake (Nasu).

441. *Distribution of Epicentres.*—Of the total number (1,327) of after-shocks recorded from 1927 Mar. 11 to 1928 July 31, 520 were registered at three stations, and in 482 of these, or 93 per cent., it was found possible to determine the positions of the epi-centre. Nasu divides these after-shocks into three classes. The first consists of the severe earthquake of Apr. 1 only, by which all three seismographs were thrown out of action during the first phase of the transverse motion, the maximum range of the vibra-

tions at Miyazu and Toyooka being 0·4 in. The second class includes 65 earthquakes of moderate intensity, and the third the remaining 416 slight shocks. Nasu has drawn nine maps showing the distribution of the epicentres during successive intervals, as well as one for the interval 1927 Mar. 12-Aug. 31. *Fig.* 79 is, for simplicity, confined to the epicentres of the 66 more important after-shocks. It shows very clearly the main features of their distribution, which are as follows: (i) while epicentres occur in different parts of the central area, they are clustered most densely on the west side of the Gomura fault and on the south side of the Yamada fault; (ii) on the east side of the Gomura fault, that is, in the Oku-Tango peninsula, epicentres are rare, suggesting that the peninsula was shifted more or less as a whole towards the north-west; (iii) many epicentres lie at sea on the west side of the continuation of the Gomura fault, and on land on the south side of the Yamada fault in both directions, suggesting, as already mentioned, that the total lengths of the two faults may be as much as 31 and 18½ miles; and (iv) a small district near Miyazu lying outside the meizoseismal area of the principal earthquake, was the seat of the important earthquake of Apr. 1 and its after-shocks. It is, however, somewhat doubtful whether this earthquake should be regarded as an after-shock of the Tango earthquake.

442. It is remarkable that, as Nasu points out, the more conspicuous after-shocks occur in groups, each of which is manifested in a well-defined portion of the central area. For instance, the first group of 11 after-shocks, between Mar. 7 and 11, most of them much stronger than the other shocks, originated within a zone lying along the Gomura fault and its seaward continuation, about half the area of the zone being north of the coast. The fourth group, of 8 after-shocks from Mar. 30 to Apr. 8, lay within a zone running nearly east and west near Miyazu. After this, the zones of epicentres migrated towards the northeast, and finally returned to the zone of the first group of earthquakes. Indeed, the last group, of 13 earthquakes, from Jan. 30 to June 16, 1928, had epicentres lying along the Gomura fault but extending much farther to the south than the zone of the first group.

443. *Focal Depth of After-Shocks.*—The seismic triangulation has enabled Nasu to determine the focal depths of as many as 477 after-shocks. The estimated depths range from 0 to 44 km. (27·3 miles), but two-thirds of the total number have depths of from 12·0 to 19·9 km. (7·5 to 12·4 miles). The mean depth of all the foci is 15·4 km. or 9·6 miles, or, excluding zero estimates, 15·9 km. or 9·9 miles.

The mean focal depths for successive intervals of about two

months are given in the following table (zero estimates being excluded) :

	miles
1927 Mar. 13-Apr. 26	10·2
Apr. 27-June 30	9·6
July-Aug.	9·8
Sep.-Oct.	8·9
Nov.-Dec.	6·4
1928 Jan.-Feb.	5·4
Mar.-Apr.	5·9
May-June	5·8

Thus, during the first eight months after the earthquake, the mean

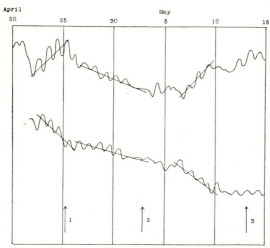

FIG. 80.—Tilting of the ground before after-shocks of the Tango earthquake (Ishimoto).

depth of focus remained nearly constant (about 10 miles), but, after the end of Oct. 1927, it somewhat abruptly decreased by about 40 per cent., the mean depth of focus during the next eight months being about 6 miles.

444. Nasu has made a very careful study of the vertical distribution of after-shock foci. Selecting a portion of the crust adjoining the Gomura fault, he projects the foci within that portion on a vertical plane at right angles to the fault. He finds that some of the points so projected can be grouped in a system of finite straight lines, parallel to one another and arranged *en échelon,* and that the points on any one line correspond usually to the foci of successive shocks. He thus concludes that the after-shocks origi-

nated on a series of parallel planes that are probably cracks produced in the blocks as the result of shearing stresses applied to them. The cracks occur at intervals of $1\frac{1}{4}$ to 3 miles. It would thus seem that the upper crust, and especially that portion that lies between depths of 6 and 12 miles is split up by these fault-planes into a number of small blocks. The faults themselves are for the most part hidden, but a few of them, such as the Gomura and Yamada faults, extend upwards to the surface. The distribution of after-shock foci shows that the Gomura fault dips from 70° to 80° towards the W.S.W. and penetrates the crust to a depth of at least 12 miles; while the Yamada fault dips from 50° to 60° to the N.N.W. and pierces the crust to a depth of more than 12 miles.

445. *Tilting of the Ground before After-Shocks.* — On Mar. 11, Ishimoto erected a pair of his tiltmeters at Miyazu, and on Mar. 26 another pair at Kawabe. Copies of the Miyazu records from Apr. 20 to May 15 are given in *Fig.* 80. The most conspicuous variation is that due to the diurnal change of temperature, but in addition there are other variations, such as those indicated by the inclined straight lines, which clearly imply a tilting of the ground. The arrows indicate the times of occurrence of strong after-shocks on Apr. 25 at 7.27 p.m., May 3 at 11.48 a.m. and May 13 at 5.43 p.m. Each of these after-shocks, and indeed all after-shocks of moderate intensity, were preceded for a few days by this characteristic tilting of the ground. Ishimoto notices that the tilting was usually towards the centre of disturbance whenever that was seated in a region of subsidence during the principal earthquake and away from the centre when it lay in an upheaved district*.

446. *Periodicity of After-Shocks.* — The after-shocks of the Tango earthquake, like those of the Kwanto earthquake of 1923, are subject to short-period fluctuations, of one day, 42 minutes, and 14·8 and 29·6 days.

For the diurnal period, taking first the Tazima earthquake of 1925 May 23, we have the following results obtained from the Toyooka record :

Interval	Number of earthquakes	Epoch	Ampl.
May 24-28	184	3 a.m.	·35
May 29-June 2	52	10-12 a.m.	·43
June 3-17	100	0½ p.m.	·69

Compared with the Tango earthquake, the Tazima earthquake was simple in its origin. During the first interval, after-shocks due to settling predominated, but, after four days, the movements to which the initial shock was due reasserted themselves, and the maximum epoch returned to the usual hour for ordinary shocks.

---

*Ishimoto, **8**, pp. 203-222.

In considering the Tango earthquake, the shocks on Apr. 1 are omitted, owing to the large numbers during the second quarter of the day. The results for different intervals are as follows:

Interval	Number of earthquakes	Epoch	Ampl.
Mar. 12-31	370	ab. 1 a.m.	·13
Apr. 2-30	334	3 a.m.	·32
May-Aug.	286	3-4 a.m.	·13
1927 Sep.-1928 July	135	1 a.m.	·38

Thus, for at least 15 months, the epoch of the diurnal period occurred at or near 3 a.m., a result that seems to follow from the complicated origin of the crust-movements long after the earth-quake ended.

447. The 42-minute period is clearly developed in both the Tazima and Tango after-shocks. For the former, we have the following results:

Interval	Number of earthquakes	Epoch min.	Ampl.
May 23-24	31	0	·36
May 24-29	184	36	·27
May 29-June 17	142	$25\frac{1}{2}$	·24

For the Tango earthquake, the results are given in the next Table, those in the first four lines being founded on the records at Toyooka and elsewhere included in the *International Seismological Summary,* and the remainder on Nasu's list. The strong earthquake that occurred on Apr. 1 was followed on the same day by 191 after-shocks.

Interval	Number of earthquakes	Epoch min.	Ampl.
Mar. 7-8	164	0	·14
Mar. 8-9	100	24	·16
Mar. 9-10	57	$7\frac{1}{2}$	·41
Mar. 10-12	38	27	·51
Mar. 12-16	143	$22\frac{1}{2}$	·30
Mar. 16-21	96	27	·27
Mar. 21-25	43	0	·63
Mar. 25-31	56	15	·22
Apr. 1	191	$34\frac{1}{2}$	·24
Apr. 2-14	214	21	·13
Apr. 15-30	120	18	·13
May 1-15	82	0	·35

After this, the period cannot be traced, but it lasted clearly for a little more than two months, during which there were at least six reversals of epoch.

448. The lunar periods of 29·6 and 14·8 days are clearly marked for the interval containing two lunations May 2-June 29

16

(188 earthquakes). The maximum epoch of the former falls a short time before full moon (ampl. ·28), while the epochs of the latter occur at the times of first and last quarters (ampl. ·23)*.

449. *Variations in Focal Depth.*—In addition to the marked change in mean focal depth after the end of the eighth month, there appear to be distinct periodic changes in the mean focal depth. Taking the mean values for each hour of the day, the epoch of maximum depth occurs at 3 a.m., the same hour as that of after-shock frequency from 1927 Mar. to 1928 July, though the amplitude is very small, only 0·02, corresponding to an increase in depth of ·2 mile.

For the 42-minute period, we have the following results :

Interval	Epoch min.	Ampl.
Mar. 12-31	21	·06
Apr. 2-30	27	·10
May	39	·03

The period is thus more distinctly marked than the diurnal period. Moreover, during the latter half of March, the maxima occur 21 minutes after the return-movements. In April, they occupy an intermediate position, while, in May, they coincide approximately with the return-movements. At the maximum epochs, the increases in depth for the three intervals are ·6, ·9 and ·3 mile, respectively.

The lunar periods for the interval May 2 to June 29 are also well marked. The maximum epoch of the 29·6 day period occurs shortly after full moon, and the epochs of the 14·8 day period fall about the times of first and last quarters. The amplitudes of the two periods are ·09 and ·06, corresponding to increases in depth at the maximum epochs of ·8 and ·6 mile.

XII. Origin of the Earthquake

450. There is but little to add on this point to what has been given above. The first movement recorded by seismographs belonged to the same class as the after-shocks of type B, and this was followed rapidly by one of the same class as the after-shocks of the type A. As the shocks of type B are associated with the Gomura fault and those of type A with the Yamada fault, Imamura infers that the first movement took place along the Gomura fault. The block on the west side of the fault had, he imagines, been subjected for a long time to stresses from northwest to southeast. As a result of these stresses, this block was at last raised very slowly. This strained condition lasted but for a few hours and then suddenly gave way, the block being uplifted and displaced towards the

---

Phil. Mag., vol. 17, 1934, p. 749.

S.S.E., while the block on the other side rebounded in the opposite direction. Very rapidly the vibrations sped towards the Yamada fault. There, also, the crust-blocks must have been on the point of motion, and so nearly that the vibrations from the Gomura fault were sufficient to precipitate the sudden movement of the block on the north side of the Yamada fault upwards and towards the east. As the displacement along the Yamada fault was thus a consequence of that along the Gomura fault, it follows that the Tango earthquake was a double earthquake and not a twin-earthquake, as it has been called by Prof. Koto and other writers.

451. This appears to have been the origin of the principal earthquake of Mar. 7. Subsequent investigations and measurements show, however, that the crust-movements did not end here, but continued for at least two years and a half. The repeated surveys of the district and the distribution of the after-shock centres lead us to infer that the earth's crust in and near the Oku-Tango peninsula is divided into numerous blocks bounded by faults or fissures new and old and that the blocks, at any rate after the earthquake, were capable of slight but independent motion. The block-movements, it is interesting to notice, were not always in the same direction during the intervals between successive surveys, but, on the whole, between the first and the last surveys, the displacement resembled that which occurred with the principal earthquake*.

XIII. BIBLIOGRAPHY

1 HYDROGRAPHIC DEPARTMENT, IMPERIAL JAPANESE NAVY. " Hydrographic survey of the sea facing the provinces of Tajima and Tango disturbed by a strong earthquake." *Earthq. Res. Inst. Bull.*, vol. 2, 1927, pp. 111-112.

2 IMAMURA, A. " On the destructive Tango earthquake of March 7, 1927." *Earthq. Res. Inst. Bull.*, vol. 4, 1928, 179-202.

3 IMAMURA, A. " The Tazima earthquake of 1925." *Imp. Earthq. Inv. Com. Bull.*, vol. 10, 1928, pp. 71-107.

4 IMAMURA, A. " Topographical changes accompanying earthquakes or volcanic eruptions." *Imp. Earthq. Inv. Com. Publ.*, no. 25, 1930, pp. 110-112, 112-121.

5 IMAMURA, A., and KISHINOUYE, F. " On the horizontal shift of the dislocation accompanied by the recent destructive earthquakes in the Kwanto district and the Tango province." *Earthq. Res. Inst. Bull.*, vol. 5, 1928, pp. 35-41.

6 IMAMURA, A., and KISHINOUYE, F. " On the horizontal shift of the dislocations accompanying the recent destructive earthquakes in the Kwanto district and the Tango province." *Tokyo Imp. Acad. Proc.*, vol. 4, 1928, pp. 112-115.

7 IMAMURA, A., and NASU, N. " On the destructive Tango earthquake of March 7, 1927 : a stereometric study of the seismic origin." *Tokyo Imp. Acad. Proc.*, vol. 3, 1927, pp. 227-231.

8 ISHIMOTO, M. " Observations sur les variations de l'inclinaison de la surface terrestre à Miyadu-mati et Kawabé-mura après le grand tremblement de terre de Tango." *Earthq. Res. Inst. Bull.*, vol. 4, 1928, pp. 203-222.

*Imamura, **2**, pp. 181-182; Koto, **12**, pp. 265-329.

9 Isii, E. "Comparison of the results of the third and fourth precise levellings in the region disturbed by the Tango earthquake." *Earthq. Res. Inst. Bull.*, vol. 7, 1929, pp. 587-588.

10 Koto, B. "The Tazima earthquake of 1925." *Tokyo Imp. Univ. Fac. Sci. Journ.*, vol. 2, 1926, pp. 1-75.

11 Koto, B. "The Tazima earthquake of 1925." *Tokyo Imp. Acad. Proc.*, vol. 3, 1927, pp. 232-235.

12 Koto, B. "The intersecting twin earthquake of Tango hinterland in 1927." *Tokyo Imp. Univ. Fac. Sci. Journ.*, vol. 2, 1928, pp. 265-329.

13 Land Survey Department, Imperial Japanese Army. "Revision of the primary trigonometrical survey in Tango earthquake districts." *Earthq. Res. Inst. Bull.*, vol. 7, 1929, pp. 187-191.

14 Land Survey Department, Imperial Japanese Army. "Revision of the secondary trigonometrical survey in the Tango district." *Earthq. Res. Inst. Bull.*, vol. 7, 1929, pp. 381-388.

15 Matuzawa, T. "Observation of some of recent earthquakes and their time-distance curves (Part I.)." *Earthq. Res. Inst. Bull.*, vol. 5, 1928, pp. 10-13, 13-17.

16 Matuzawa. T. "Observation of some recent earthquakes and their time-distance curves. (Part II.)." *Earthq. Res. Inst. Bull.*, vol. 6, 1929, pp. 187-189.

17 Muto, K. "A study of displacements of triangulation points." *Earthq. Res. Inst. Bull.*, vol. 10, 1932, pp. 384-392.

18 Nakamura, S. "On the earthquake of 7th March, 1927, in Tango, Japan." *Tohoku Imp. Univ. Sci. Reps.*, vol. 18, 1929, pp. 419-472.

19 Nasu, N. "On the aftershocks of the Tango earthquake." *Earthq. Res. Inst. Bull.*, vol. 6, 1929, pp. 245-331.

20 Nasu, N. "Further study of the aftershocks of the Tango earthquake." *Earthq. Res. Inst. Bull.*, vol. 7, 1929, pp. 133-152.

21 Nasu, N. "Further note on the stereometrical study of the origins of the great Tango earthquake and its aftershocks." *Tokyo Imp. Acad. Proc.*, vol. 4, 1928, pp. 378-381.

22 Nasu, N. "A stereometrical study of the aftershocks of the great Tango earthquake with special reference to the mechanism of their occurrence." *Tokyo Imp. Univ. Fac. Sci. Journ.*, vol. 3, 1929, pp. 29-129.

23 Nasu, N. "On the crustal block that played an important rôle in the destructive Tango earthquake of 1927." *Tokyo Imp. Acad. Proc.*, vol. 5, 1929, pp. 164-166.

24 Omura, H. "Horizontal displacements of the primary and secondary triangulation points, observed after the earthquake of March 7, 1927, in Tango districts." *Earthq. Res. Inst. Bull*, vol. 4, 1928, p. 223.

25 Omura, H. "Comparison of the results of the first and second precise levellings in the region disturbed by the Tango earthquake." *Earthq. Res. Inst. Bull.*, vol. 4, 1928, p. 225.

26 Omura, H. "Comparison of the results of the second and third precise levellings in the region disturbed by the Tango earthquake." *Earthq. Res. Inst. Bull.*, vol. 5, 1928, p. 165.

27 Omura, H. "Horizontal displacements of the primary and secondary triangulation points, observed after the earthquake of March 7, 1927, in Tango districts. Second Report." *Earthq. Res. Inst. Bull.*, vol. 7, 1929, pp. 185-191.

28 Suyehiro, K. "Geophysical investigations on the severe earthquake in the province of Tango." *Earthq. Res. Inst. Bull.*, vol. 3, 1927, pp. 163-165.

29 Suyehiro, K. "First report on the precise levelling across the province of Tango." *Earthq. Res. Inst. Bull.*, vol. 3, 1927, pp. 167-169.

30 Tada, F. "Physiographic history of the Oku-Tango peninsula." *Earthq. Res. Inst. Bull.*, vol. 5, 1928, pp. 111-121.

31 Taniguchi, T. "Damages of buildings in the province of Tango due to a destructive earthquake." *Earthq. Res. Inst. Bull.*, vol. 3, 1927, pp. 133-162.

32 TERADA, T., and HIGASI, S. " Vertical displacements of sea bed off the coast of the Tango earthquake district." *Tokyo Imp. Acad. Proc.*, vol. 4, 1928, pp. 296-299.

33 TERADA, T., and MIYABE, N. " On the horizontal displacements of earth crust produced by the Tango earthquake." *Tokyo Imp. Acad. Proc.*, vol. 4, 1928, pp. 211-214.

34 TERADA, T., and MIYABE, N. " Relation between horizontal deformation and postseismic vertical displacement of earth crust which accompanied the Tango earthquake." *Tokyo Imp. Acad. Proc.*, vol. 4, 1928, pp. 215-217.

35 TERADA, T., and MIYABE, N. " Postseismic slow vertical displacement of earth crust and isostasy." *Tokyo Imp. Acad. Proc.*, vol. 4, 1928, pp. 218-221.

36 TERADA, T., and MIYABE, N. " Deformation of the earth crust and topographical features." *Tokyo Imp. Acad. Proc.*, vol. 5, 1929, pp. 322-325.

37 TSUBOI, C. " On the postseismic block movements in the Tango earthquake district." *Tokyo Imp. Acad. Proc.*, vol. 4, 1928, pp. 529-532.

38 TSUBOI, C. " An interpretation of the results of the repeated precise levellings in the Tango district after the Tango earthquake of 1927." *Earthq. Res. Inst. Bull.*, vol. 6, 1929, pp. 71-83.

39 TSUBOI, C. " Investigation on the deformation of the earth's crust in the Tango district connected with the Tango earthquake of 1927." *Earthq. Res. Inst. Bull.*, vol. 8, 1930, pp. 153-220, 338-345.

40 TSUBOI, C. " A characteristic mode of displacements of triangulation points in the Tango district after the Tango earthquake of 1927." *Tokyo Imp. Acad. Proc.*, vol. 6, 1930, pp. 56-58.

41 TSUBOI, C. " On the results of fifth precise levelling in the Tango earthquake district." *Tokyo Imp. Acad. Proc.*, vol. 7, 1931, pp. 234-237.

42 TSUBOI, C. " Investigation on the deformation of the earth's crust in the Tango district connected with the Tango earthquake of 1927 (Part III.)." *Earthq. Res. Inst. Bull.*, vol. 9, 1931, pp. 423-434.

43 TSUBOI, C. " Investigation on the deformation of the earth's crust in the Tango district connected with the Tango earthquake of 1927 (Part IV.)." *Earthq. Res. Inst. Bull.*, vol. 10, 1932, pp. 411-434.

44 TSUYA, H. " On the geological structure of the Tango earthquake region." *Earthq. Res. Inst. Bull.*, vol. 4, 1928, pp. 139-158.

45 WATANABE, K., and SATO, H. " The Tango earthquake of 1927." *Japan Imp. Geol. Surv. Rep.*, no. 100, 128 pp.

46 YAMASAKI, N. " On the cause of the Tazima earthquake of 1925." *Imp. Earthq. Inv. Com. Bull.*, vol. 10, 1928, pp. 109-113.

47 YAMASAKI, N., and TADA, F. " The faults of the Tango earthquake of 1927." *Tokyo Imp. Acad. Proc.*, vol. 3, 1927, pp. 223-226.

48 YAMASAKI, N., and TADA, F. " The Oku-Tango earthquake of 1927." *Earthq. Res. Inst. Bull.*, vol. 4, 1928, pp. 159-177.

49 YONEMURA, S. " Report of the results of soundings in the region off the coast of the Tango province, after the earthquakes of 1927." *Earthq. Res. Inst. Bull.*, vol. 4, 1928, pp. 227-230.

CHAPTER XV

IDU EARTHQUAKE : 1930 Nov. 26

1. INTRODUCTION

452. The Idu* peninsula runs southward from the southeast coast of the Main Island of Japan, separating the two deep bays of Suruga and Sagami. During the great Kwanto earthquake of 1923 remarkable displacements occurred in the bed of Sagami Bay, and along its northwestern, northern and eastern shores. Along the west coast, at Ito and Atami, the earthquake was much less destructive than farther to the north, only 9·6 per cent. of the houses at Ito, and 11·2 per cent. of those at Atami, being destroyed by the shock.

It was chiefly in the neighbourhood of these two places that the earthquakes of the year 1930 occurred. For more than two months from Feb. 13, the town of Ito was shaken almost daily by storms of earthquakes. On May 7, a second, but feebler, series began that lasted until the following August. Then, for about three months, there was comparative rest in the peninsula of Idu, until Nov. 7, when the fore-shocks, that were to culminate in the great earthquake of Nov. 26, began.

453. It is of interest to notice, as Imamura points out, that, in the Kwanto region, adjoining the Idu peninsula to the east, there have been three great periods of activity, in 818, 1703 and 1923. Twenty-three years after the first period, on 841 July 30, the Idu province was disturbed by a local destructive shock. Again, seven years after the third period, on 1930 Nov. 26, came the destructive shock that forms the subject of the present chapter.

Though not one of Japan's great disasters, the Idu earthquake and its predecessors at Ito are among the most interesting disturbances that have visited the country. No other earthquake in any land has been studied in greater detail, nor has any other manifested phenomena so varied or so remarkable.

---

*Sometimes written as Idzu or Izu.

II. Ito Earthquakes of 1930

454. The first series of Ito earthquakes began on Feb. 13 and ended on Apr. 11. They were recorded at the observatory of Misaki, about 31 miles E.N.E. of Ito. The daily frequency of the shocks is represented by the curve in *Fig.* 81. In this curve, only those shocks with an amplitude of more than 1 micron at Misaki are included, that is, practically, those that were felt by the unaided senses at the Ito station. The total number of such shocks was 3,684.

It will be seen from this diagram that the daily numbers of shocks varied greatly, on as many as 16 days amounting to 100 or more. The maximum number (209) was reached on Mar. 9. Although no serious damage was caused by any shocks, some of them were strong enough to throw down gravestones and crack plaster walls. The strongest but one occurred on Mar. 9 at 7.55 p.m., the amplitude of the largest vibration at the Ito station being 4 mm. In the greatest earthquake, on Mar. 22 at 5.51 p.m., the amplitude at Ito was 12 mm., but, at another station on the sandy beach about midway between Ito and the epicentral area, it amounted to 50 mm. The walls of some houses were cracked by this earthquake.

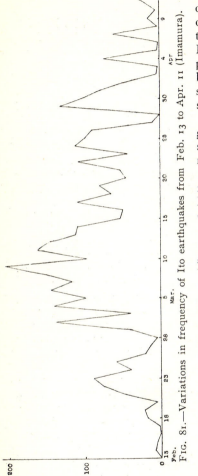

Fig. 81.—Variations in frequency of Ito earthquakes from Feb. 13 to Apr. 11 (Imamura).

455. After a pause of nearly a month, a new series began on May 7, and reached their greatest frequency about the middle of the month. After the end of May, few shocks occurred, and by August they had ceased altogether. The total number of shocks in the two series recorded at Misaki was not less than 6,000, and of those sensible at Ito was more than

4,880. The disturbed area of 20 of these shocks exceeded 12,000 sq. miles.

456. As soon as the importance of the earthquake series was realised, tromometers were erected at a network of five stations surrounding the epicentre, namely, Aziro, Hasima, Ito, Kawana and Usami, starting from Mar. 6 (*Fig.* 82).

From the records obtained at these stations, Mr. N. Nasu determined the surface-position and depth of the foci. He found that the epicentres of the shocks up to the end of March were, as a rule, clustered within a small circular area, about 2½ miles in diameter, on the sea-bed of the Bay of Ito. In *Fig.* 82, this area is bounded by the circular broken-line. Projecting the foci on two vertical planes at right angles to one another, it was seen that nearly all the foci were clustered within an inverted cone, the apex of which was at a depth of about 3¾ miles. The foci, especially those of the stronger shocks, were densely packed at the top of the cone and thinned out gradually downwards. This remarkable distribution suggests, as Nasu points out, that the foci may be connected with a hidden extinct volcano with the cone as crater. In the second series of earthquakes in May, the foci broke through on the east side of the cone, thus enlarging the neck on that side.

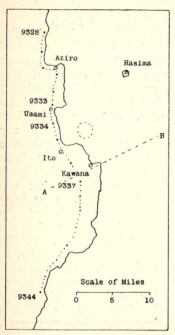

FIG. 82.—Epicentres of the Ito earthquakes (Nasu).

In addition to this cluster of foci beneath Ito Bay, there were also centres lying on a line passing close to Kawana in the north-east direction. It is worthy of notice, as Nasu points out, that this line, if continued, crosses some of the regions of Sagami Bay that were most distorted during the earthquake of 1923[*].

457. *Tidal Frequency of Ito Earthquakes.*—After preparing a table of the hourly frequency of the shocks, Nasu and his colleagues compared the variations in the resulting curve with the times of

[*]Imamura, etc., **5**, pp. 190-193; Nasu, etc., **12**, pp. 22-28.

the neighbouring tides. The graph shows that the shocks usually came in groups, of sometimes as many as 80 in one hour, and that the beginning of the groups coincided with low water and the close with that of high water. Towards the end of March, however, the connexion was less apparent. Kunitomi has also pointed out the same relation between unusual seismic activity and the times of the tides. For the first series, from Feb. 13 to Apr. 11, he has counted the numbers of earthquakes felt during the hour, including low tide and during each of the five hours on either side, the numbers being

-5	-4	-3	-2	-1	hour of low tide	1	2	3	4	5
27	21	33	34	64	80	64	41	55	39	42

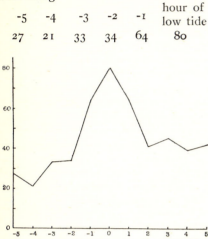

FIG. 83.—Relation between the frequency of Ito earthquakes and height of the tide (Kunitomi).

Fig. 83 represents these variations and shows very clearly the relation between the maximum frequency of earthquakes and the minimum height of the tide. Kunitomi remarks that a more detailed study shows that the earthquake maximum occurs slightly before the time of low tide*.

458. *Tilting of the Crust.*—On Mar. 12, a pair of tiltmeters were erected at Ito, and a week later a similar pair at Kawana. At both places, they were installed in caves hollowed out of the mass of volcanic scoria.

Vector diagrams were drawn by Ishimoto and Takahasi to represent the varying tilts at the two stations. These curves showed that slight shocks occurred at the times when the changes of inclination were small and complicated, and the stronger shocks when the changes were rapid and simple and usually in the west and east directions†.

459. *Changes in the Level of the Ground.*—Few seismic districts have been so carefully surveyed as that in the neighbourhood

---

*Imamura, etc., **5**, pp. 190-193; Kunitomi, **9**, pp. 79-80. In the curve reproduced in *Fig.* 83, the number of shocks for the third hour after low water is taken by Kunitomi as 45.

†Ishimoto, etc., **8**, pp. 427-458.

of Ito. The positions of the bench-marks and the route of the levelling are shown in *Fig.* 84. The dates of the different series of levellings carried out by the Land Survey Department of the Imperial Army are as follows :—

  I.   1923-24, after the Kwanto earthquake,
 II.   1930 Mar. 15-Apr. 14,
III.   1930 Nov. 9-Dec. 3,
 IV.   1930 Dec. 19-1931 Jan. 3,
  V.   1932 Dec. 25-1933 Mar. 16.

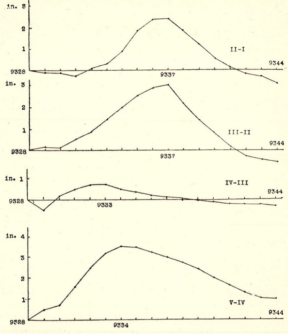

FIG. 84.—Variations in the level of the ground along the east coast of the Idu peninsula after the Ito earthquakes (Tsuboi).

Most of the series III. was finished before the occurrence of the Idu earthquake on Nov. 26, the central region of which was about $4\frac{1}{2}$ miles from the route. On two sections (B.M. 9,339-41), however, the survey was carried out in one direction on the day before the earthquake and in the opposite direction immediately afterwards. In these two sections, at any rate, there was no change of level at the time of the earthquake.

Assuming that the height of the northern bench-mark (No. 9,328) remained unchanged, the variations during the four intervals are represented in *Fig.* 84. The maximum uplifts were 3·78 in. at B.M. 9,337 (a short distance south of Ito) in the first interval, 4·77 in. at the same bench-mark in the second, 1·06 in. at B.M. 9,333 in the third, and 5·35 in. at B.M. 9,334 in the fourth. The northerly shift of the greatest uplifts in the two later intervals may, perhaps, be connected with the occurrence of the Idu earthquake and its remarkable series of fore-shocks. It is interesting to notice that, in the last interval of two years, the region was almost inactive seismically, although the crustal deformation continued as before*.

III. INVESTIGATION OF THE EARTHQUAKE

460. The investigation of the Idu earthquake and of the Ito series of shocks was conducted by Prof. A. Imamura and several members of the Earthquake Research Institute, and by Mr. S. I. Kunitomi, of the Imperial Meteorological Observatory. The luminous phenomena that accompanied the earthquake were studied by Prof. T. Terada and Mr. K. Musya, and the sound-phenomena by Messrs. W. Inouye and T. Sugiyama. The repeated precise levellings and the re-triangulation of about 540 sq. miles of the central district were carried out by the Land Survey Department of the Imperial Army.

The investigation of the Idu earthquake is, however, most notable for the careful study of the subsequent movements of the disturbed crust. The seismometric observations of the Ito earthquakes were discontinued when they became infrequent in July, except at the one station of Ito. But, when fresh swarms of earthquakes began early in November, Messrs. N. Nasu and F. Kishinouye were sent on Nov. 25 to take charge of the stations at Ito and Aziro. Instruments were also erected at three other stations, Hiyekawa, Yosiwara and Koyama. Two similar seismometers were placed at Tanna, one on the ground surface, the other in the tunnel directly below it. Observations with tiltmeters in the Ito district had ceased in October, but, on Dec. 1, three sets of such instruments were placed in the western portion of the Tanna tunnel and one set in the eastern portion. Dial gauges were fitted on Dec. 30 to the slickensides that appeared in the same tunnel. The precise levelling of the tunnel was carried out at various times by Mr. R. Takahasi.

IV. LOSS OF LIFE AND PROPERTY

461. According to Imamura, the total number of lives lost during the earthquake was 259, while 2,142 dwellings and 5,957

---

*Suyehiro, **15**, pp. 399-400; **16**, pp. 375-376; **17**, pp. 109-110; Tsuboi, **22**, pp. 151-158.

houses of various kinds were destroyed. Kunitomi's figures are somewhat different, though he does not state the authority for them. They are as follows:

Prefecture	Number of persons		Number of houses destroyed
	killed	wounded	
Shizuoka	260	1,204	8,714
Kanagawa	13	81	294
Total	273	1,285	9,008

In order to draw the isoseismal lines in the epicentral area (*Fig.* 87), Imamura has estimated the percentage of houses destroyed in 133 towns and villages. In several of these, the percentage is unusually high, rising to 76 at Harai, 80 at Yamanakasinden, 83 at Nandyo, 90 at Utinaka and 98 at Nagasaki*.

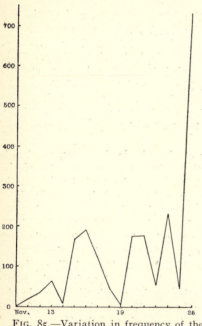

FIG. 85.—Variation in frequency of the fore-shocks of the Idu earthquake, Nov. 10-25 (Kunitomi).

V. PREPARATION FOR THE EARTHQUAKE.

462. After the second series of Ito earthquakes had declined in frequency at the end of May, the Idu peninsula was but seldom disturbed for about five months. On Nov. 7, a very slight shock was recorded at the Misima observatory. On Nov. 11, the number increased to 19, and, except on two days (Nov. 14 and 19), the daily number of fore-shocks never fell below 36. On seven days, it exceeded 100, rising to 233 on Nov. 23 and 734 on Nov. 25. The total number recorded at Misima from Nov. 7 to 4.3 a.m. on Nov. 26 was 2,165, of which 184, or 8·5 per cent., were felt. The daily variation in the number of fore-shocks at Misima is represented by the curve in *Fig.* 85.

463. At Ito, similar large numbers of fore-shocks were re-

---

*Imamura, **2**, p. 419; **3**, p. 51; Kunitomi, **9**, pp. 92-95.

corded, such as 319 on Nov. 16, 565 on Nov. 20, 623 on Nov. 21 and 690 on Nov. 25. On these days, great activity was concentrated within a few hours, the numbers recorded during successive hours being 119 and 63 on Nov. 16; 236, 123 and 71 on Nov. 20; 209, 152, 98 and 48 on Nov. 21; and 127, 162, 145 and 76 on Nov. 25. It is worthy of notice that on Nov. 26, before the occurrence of the great earthquake at 4·3 a.m., the hourly numbers were only 5, 38, 5 and 3.

464. A remarkable feature of these fore-shocks is that, without exception, the initial motion at Ito had a northwest direction, and the duration of the preliminary tremors was 1·5 to 2 sec. At Aziro, the direction was E.N.E. and the duration about 1 sec. At Misima, in nearly all the fore-shocks, the direction was southeast and the duration 2·5 sec. From these data, Nasu infers that the fore-shocks originated near Ukihasi, a town lying about $6\frac{1}{4}$ miles northwest of Ito.

465. During the early series of earthquakes at Ito, it was noticed that hours of high frequency usually corresponded with the times of low tide at the neighbouring station of Misaki. Nasu and his colleagues found that the same relation existed with the earlier fore-shocks of the Idu earthquake. Though well-marked at first, however, the relation gradually became less distinct, and in time it ceased to hold. It may thus be inferred that, during the early stages of preparation, the withdrawal of the tidal load tended to precipitate the occurrence of the daily earthquake swarms*.

VI. INTENSITY OF THE SHOCK

466. The isoseismal lines throughout the country have been traced by Kunitomi (*Fig.* 86). Under the charge of the Imperial Meteorological Observatory, there are more than 2,000 minor observatories and stations scattered over the islands. The intensity of the shock was estimated at each of these places that lay within the disturbed area, according to the six degrees of the Japanese scale. The corresponding intensities in terms of the Cancani scale, which is merely the Mercalli scale with two additional degrees (11 and 12), are

Cancani	1	2	3	4	5	6	7	8	9	10	11	12
Japanese			1		2		3		4	5	6	

467. The isoseismal 6, that bounds the area of great damage, is an elongated ellipse with its longer axis directed north and south. The isoseismal 3, including the area of slight damage, contains

---

*Imamura, **3**, pp. 51-53; Kunitomi, **9**, pp. 77-79, 95-97; Nasu, etc., **12**, pp. 28-34.

about 38,000 sq. miles. The land-area shaken is estimated by Kunitomi to cover about 133,000 sq. miles. The mean radius of the outermost curve, as drawn on the map, is about 277 miles, and

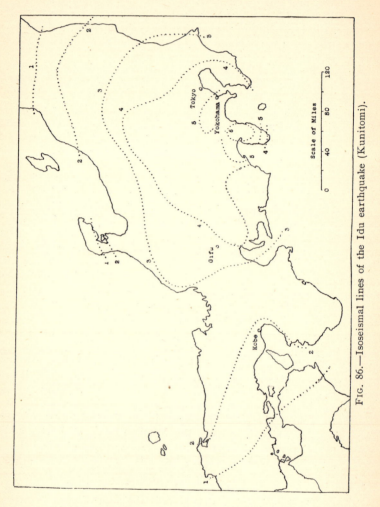

FIG. 86.—Isoseismal lines of the Idu earthquake (Kunitomi).

thus the whole disturbed area must contain about 240,000 sq. miles.

Fig. 87 shows the distribution of intensity in the epicentral area, as measured by the percentage of houses overthrown. The outer curve included all places in which at least 1 per cent. of the houses were destroyed. The other curves, I.-IV., surround all the places within which the percentage was not less than 25.

468. The areas of these four curves are some indication of the relative intensity within them, I. being the smallest, and III. the largest. A better test of intensity, however, is the percentages

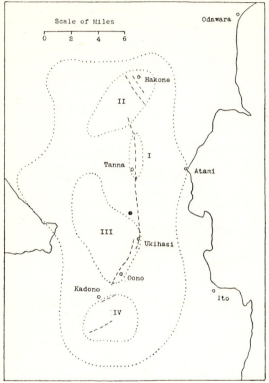

FIG. 87.—Isoseismal lines and fault-lines in the central area (Imamura).

of houses destroyed. In area I. we have such figures as 40, 41, 50 and 55; in area II., 30, 35, 42 and 80; in area III., 76, 77, 83, 90 and 98; and, in area IV., 53, 58, 66 and 68*.

VII. POSITION OF THE EPICENTRES

469. Imamura has made a careful study of the seismograms obtained at Tokyo and has deduced from them results of

*Kunitomi, 9, pp. 73, 83-84.

much interest. The records were provided by six instruments, of which the most useful in the present case were the vertical motion seismograph and the long-period horizontal pendulum. He points out that, in both the early series of vibrations, sets of waves can be distinguished, that seem to have emerged from different origins. The times at which they reached Tokyo (to the nearest second) were 4h. 3m. 6s., 4h. 3m. 8s., 4h. 3m. 10s. and 4h. 3m. 14s., a.m. The directions of the initial vibrations were S. 46° W. (mean), S. 51° W., S. 39° W. and S. 37° W. From these directions and from the durations of the corresponding preliminary tremors, he infers that source II. was in the northern end of the peninsula, and sources I., III. and IV. in the southern, in the order named. The intensities of the secondary phases of the shocks from sources I. to IV. were in the ratios 1 : 5 : 8 : 7, those from the last three sources being especially destructive.

The position of the epicentre of the first series was lat. 35° 2′ N., long. 139° 0′ E., or close to the town of Ukihasi*.

VIII. DISLOCATIONS OF THE CRUST

470. A large number of faults, most of them small, appeared in the central district. Of these four are especially worthy of notice. They are represented by broken-lines in *Fig.* 87.

(i) The Tanna fault, running north and south through the axis of the district I. (*Fig.* 87) for a distance of 10 or 11 miles. It is crossed at right angles by the Tanna tunnel at a depth of 525 ft. below the surface. At this level, the crust-block on the west side of the fault, relatively to that on the other, was shifted to the south and depressed, the maximum displacements in these directions being 7 ft. 10½ in. and 1 ft. 11½ in., respectively. On the ground above the tunnel, the displacements were much less. Similar movements, though on a smaller scale, occurred along this fault during the Kwanto earthquake of 1923 and during one or both of the Odawara earthquake of 1853 and the Tokaido earthquake of 1854.

(ii) The Hakone fault, at the north end of the preceding, and probably a member of the same system. It runs in a northwest direction for 2½ miles, passing not far from Hakone, where 50 per cent. of the houses were destroyed.

(iii) The Oono fault, trending S. 30° W. for 4½ miles from Ukihasi, and passing through Oono, at which 77 per cent. of the houses were ruined. The block on the west side was displaced relatively to the south, the maximum shift being 3 ft. 3 in.

(iv) The Kadono fault, about 1½ miles long, apparently a branch of the preceding, trending S. 70° W. The block on the

---

*Imamura, **3**, pp. 56-61.

west side was, relatively, shifted to the south and elevated, the maximum amounts in these directions being 4 ft. 3 in. and 1 ft. 11½ in., respectively.

Thus, throughout the whole length of the fault-system, the block on the west side was shifted relatively to the south, but the block was tilted in a northerly direction, the neutral line of the tilt being near the southern margin of the Tanna basin.

471. It will be noticed that these four faults are connected rather closely with the four areas (I.-IV.) in which at least 25 per cent. of the houses were thrown down. It is remarkable, however, that, near the fault (the Tanna fault) with the greatest crust displacement, the intensity of the shock was much less than in the other three areas. Imamura attributes the comparative immunity in the first area to the smoothness of the movement along the Tanna fault. Is it not also possible that the strain along this fault had been to a great extent relieved by the numerous minor slips that gave rise to the fore-shocks near Ukihasi*?

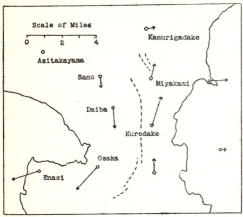

Fig. 88.—Horizontal displacements of the primary and secondary triangulation points (*Earthquake Research Institute*).

IX. Horizontal Displacements of the Ground

472. After the great Kwanto earthquake of 1923, a revision of the triangulation of the disturbed region, including the province of Idu, was made by the Land Survey Department of the Imperial Army. This was carried out in 1925-26. It was repeated in Feb.-Mar. 1931 in the Idu peninsula in order to determine the displacements of the primary and secondary triangulation points during the earthquake of 1930. These changes are represented in *Fig.* 88, in which the lengths of the arrows are proportional to the displacements observed. It is clear from this map that the movements were similar to those that occurred along the San Andreas

---

*Imamura, **2**, pp. 419-422; **3**, pp. 62-63; Kunitomi, **9**, pp. 97-102.

rift in 1906, that is to say, the crust-blocks on either side of the Tanna fault moved in opposite directions, that on the west side southwards and that on the east side northwards. Near the centre of the fault, the horizontal shift at Daiba was found to be 28·0 in. in the direction of S. 4° E., and that at Kurodake 39·0 in. in the direction N. 27° E., the sum of the two displacements being 5 ft. 7 in., or 2 ft. 3 in. less than that observed within the Tanna tunnel. The greatest amounts were measured at two stations west of the south end of the Tanna fault, namely, 47·6 in. in the direction S. 44° W. at Osaka and 41·3 in. in the direction S. 72° W.*

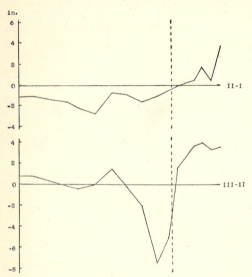

FIG. 89.—Variations in the level of the ground along a line crossing the Tanna fault (Tsuboi).

x. Vertical Displacements of the Ground

473. Series of precise levellings were carried out by the Land Survey Department of the Imperial Army in 1896 across the neck of the Idu peninsula and in 1903 along a route clinging to the coast. They were repeated in 1923-24, and again in 1930 Dec.-1931 Jan. The changes in both intervals have been analysed by Tsuboi, who attributes those in the first interval mainly to the Kwanto earthquake of 1923, and those in the second to the Idu earthquake of 1930.

The displacements in the second interval (1924-30) along the line crossing the Tanna fault are represented by the curve in *Fig.* 89. The position of the Tanna fault is indicated by the broken-line. Thus, the bench-mark immediately to the east of the fault was raised by 1·9 in., while the two bench-marks adjoining it to the west were lowered by 5·2 and 7·8 in.

474. The changes in the neighbourhood of Ito have been

Earthq. Res. Inst., **1**, pp. 262-263. In estimating these displacements, it was assumed that the position of the triangulation-point Asitakayama and the direction from it of the adjoining point Kamurigadake remained unchanged.

described above.   Along the west coast, small changes also occurred in the interval 1924-30.   The greatest was the elevation by 2·9 in. of the bench-mark at the head of the bay, the most remarkable movements, though small in magnitude, were those of the crust-blocks along the northwestern coast of the peninsula. Though an individual block seems to move independently of those on either side, there must, as Tsuboi remarks, be some order in their displacements.   The outlines of five crust-blocks are shown in *Fig.* 90, and Tsuboi has determined the direction and magnitude of tilting of each block.   Beginning with the southern block, the directions of tilting of successive blocks were N. 30° W., S. 40° W., N. 70° W., N. 50° W. and N. 60° E., while the magnitudes were 0·5″, 2″, 2·5″, 3·5″ and 4″. Thus, as we proceed from south to north, there was a clockwise change in the direction of tilting, as though the land as a whole had been twisted like a plate*.

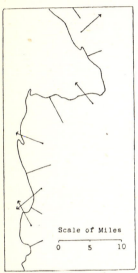

Scale of Miles

0   5   10

FIG. 90.—Tilting of crust-blocks in the north-western portion of the Idu peninsula (Tsuboi).

X. LUMINOUS PHENOMENA ACCOMPANYING THE EARTHQUAKE

475.   Luminous phenomena have often been described as accompaniments of great earthquakes, but their reality has been more or less doubtful until the occurrence of the Idu earthquake.   They were observed by Mr. K. Musya of the Earthquake Research Institute, by whom, and by Prof. T. Terada, the phenomena were investigated.   Musya collected about 1,500 observations of luminous phenomena, and, though their origin is still unexplained, there can be little doubt now as to their reality or their direct connexion with the earthquake.

The lights were seen on both the east and west coasts of the Idu peninsula, along the shores of Sagami Bay, in the valley of the Sagami River, and on the coasts of Tokyo Bay and the Boso peninsula, that is, over an area extending 50 miles to the east of the epicentre, 68 miles to the northeast and 43 miles to the west.

As a rule, the directions in which they were seen coincided nearly with that of the epicentral area, but there were some excep-

*Tsuboi, **23**, pp. 271-290.

tions that are difficult to explain. In the Sagami River valley, they were usually seen in the southeast, near Tokyo in the south and southeast.

In a few cases, the lights were seen before 4.3 a.m., when the earthquake occurred. Near the epicentre, they continued for at least an hour after that time. There is no doubt, however, that the lights were most conspicuous about the middle of the shock. As a rule, the duration of each light seemed longer than that of lightning, and, according to some careful observers, more than a minute.

Their form and colour varied. Most of the lights were radiated like the rays of the rising sun, some were shaped like searchlights, others like fireballs. According to one observer, ball-shaped lights of great brilliancy were arranged in a straight row. In most cases, the colour was described as bluish, but reddish-yellow, yellow and reddish-blue lights were also seen. The lights were evidently brilliant. At one place 30 miles from the epicentre, they were brighter than moonlight, and, even, in Tokyo, a number of observers state that objects illuminated by them could be discerned*.

XI. OSCILLATIONS OF LAKE ASINO-HO

476. Lake Asino-ho lies in the northern part of the epicentral area of the earthquake. Its length is about 3·7 miles and its greatest width about 1·2 miles; its mean depth is about 87 ft. A limnograph, installed at Hakonemati, near the south end of the lake, showed no disturbance on Nov. 25. At 4.3 a.m. the next day, it was dismounted by the great earthquake, and was not repaired until 7.20 a.m., when it revealed the existence of oscillations of considerable size. At 9 a.m., their amplitude was 3·6 in., at 8 p.m. 2·0 in., and 10 a.m. on Nov. 27, 0·4 in., and for 48 hours after the earthquake, the oscillations were still measurable. Imamura and Kodaira, who have studied them, have determined a relation between the amplitude and the time. Assuming that it applies to the first oscillation, the initial amplitude of the oscillations would be 4·3 in. The mean period was 6·64 min., corresponding to binodal oscillations of the water of the lake, but, as alternate oscillations were of greater amplitude, it would seem that others of double the period, that is, uninodal oscillations, were also present.

Whether they were caused directly by the shock or by the tilting of the ground cannot now be determined. In the section on after-shocks, it will be seen that they occurred on the day or days preceding swarms of after-shocks, and this suggests that in such cases they must be due rather to the tilting of the ground†.

---

*Musya, **10**, pp. 177-215; Terada, **20**, pp. 225-255.
†Imamura, etc., **6**, pp. 115-125.

XII. INTENSITY OF EARTHQUAKES IN THE TANNA TUNNEL

477. The Tanna tunnel was planned in order to shorten the main line from Tokyo to Kobe. Its total length will be 8,535 yd. Work was begun at both ends and, at the time of the Idu earthquake, the eastern portion had advanced about 3,663 yd. and the western about 3,991 yd., the latter having just crossed the Tanna fault at the depth of 525 ft. Except for the displacement along the fault and a few cracks made in its walls, the tunnel was unharmed by the earthquake, though, in the village of Karuizawa, vertically over the tunnel, 55 per cent. of the houses were thrown down. Nasu installed two similar seismographs, one on the surface of the Tanna Basin, the other in the tunnel below, having previously tested both in a room of the Earthquake Research Institute and obtained identical results. From Jan. 15 to June 30, 1931, 14 strong or moderately strong earthquakes were recorded. If the period of the vibrations was less than one second, the amplitude on the surface was always more than twice, in one case 4·8 times, as great as in the tunnel. If, however, the period was as much as 4 or 5 sec., the amplitudes at both stations were almost exactly equal*.

XIII. CHANGES IN THE LEVEL OF THE TANNA TUNNEL

478. The most remarkable dislocation observed in the tunnel was that along the Tanna fault, by which the crust on the west side was shifted relatively 7 ft. 10½ in. to the south and 1 ft. 11½ in. downwards. In addition to the levelling and triangulation surveys made on the surface, Takahasi carried out several interesting series of levellings in the tunnel itself just below the regions where, as shown in the second curve in *Fig.* 91, the surface-tilting was greatest. Ring-shaped bench-marks attached to iron bolts were fixed at intervals of about 22 yd. to the wall of the tunnel. Their displacements were measured by instruments that were essentially U-tubes, the graduated end of which were fitted into the bench-marks.

Observations were begun on Dec. 29 and six series were made, the last four (on Feb. 5-12, Mar. 3-9, Apr. 13-18 and July 18-24, 1931) being carried out both ways and therefore more accurate than the others. The curves in *Fig.* 91 represent the changes that occurred during the last three intervals of 28, 40 and 90 days. Though the movements are extremely minute, being less than one-eighth of an inch in any interval, the curves are remarkably similar in form. It is interesting to notice that: (i) the deformations were most marked at the points where the tunnel is crossed by faults or

---

*Nasu, **11**, pp. 454-472.

where there are sudden changes in the strength of the rocks, in
other words, the boundaries of crust-blocks, and (ii) the block that
tilted so greatly at the time of the earthquake rapidly became almost
immobile, as shown by this survey.

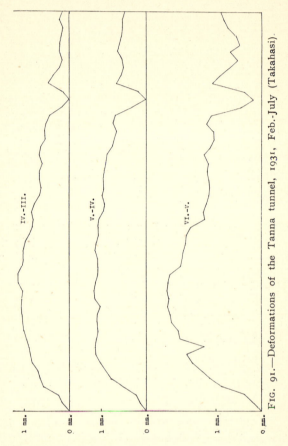

FIG. 91.—Deformations of the Tanna tunnel, 1931, Feb.-July (Takahasi).

479. The great displacement of 7 ft. 10½ in. in the tunnel
revealed a fresh slickenside. Two indicators were attached to it in
order to measure the horizontal and vertical movements along the
fault. They showed that the displacement that occurred with the
earthquake was continued in the same directions, though the total
amount during the first half of 1931 was little more than ·04 in.*

*Takahasi, **19**, pp. 435-453

XIV. AFTER-SHOCKS

480. *Distribution in Time.*—Like the fore-shocks, the after-shocks occurred in swarms*.   On Nov. 26, 251 shocks were recorded at Ito, and 66 and 68 on the succeeding days. From Nov. 29 to Dec. 1, the numbers were 16, 29 and 15; then on Dec. 2 and 3, they rose to 240 and 342, falling on Dec. 4-6 to 21, 27 and 7; on Dec. 7, 286 were recorded, on the next two days 7 and 1, and, on Dec. 10, 592. From Dec. 11 to Jan. 28, the total number recorded was 104, the greatest number on any day being 20, and the least none on 22 days. On Jan. 29, the number rose to 313, on the next four days, the numbers were 103, 264, 48 and 40. From Feb. 3 to Mar. 6, the total number recorded was 39. Thus, during the hundred days following the earthquake, there were four "earthquake swarms," namely, on Dec. 2-3, Dec. 7, Dec. 10 and Jan. 29-31.

It is interesting to notice that oscillations on Lake Asino-ho were registered on Dec. 1, 6 and 9, on the days immediately preceding three of the above swarms, and also on Jan. 27, though the connexion of the latter with the last swarm is not established†.

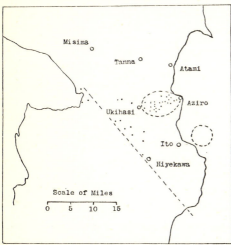

FIG. 92.—Distribution of after-shocks of the Idu earthquake in space (Nasu, etc.).

481. *Distribution in Space.* — The distribution of the after-shock centres was entirely different from that of the fore-shocks and of the earthquakes at Ito. The epicentres of the last-named lie within a small circular area near Ito. Those of the fore-shocks are almost confined to the neighbourhood of Ukihasi or at any rate that of the Tanna fault.   The after-shock centres are conspicuously

*The daily numbers of shocks from 1930 Nov. 1 to 1931 Mar. 31 are given by Imamura and Kodaira in their paper on the oscillations observed in Lake Asino-ho.

†Imamura, etc., **6**, pp. 123-124. Before the great earthquake, oscillations were also registered on Nov. 16, 19 and 20, the days preceding swarms of fore-shocks when 64, 530 and 624 fore-shocks were recorded.

absent from both districts. As determined by the records at the four stations of Ito, Aziro, Hiyekawa and Tanna Basin, they are represented by dots in *Fig.* 92. It will be seen that they are grouped mainly in two regions. One of these is a small area in the neighbourhood of Aziro, where the centres are clustered in the same way as those of the earlier Ito earthquakes. The other is a narrow band running in a northwest direction across the peninsula. There seems to be no definite fault lying along this band, and the cause of the distribution is at present unknown. It will be noticed that the line joining the centres of the Ito and Aziro clusters is roughly parallel to this band*.

XV. BIBLIOGRAPHY

1 EARTHQUAKE RESEARCH INSTITUTE. " Horizontal displacements of the primary and secondary triangulation points in Idu earthquake district." *Earthq. Res. Inst. Bull.,* vol. 10, 1932, pp. 262-263.

2 IMAMURA, A. " On the recent destructive Idu earthquake of 1923 [1930]." *Tokyo Imp. Acad. Proc.,* vol. 6, 1930, pp. 419-422.

3 IMAMURA, A. " A seismometric study of the North Idu earthquake of November 26, 1930." *Japan Journ. Astr. Geoph.,* vol. 8, 1931, pp. 51-65.

4 IMAMURA, A. " Seismometric study of the recent destructive North Idu earthquake." *Earthq. Res. Inst. Bull.,* vol. 9, 1931, pp. 36-49.

5 IMAMURA, A., NASU, N., KISHINOUYE, F., and YASUDA, C. " On the recent Ito earthquakes." *Tokyo Imp. Acad. Proc.,* vol. 6, 1930, pp. 190-193.

6 IMAMURA, A., and KODAIRA, T. " On the seiches of Lake Asino-ho with special reference to the N. Idu earthquake of 1930." *Japan Journ. Astr. Geoph.,* vol. 9, 1932, pp. 115-125.

7 INOUYE, W., and SUGIYAMA, T. " On sound-phenomena of the Idu earthquake of Nov. 26th, 1930." *Earthq. Res. Inst. Bull.,* vol. 9, 1931, pp. 168-176.

8 ISHIMOTO, M., and TAKAHASI, R. " Séismes d'Ito et l'observation sur les variations de l'inclinaison de la surface terrestre." *Earthq. Res. Inst. Bull.,* vol. 8, 1930, pp. 427-458.

9 KUNITOMI, S. I. " Note on the North Idu earthquake of 1930." *Tokyo Geoph. Mag.,* vol. 4, 1931, pp. 73-102.

10 MUSYA, K. " On the luminous phenomena that attend the Idu earthquake, November 26th, 1930." *Earthq. Res. Inst. Bull.,* vol. 9, 1931, pp. 177-215.

11 NASU, N. " Comparative studies of earthquake motions above-ground and in a tunnel (Part I.)." *Earthq. Res. Inst. Bull.,* vol. 9, 1931, pp. 454-472.

12 NASU, N., KISHINOUYE, F., and KODAIRA, T. " Recent seismic activities in the Idu peninsula (Part I.)." *Earthq. Res., Inst. Bull.,* vol. 9, 1931, pp. 22-35.

13 OTUKA, Y. " The geomorphology of the Kano-gawa alluvial plain, the earthquake-fissures of Nov. 26, 1930, and the pre- and post-seismic crust deformations." *Earthq. Res. Inst. Bull.,* vol. 10, 1932, pp. 235-245.

14 OTUKA, Y. " The geomorphology and geology of northern Idu peninsula, the earthquake fissures of Nov. 26, 1930, and the pre- and post-seismic crust deformations." *Earthq. Res. Inst. Bull.,* vol. 11, 1933, pp. 530-573.

15 SUYEHIRO, K. " The result of the precise levellings carried out along the east coast of the province of Idu just before the occurrence of the strong Idu earthquake." *Tokyo Imp. Acad. Proc.,* vol. 6, 1930, pp. 399-400.

16 SUYEHIRO, K. " Precise levellings in the province of Idu." *Earthq. Res. Inst. Bull.,* vol. 8, 1930, pp. 375-376.

*Kunitomi, **9**, pp. 95-97.

17 SUYEHIRO, K. " Comparison of the results of the first and second precise levellings on the east coast route of the province of Idu." *Earthq. Res. Inst. Bull.,* vol. 9, 1931, pp. 109-110.
18 SUYEHIRO, K. " Outline of investigations of the great Idu earthquake." *Earthq. Res. Inst. Bull.,* vol. 9, 1931, pp. 111-114.
19 TAKAHASI, R. " Results of the precise levellings executed in the Tanna railway tunnel and the movement along the slickenside that appeared in the tunnel." *Earthq. Res. Inst. Bull.,* vol. 9, 1931, pp. 435-453.
20 TERADA, T. " On luminous phenomena accompanying earthquakes." *Earth. Res. Inst. Bull.,* vol. 9, 1931, pp. 232-243.
21 TERADA, T. " On swarm earthquakes." *Earthq. Res. Inst. Bull.,* vol. 10, 1932, pp. 29-34.
22 TSUBOI, C. " A note on the results of the repeated precise levellings across the Ito earthquake area." *Earthq. Res. Inst. Bull.,* vol. 9, 1931, pp. 151-158.
23 TSUBOI, C. " On the results of repeated precise levellings around Idu peninsula." *Earthq. Res. Inst. Bull.,* vol. 9, 1931, pp. 271-290.
24 TSUBOI, C. " Investigation on the deformation of the earth's crust in Idu peninsula connected with the Idu earthquake of Nov. 26, 1930." *Earthq. Res. Inst. Bull.,* vol. 10, 1932, pp. 435-448.
25 TSUBOI, C. " Vertical crustal displacement in the seismic region of Ito, on the east coast of the Idu peninsula." *Earthq. Res. Inst. Bull.,* vol. 11, 1933, pp. 488-498.
26 TSUYA, H. " On the geological structure of Ito district." *Earthq. Res. Inst. Bull.,* vol 8, 1930, 409-426.
27 TSUYA, H. " Neogene and quaternary vulcanism in the Idu district (preliminary report)." *Earthq. Res. Inst. Bull.,* vol. 10, 1932, pp. 247-259.

CHAPTER XVI

HAWKE'S BAY EARTHQUAKE : 1931 Feb. 3.

I. INTRODUCTION

482. The islands of New Zealand were first visited by missionaries in 1814, and our knowledge of their earthquakes begins with the year 1826. The most important of these earthquakes are those of the years 1826-27, 1848 Oct. 16, 17 and 19, 1855 Jan. 25, 1929 June 17 and 1931 Feb. 3, with all of which crustal changes occurred. The earthquakes of 1826 and 1929 are of great interest, but they cannot be said to have had any close connexion with the subject of the present chapter.

II. EARLY EARTHQUAKES IN NEW ZEALAND

483. *Earthquakes of 1848.*—There were three strong earthquakes:

(i) Oct. 16, 1.40 a.m., at Wellington, the shock is said to have lasted 10 min., and, at its height, it was difficult to stand. Many chimneys in the town were thrown down.

(ii) Oct. 17, 3.40 a.m., a stronger shock. The earth was seen to move in waves, about a foot in height. At Wellington, several buildings were thrown down and 3 lives were lost.

(iii) Oct. 19, 5 a.m., the strongest shock of the series, lasting about 8 min. By this shock, the destruction of brick buildings in the central district was completed.

484. The most remarkable result of this earthquake was a great rent made in a mountain-range that runs southward from Cloudy Bay in the South Island, a range that may be considered as a prolongation of the Remutaka Mountains in the North Island (*Fig.* 93). The fissure was not more than 18 in. in average width, but it was traced by careful observers for 60 miles, running in the S.S.W. direction, parallel to the axis of the chain.*

485. *Wellington Earthquake: 1855 Jan. 23.* — One of the greatest of all New Zealand earthquakes, the shock was felt over the whole country from the extreme south to East Cape in the North Island. The total area disturbed was about 360,000 sq.

---

*Hector, **6**, pp. 522-531 ; Lyell, **8**, p. 89.

miles. In Wellington, all the brick buildings were overthrown or seriously injured.

The earthquake occurred at 8.50 p.m., and its total duration was estimated to be 1m. 20s. or 1m. 30s. The hillsides opposite Wellington were so shaken that about one-third of their surface was bared of trees.

486. With this earthquake, there occurred a remarkable uplift of the land near Wellington. It was estimated that a tract of land, 4,600 sq. miles in area, was permanently elevated from 1 to 9 ft. At a point on the west coast 16 miles north of Wellington (*Fig.* 93), there was no perceptible rise, but, from there, the amount of upheaval gradually increased to 9 ft. along the eastern flank of the Remutaka Mountains. Along the base of the hills in which the range ends at Cook Strait, the vertical movement ceased abruptly, the low country to the east being unaffected. Between the two portions of the cliff runs a distinct line of fault.

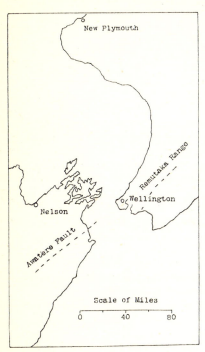

FIG. 93.—Map of the faults connected with the New Zealand earthquakes of 1848 and 1855.

This line of fault runs inland along the base of the Remutaka Mountains, its course being shown by a nearly vertical cliff of fresh aspect 9 ft. in height. It was traced to the extraordinary distance of 90 miles.

On the south side of Cook Strait, the movement was, as a rule, downward. The valley of the Wairau, with parts of the adjoining coast, subsided about 5ft.*

III. Seismic History of the District

487. New Zealand lies at the south end of a sub-oceanic ridge that extends in a nearly straight line for 1,600 miles southwest

*Hector, **6**, p. 522; Lyell, **8**, pp. 83-89; Mallet, R., *Brit. Ass. Rep.*, 1858, pp. 105-106.

from Tonga. On the southeast side of the ridge, there runs a deep and narrow trench, including the Tonga and Kermadec Deeps, the beds of which are more than 5,000 fathoms below sea-level. The latter deep ends about 200 miles northeast of East Cape, but is continued as a trench, more than 1,600 fathoms in depth, extending along the east coast of the North Island to a point about opposite to Cook Strait.

The east coast of the North Island runs in a nearly straight line N.N.E. from Cape Palliser to East Cape, except that it is broken by the large indentation of Hawke's Bay, the distance across which is about 50 miles. Napier is built on the south coast of the bay, Hastings about 6 miles inland.

Only a few earthquakes have been recorded in the district since its settlement by Europeans.

The first of which we have any record occurred on 1863 Feb. 23. Its intensity was 9 (Rossi-Forel scale), several houses in Napier being destroyed. As the shock was felt from Auckland on the north to Otago on the south, its disturbed area may have exceeded 300,000 sq. miles.

On 1890 Mar. 7, a sharp shock was felt at Napier, its centre being about 180 miles to the southeast.

On 1904, Aug. 9, Hawke's Bay was severely shaken. The intensity at Napier was 8 or 9. The epicentre lay about 200 miles to the southeast. That is, the earthquakes of 1890 and 1904 both belong to the submarine zone referred to above, and the areas disturbed by them must have greatly exceeded 100,000 and 125,000 sq. miles.

On 1921 July 21, a strong local earthquake shook Hawke's Bay, with its epicentre about 20 miles inland.

After this, for nearly ten years, no earthquake of any importance occurred in the Hawke's Bay region, though a number of shocks, of slight or moderate intensity, occurred either inland or some distance out at sea. Thus, the Hawke's Bay region remained inactive for ten years, until it was suddenly shaken at 10.17 a.m. on 1931 Feb. 3. Fore-shocks, indeed, seem to have been entirely absent. Six days before the earthquake, a Wood-Anderson seismograph had been erected at Wellington, but this sensitive instrument recorded no movement whatever in the Hawke's Bay region*.

IV. LOSS OF LIFE AND PROPERTY

488. Until 1931, no earthquake in New Zealand was attended by serious loss of life, the greatest number of deaths previously recorded being 17 during the Buller earthquake of 1929. For the

*Adams, etc., **3**, pp. 95-96.

first time, on 1931 Feb. 3, the islands were visited by a destructive earthquake in the neighbourhood of towns such as Napier (population 16,025), Hastings (10,850) and Gisborne (13,635). The number of deaths was not less than 256, of which 161 were in Napier, 93 in Hastings and 2 in Wairoa.

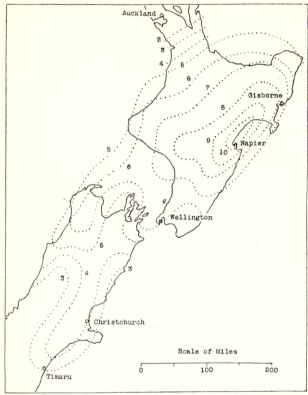

FIG. 94.—Isoseismal lines of the Hawke's Bay earthquake (Adams).

Not even a rough estimate can be given of the value of the property destroyed. After the earthquake, the whole town of Napier looked as if it had been subjected to a severe artillery engagement.

v. INTENSITY OF THE SHOCK

489. The isoseismal lines, depending on the Rossi-Forel scale of intensity, are shown in *Fig.* 94. The devastated area, bounded

by the isoseismal 9, reaches from just north of Wairoa to near Waipawa and Waipukurau. It is about 100 miles long, about 30 miles wide, and contains about 2,300 sq. miles. Within it, there is a smaller area, similar in form, inside which the intensity was 10. The isoseismal 8 covers an area of about 9,000 sq. miles. Towards the southwest, it extends almost across the island, to Wanganui, 115 miles from the epicentre. The isoseismal 6, which bounds the area in which the earthquake would be considered as strong, crossed over Cook Strait and included part of the South Island, the curve passing close to Murchison.

The remaining isoseismals show that the intensity of the shock decreased regularly in the North Island, but with some irregularity in the South Island. In the former, it was not reported as having been felt at Auckland, 200 miles northwest of the epicentre, while, in the latter, it was distinctly felt at Timaru, 460 miles southwest of the epicentre. Under such conditions, it is difficult to estimate the magnitude of the disturbed area, but, if the curves are continued, the outermost isoseismal (of intensity 2) appears to be about 630 miles long and 380 miles wide and to contain about 185,000 sq. miles*.

VI. Nature of the Shock

490. The absence of all fore-shocks has been already noticed. The earthquake, indeed, began suddenly at 10.17 a.m. on Feb. 3, N.Z.M.T. (Feb. 2, 10.47 a.m., G.M.T.). The main shock at Napier was in two parts. The first grew rapidly in strength and there was a distinctly uplifting motion associated with violent and confused swaying. Then followed a pause of half a minute, after which came the second part with a sharp motion downwards. An observer facing a clock found the total duration of the earthquake to be $2\frac{1}{2}$ min.†

VII. Position of the Origin

491. Seismograph records obtained at three New Zealand stations (Wellington, Arapuni and Takaka) show that the epicentre lay close to the coast-line a few miles (5 to 15) north of Napier, in lat. 39° 20′ S., long. 177° 0′ E. This point is represented by the black spot in *Fig.* 97. From the same records, it was found that the focal depth of the earthquake was about 13 miles, and this estimate is confirmed by the fact that the same depth was obtained for several of the after-shocks‡.

---

*Adams, etc., **3**, pp. 97-99.
†Callaghan, **5**, p. 7.
‡Adams, etc., **3**, p. 102.

VIII. DISLOCATIONS OF THE CRUST

492. *Surface-Indications of Deep-Seated Fractures.* — To-wards the south, such indications first occurred near Lake Poukawa (*Fig.* 95), about 22 miles southwest of Napier. Here, in the Poukawa Valley for a distance of 6 miles northeast of the lake, a series of ridges, rents and cracks extends across the valley. The ridges are usually 3 or 4 feet, in places 6 to 8 feet, above the general surface of the ground. Their continuity for miles and the fact that, as a rule, no gaping cracks occur higher up the slope show that they are not mere surface slips, but are due to a shortening of the surface by a movement of the country on the west side of a fracture towards the east. From the slackness of the wires in fences that cross the line, it would seem that the movement must be measured in feet rather than in inches.

The fracture has a general northeast course for $3\frac{1}{2}$ miles from Lake Poukawa. It then turns nearly due east for about a mile, displaces the railway and road horizontally between 6 and 7 feet, and passes over low hills to the strike valley of Sutro Creek, after which it resumes its northeast course and dies out about a mile farther on. The direction of the horizontal movement seems to have been nearly due east.

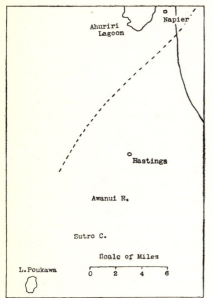

FIG. 95.—Central area of the Hawke's Bay earthquake (Henderson).

At the head of the Awanui Vally, another series of ridges begins, running parallel to, and about a mile northwest of, the Poukawa series. The pressure ridges indicate that the crust-block to the west of the fracture moved relatively to the southeast and tended to override the eastern block. A little less than a mile to the north of this dislocation, a third series of ridges extends for about a mile, a fence at one point being displaced about 9 in. horizontally*.

*Henderson, 7, pp. 51-61.

493. *Changes Revealed by Re-Levelling.* — The elevation of the coast at and beyond Napier was at once evident and will be described later (art. 494). In the low-lying plain to the south of the town, however, the changes of level could be traced only by the movements of the bench-marks. A new series of levellings was carried out along the railway-line from Wairoa to Opapa (28 miles south of Napier) and three new series were made along dykes that cross the plain from northwest to southeast at distances of about 3, 6 and 10 miles to the southwest of Napier. The curves showing the changes of level along these three lines are similar in form and amount, and show that:

(i) A line or narrow band of no change runs in a south-westerly direction from a point on the shore a little more than a mile south of Napier. The course of this band is parallel to the line of the Poukawa shift, and is denoted by the broken-line in *Fig.* 95.

(ii) On the northwest side of this line, the crust was raised. Each of the three curves shows that the greatest uplift occurred about 3 miles from the neutral line. Along the middle section, the uplift on this crest was 5 ft. 1 in., decreasing to 3 ft. 3 in. in a distance of $3\frac{1}{4}$ miles. If this rate is maintained, the change of level must vanish at a point about $9\frac{1}{4}$ miles from the neutral line. The extent of the uplifted country is considerable. As will be seen, the uplift of the coast extends to a point about 20 miles north of Napier. To the southwest, the farthest bench-mark is 17 miles from that city, and at this point the uplift was 3 ft. 11 in.

(iii) To the southeast of the neutral line, the whole of the plain seems to have subsided, in two places by as much as 2 ft. 6 in. and 3 ft. 5 in.*

494. *Uplift of the Coast.* — The part of the coast uplifted is shown in *Fig.* 96. At a point 10 miles south of Napier, no movement of the shore-line could be detected. The first signs of change were noticed at a point 2 miles to the north, where small ridges and furrows about a foot deep in the shingle were seen. Two miles farther to the north, these became more pronounced, the beach being thrown into a series of ridges and furrows, the maximum height from crest to trough being 4 feet. Towards Napier, the upheaval increased. Close to the east side of the peninsula on which Napier is built, there is an outlying reef of rocks, which, before the earthquake, was rarely uncovered, but afterwards it was almost bare even at high water. At the northeast corner of the peninsula, the tide-gauge on the breakwater showed an uplift of 6 feet. Calcareous seaweeds on the elevated piles of the wharf were bleached by the sun, and marked the line of the former sea-level.

---

*Henderson, **7**, pp. 61-67.

Between the breakwater and the entrance of Port Ahuriri, the effect of the uplift was evident from the bleaching of the calcareous algæ that formed a white band along the shore. At the entrance to Port Ahuriri, the tide-gauge marked a rise of 5 feet. The Ahuriri Lagoon is shallow and its bed is flat. The outer margin was raised 6 feet and the inner 3 ft. 9 in. In consequence, large areas of the lagoon floor are now bare at all states of the tide. The total area of new land is estimated at about 5 sq. miles.

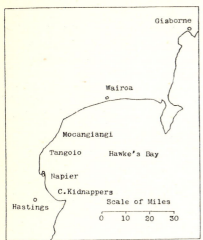

FIG. 96.—Uplift of coast during the Hawke's Bay earthquake of 1931 (Marshall).

The gravel spit 5 miles long from Port Ahuriri to Petane shows the same amount of rise, of about 6 feet, though perhaps increasing towards Petane. From about $6\frac{1}{2}$ feet at Tangoio, the uplift gradually increased to 9 feet at Mocangiangi. Two miles beyond this, the amount of uplift seemed to lessen rapidly, but, still farther, the coast-line is so covered with slips that no movement could be detected. Near the mouth of the Waikare River and for some miles northward and eastward, the movement of the coast, if any occurred, was very slight. The only exception is a small area to the west of the Wairoa River, where there was a rise of about 2 feet[*].

670. *Rise of the Sea-Bed.*—The bed of Hawke's Bay is very free from irregularities, and the depth of water increases slowly from the beach outwards to about 8 fathoms at the distance of a mile. After the earthquake, a series of soundings was made over the bay. Their main result was to show that, near Napier, the depth of water had been reduced about 6 feet, but that, at about the point at which the uplift of the coast ceased to be evident, the depth was practically the same as before. There was clearly no marked distortion of the sea-bed, such as occurred in Sagami Bay at the time of the Kwanto earthquake of 1923[†].

496. *Conclusions.*—(i) The fracture or fracture-zone under the

[*]Marshall, **9**, pp. 79-92.
[†]Marshall, **9**, p. 92

loose deposits of the plain to the south of Napier may be supposed to extend north-east on the floor of Hawke's Bay to north of Arapawanui. From Lake Poukawa to the latter point is about 40 miles, so that the length of the dislocation is comparable with the lengths of those formed with the earthquakes of 1848 and 1855 (about 60 and 90 miles, arts. 483, 485).

(ii) As the actual fracture would extend some distance farther in both directions, Mr. Henderson concludes that an earth-block 60 miles long from northeast to southwest and at least 10 miles wide in one part was uplifted.

(iii) Measurements along the three lines on which levelling could be repeated show that the central portion of this block was tilted gently and uniformly to the northwest. It is probable that the whole block was tilted in the same way*.

497. *The Sponge Bay Uplift.* — A fortnight after the earth-quake, on the afternoon of Feb. 17, a remarkable uplift occurred in Sponge Bay near Gisborne. Some men who were working on the beach of Tuamotu Island saw a boulder-bank rise out of the sea without any warning and quickly attain an average height of 7 feet. The newly raised area covers about 2 acres, and lies half a mile west of Tuamotu Island and about $2\frac{1}{4}$ miles from Gisborne. Two months before, the reef was covered by one or two feet of water at low tide. The new reef has a flat dome-shaped profile. While the sea-floor rose on the seaward side of the Sponge Bay beach, the area on the land side was depressed a few feet and broken into segments by numerous small crevices.

At the time of the upheaval, no pronounced earth-tremors were felt, and none was recorded in the surrounding district†.

IX. AFTER-SHOCKS

498. *Decline in Frequency.* — The principal earthquake occurred on Feb. 2 at 10h. 46m. 43s., p.m. (G.M.T.). The times of the numerous after-shocks are given in Greenwich mean time. On Feb. 3, 151 shocks were recorded by the Wood-Anderson seismograph at Wellington, and, on successive days, 55, 50, 29, 24, 21, 12, 17, 9 and 7, thus showing the usual rate of decline. On Feb. 13, a severe shock (intensity 8) occurred, with its origin halfway between the extreme points of Hawke's Bay. This shock, which may almost be regarded as a second principal earthquake, was followed by a large number of after-shocks, 81 on Feb. 13, and 23, 18, 19, 9, 9, 12, etc., on succeeding days, the total number recorded until May 31 being 674.

---

*Henderson, **7**, pp. 69-75.
†Strong, **10**, pp. 76-78.

The after-shocks were also recorded by a Milne-Jaggar seismograph at Hastings, the numbers during the remainder of February being 596, and, during successive months, 78, 50, 44, 42, 28 and so on, with a total of 938 until the end of the year.

The strongest shocks were those of Feb. 3 at 10.25 a.m. and 10.27 a.m. (both of intensity 7), Feb. 13 at 0.57 p.m. (int. 8), Mar.

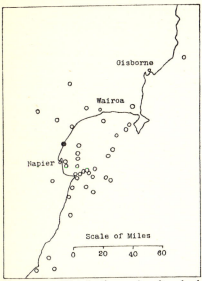

8, 11.21 p.m. (int. 7), Apr. 22, 11.10 a.m. (int. 7), and 1932 May 5, 7.54 p.m. (int. 8). On 1932 Sep. 16, at 1.25 p.m., a strong shock occurred, of int. 8-9 at Gisborne and Wairoa, with its epicentre about 60 miles east of Wairoa.*

499. *Distribution in Space.*—The map in *Fig.* 97 shows the distribution of the epicentres of the 40 principal after-shocks from Feb. 3 to Sep. 11. These are represented by the small circles, while the black spot denotes the epicentre of the principal earthquake.

Most of the after-shocks, it will be seen, originated beneath Hawke's Bay, especially its southern portion. One line of epicentres runs in a

FIG. 97.—Distribution of after-shock epicentres of the Hawke's Bay earthquake (Adams).

northerly direction from Cape Kidnappers, and another from the same cape first in the E.N.E. direction and then turning northeast across the mouth of the bay†.

500. *Periodicity of After-Shocks.* — The most significant period is that of 42 minutes. During the first three days (Feb. 3-5), the maxima of the period coincided closely with the return-movements; during Feb. 6-13, the minima; from Feb. 14 to the end of Mar., the maxima; during Apr. and May, the minima; and, during June, the maxima. Thus, the frequency of the after-shocks was affected by the 42-minute period for nearly 5 months, during which there were at least four reversals of epoch. During the first, third

*Adams, etc., **3**, pp. 102-106.
†Adams, etc., **3**, p. 107.

and fifth intervals, most of the crust-displacements occurred in the same direction as that which caused the principal earthquake, and, during the second and fourth, in the opposite direction*.

x. BIBLIOGRAPHY

1 ADAMS, C. E. "Seismological report for the year 1931." *Wellington Dom. Obs. Seis. Bull.,* E. 27-31.
2 ADAMS, C. E. "Seismology of New Zealand." *N.Z. Official Yearbook,* 1931, 8 pp.
3 ADAMS, C. E., BARNETT, M. A. F., and HAYES, R. C. "Seismological report of the Hawke's Bay earthquake of 3rd February, 1931." *New Zealand Journ. Sci. Tech.,* vol. 15, 1933, pp. 93-107.
4 BRODIE, A., and HARRIS, A. G. "Damage to buildings [Hawke's Bay earthquake, 1931]." *New Zealand Journ. Sci. Tech.,* vol. 15, 1933, pp. 108-115.
5 CALLAGHAN, F. R. "The Hawke's Bay earthquake : General description." *New Zealand Journ. Sci. Tech.,* vol. 15, 1933, pp. 3-38.
6 HECTOR, SIR J. "Report of the Committee appointed to investigate and report upon seismological phenomena in Australasia." *Austr. Ass. Trans.,* vol. 3, 1891, pp. 505-532.
7 HENDERSON, J. "The geological aspects of the Hawke's Bay earthquakes." *New Zealand Journ. Sci. Tech.,* vol. 15, 1933, pp. 38-75.
8 LYELL, SIR C. "New Zealand earthquake of 1855." *Principles of Geology,* 10th edit., 1868, vol. 2, pp. 82-89.
9 MARSHALL, P. "Effects of earthquake on coast-line near Napier." *New Zealand Journ. Sci. Tech.,* vol. 15, 1933, pp. 79-92.
10 STRONG, S. W. S. "The Sponge Bay uplift, Gisborne, and the Hangaroa mud blowout." *New Zealand Journ. Sci. Tech.,* vol. 15, 1933, pp. 76-78.

---

*Amer. Seis. Soc. Bull., vol. 23, 1933, p. 73.

SUBJECT INDEX

Acceleration, Maximum, of earth-quake-motion, in Mino-Owari earthquake, 111; Assam earthquake, 143; California earthquake, 187; Messina earthquake, 204; Tango earthquake, 217.

After-shocks, Early study of, by Pignatari (1783), 41; Drake and Brooks (1811), 55; Mrs. Graham (1822), 82.

After-shocks of: Lisbon earthquake, 23; Calabria earthquakes, 45, 49; New Madrid earthquakes, 66; Cutch earthquake, 75; Valparaiso earthquake, 82; Concepcion earthquake, 94; Owens Valley earthquake, 102; Mino-Owari earthquake, 119; Sanriku earthquake, 134; Assam earthquake, 152; Alaska earthquake, 173; California earthquake, 197; Messina earthquake, 209; Tango earthquake, 234; Idu earthquake, 263; Hawke's Bay earthquake, 274.

After-Shocks, Number of, in Lisbon earthquake, 23; Calabria earthquake, 45; Concepcion earthquake, 94; Assam earthquake, 153; Messina earthquake, 210; Decline in frequency, Mino - Owari earthquake, 120, 122; Assam earthquake, 155; Tango earthquake, 236; Idu earthquake, 263; Hawke's Bay earthquake, 274; Distribution in space, Calabria earthquakes, 45; Mino-Owari earthquake, 123; Assam earthquake, 153; California earthquake, 197; Tango earthquake, 237; Idu earthquake, 263; Hawke's Bay earthquake, 275; Types of aftershocks in Tango earthquake, 235; Determination of foci, 235; Focal depth in Tango earthquake, 238; Tilting of ground before after-shocks of Tango earthquake, 240; Periodicity of after-shocks in Calabria earthquakes, 46; Mino-Owari earthquake, 124; Sanriku earthquake, 134; Assam earthquake, 156; California earthquake, 197; Messina earthquake, 210; Tango earthquake, 240; Hawke's Bay earthquake, 275;

Periodic variations in focal depth, in Tango earthquake, 242.

Africa, North, Seawaves of Lisbon earthquake in, 21.

Alaska earthquake of 1899 Sep. 3, 160.

Alaska earthquake of 1899 Sep. 10, 158; introduction, 158; investigation of the earthquake, 159; preparation for the earthquake, 160; nature and effects of the shock, 161; disturbed area, 161; evidence of change of level, 162; physiographical evidence of uplift, 162; biological evidence, 164; human evidence, 165; evidences of submergence, 165; dislocations of the crust, 166; vertical displacements, 166; evidence of faulting, 168; minor faults, 169; seismic sea-waves, 170; landslips, 171; effects of earthquakes on glaciers, 171; shattering of glaciers, 171; advance of the Yakutat Bay glaciers, 171; after-shocks, 173; origin of the earthquakes, 173; bibliography, 174.

Algiers, Subsidiary centre of Lisbon earthquake, near, 5, 12.

Allah Bund (Cutch), 72.

Alluvium, Displacements of, during Assam earthquake, 151.

Annual periodicity of after-shocks, 156.

Assam earthquake of 1897, 138; introduction, 138; Assam earthquakes before 1897, 138; investigation of the earthquake, 139; loss of life and property, 140; intensity of the shock, 140, 143; nature of the shock, 142; visible waves, 142; seismic seiches, 143; rotation of pillars, 144; dislocations of crust, 144; faults and fractures, 146; formation of pools, 148; changes in the landcape, 148; re-triangulation of the epicentral area, 149; effects of the earthquake on the ground, 150; landslips, 150; displacements of alluvium, 151; extrusion of sand and water, 152; after-shocks, 152; distribution of epicentres, 153; periodicity of after-shocks, 156; bibliography, 157.

INDEX OF AUTHORS QUOTED

MURBY'S
BOOKS IN SCIENCE

SPRING 1937

Forthcoming Books and Books published since January, 1935, are marked thus ●.

N.B.—In the following list the particulars are brief. Fuller information will be sent on application.

Imported Books (marked ‡) for which we are agents are subject to variations in price owing to fluctuations in the rate of exchange.

GEOLOGY

Regional Geology

HANDBOOK OF THE GEOLOGY OF GREAT BRITAIN. Edited by J. W. EVANS, C.B.E., D.Sc., F.R.S., and C. J. STUBBLEFIELD, PH.D. Contributors: P. G. H. Boswell, D.Sc., A. Morley Davies, D.Sc., C. Davison, Sc.D., H. Dewey, J. W. Evans, C.B.E., D.Sc., F.R.S., E. J. Garwood, Sc.D., F.R.S., J. W. Gregory, D Sc., F.R.S., A. Harker, F.R.S., O. T Jones, D.Sc., F.R.S., P. F. Kendall, D.Sc., F.R.S , J. Parkinson, Sc.D., G. H. Plymen, Ph.D., Linsdall Richardson, F.R.S.E., G. Slater, D.Sc., H. C. Versey, D.Sc., W. W.Watts, Sc.D., F.R.S., W. B. Wright, Sc.D. "The book represents an authoritative conspectus of the present state of our knowledge of British Stratigraphy." xii + 556 pp., 24 Tables, 67 Figures. Full Bibliographies and Index. **24s.** net. Postage : foreign 1s. 2d., inland 7d.

STUDENT'S ISSUE of the above with same contents, bound in brown cloth, ink lettering, **20s.** net.

HANDBOOK OF THE GEOLOGY OF IRELAND. By the late PROFESSOR GRENVILLE A. J. COLE. D.Sc,. F.R.S , M,R.I.A., Director of the Geological Survey of Ireland and T. HALLISSY, B.A., M.R.I.A., of the Geological Survey of Ireland **8s. 6d.** net. postage 5d.

Thomas Murby & Co., 1, Fleet Lane, Ludgate Circus, London, E.C.4

AN INTRODUCTION TO STRATIGRAPHY (British Isles). By L. DUDLEY STAMP, B.A., D.Sc., A.K.C., F.G.S. Second edition revised throughout and enlarged. **10s.** net. Postage : inland 6d., abroad 7d.

● **THE DORSET COAST : A Geological Guide.** By G. M. DAVIES, M.Sc., F.G.S. Cloth **6s.** net. In two parts (paper covers), Part I., Western Section, **2s. 6d.** net. Part II., Central and Eastern Sections, **3s. 6d.** net. Postage : Bound 4d., Parts 2d.

GEOLOGICAL SECTIONS OF PARTS OF THE DORSET COAST. By G. M. DAVIES, M.Sc., F.G.S. (i.) Cliff Sections from Pinhay Bay to Burton Cliff. (ii.) Vertical Section of the Jurassic Rocks of S.W. Dorset. (iii.) Section through Black Ven. 50 sets of three diagrams, **13s. 6d.** : 25 sets, **7s.** ; Single sets, **4d.**

UNDERGROUND SOUTH-EASTERN ENGLAND. A Three Dimensional Map of the Weald, London Basin and Chiltern Hills. By L. J. CHUBB, M.Sc., F.G.S. In coloured sheets to be made up. **12s. 6d.** net. Binding equipment 2s. Made up **35s.** Postage : Sheets, inland 6d., abroad 10d. Made up, inland 6d., abroad 10d.

THE IGNEOUS ROCKS OF THE MOUNTSORREL DISTRICT. By E. E. LOWE, B.Sc., Ph.D. **6s. 6d.** net, postage 3d.

GEOLOGICAL MAP OF THE BRITISH ISLES. In 10 colours. Natural Scale 1 : 3,500,000. **2½d.**, postage 1d.

MAP OF THE BRITISH ISLES with Geological Boundaries. For students to colour, **2d.** each, postage 1d. **1s. 3d.** per doz. ; **14s.** per gross, postage extra.

LOCAL GEOLOGY. A Guide to Sources of Information on the Geology of the British Isles. By A. MORLEY DAVIES, D.Sc., F.R.G.S., F.G.S. 2nd Edition revised 1927. **1s.** net, postage 1d.

● **GEOLOGY OF CHINA.** By J. S. LEE, D.Sc., Professor of Geology in the Peking University. The book deals with the physical geography, stratigraphy and tectonics of China, with a discussion on wider problems of continental movement. Numerous maps, diagrams and half-tone illustrations of fossils and land-forms. *In the press.*

● **LEXICON DE STRATIGRAPHIE. VOL. I. : AFRICA.** Compiled by a Commission appointed by the XVth International Geological Congress. *In the press. It is hoped that this volume will be published early in 1937.* Subscription price **27s. 6d.** Price after publication **31s. 6d.**

● **GEOLOGY OF S. W. ECUADOR.** By Dr. G. SHEPPARD, State Geologist of the Republic of Ecuador, with a Chapter on the Tertiary Larger Foraminifera of Ecuador by Dr. T. WAYLAND VAUGHAN. *In the press.* Deals with the Physical Geography and Stratigraphy of the area ; and with the Petroleum Geology.

Thomas Murby & Co., 1, Fleet Lane, Ludgate Circus, London, E.C.4

- ‡**GEOLOGY OF THE TAMPICO REGION, MEXICO.** By John M. Muir. 300 pp., 15 half-tone plates, 41 line drawings, 9 tables. *Ready September, 1936.* **19s. 6d.**

- ‡**GULF COAST OIL FIELDS.** A Symposium on Gulf Coast Cenozoic. By 52 authors. Chiefly papers reprinted from the *Bulletin of the American Association of Petroleum Geologists.* 1,100 + pp., 292 figs, 19 half-tone plates. *Probably ready February, 1937.*

‡**ALBERTA STRATIGRAPHY. (Stratigraphy of Plains of Southern Alberta.)** A symposium by sixteen contributors. Reprinted from the Bulletin of the American Association of Petroleum Geologists, 1931. 166 pages, 60 illustrations including geological map. **$3.00.** Present price **13s. 6d.**

‡**THE GEOLOGY OF CALIFORNIA.** By R. D. Reed. **$5.** Present price **£1 2s. 6d.** Postage; inland 6d., abroad 9d.

‡**THE GEOLOGY OF VENEZUELA AND TRINIDAD.** By Ralph Alexander Liddle. xxix. + 552 pp. 709 illustrations; 24 sections and maps, **$7.50.** Present price **33s. 6d.** Postage : inland 7d., foreign 1s. 3d.

‡**GÉOLOGIE DE LA MÉDITERRANÉE OCCIDENTALE.** Études et observations faites au cours du Congrès Géologique International 1926. Vol. I. Le XIVe Congrès Géologique International et les excursions dans les Pays Catalans. Edited by Prof. J. Marcet Riba. Vol. I. now ready. **£1 17s. 0d.**
Vol. II. 1930-1931 : **Communications faites sur la Région Catalane à l'occasion des Excursions du Congrès.** Nos. 1-4. **7s. 6d.** Prices of additional numbers and other particulars on application.

‡**BIBLIOGRAPHIE GÉOLOGIQUE DE L'ESPAGNE.** 1s. 6d. net.

Geological Mapping

METHODS IN GEOLOGICAL SURVEYING. By Dr. E. Greenly and Dr. Howel Williams. **17s. 6d.** net. Postage : inland 6d., foreign 10d.

DIP AND STRIKE PROBLEMS, mathematically surveyed. By Kenneth W. Earle, D.Sc., F.G.S. Deals with the trigonometrical, geometrical and graphical solution of such problems as are likely to confront the practical and mining geologist in the field. **12s. 6d.** net, postage 5d.

A SERIES OF ELEMENTARY EXERCISES UPON GEOLOGICAL MAPS. By John I. Platt, M.Sc., F.G.S. *Revised Series of maps in the press.*

SIMPLE GEOLOGICAL STRUCTURES. A Series of Notes and Map-Exercises. By John I. Platt, M.Sc., F.G.S., and John Challinor, M.A., F.G.S. **3s. 6d.** net, postage 3d.

NOTES ON GEOLOGICAL MAP READING. By A. Harker, LL.D., F.R.S., F.G.S., with 40 illustrations. **3s. 6d.** net, postage 3d.

PROFILE SHEETS, for drawing sections from Contour Maps. **1d.** each, 10 for **6d.**, postage 1½d. ; 100 for **4s. 6d.**, postage 6d.

Thomas Murby & Co., 1, Fleet Lane, Ludgate Circus, London. E.C.4

AN INTRODUCTION TO PALÆONTOLOGY. By A. Morley Davies, A.R.C.S., D.Sc., F.G.S., Assistant Professor of Palæontology, Imperial College of Science. Now **10s. 6d.** net. postage 5d.

TYPE AMMONITES. By S. S. Buckman. Complete in 72 parts, now **9s.** per part. (Parts LXXI. and LXXII. are combined, **18s.**) Complete Work, Vols. I.-VII. **£30.**

● **TERTIARY FAUNAS.** A text-book for Oilfield Palæontologists and Students of Geology. By A. Morley Davies, A.R.C.S., D.Sc. F.G.S. *Vol. II.*, The Sequence of Tertiary Faunas. **15s.** net. Postage : inland 6d., foreign 8d. *Vol. I.*, The Composition of Tertiary Faunas. **22s. 6d.** net. Postage : inland 6d., abroad 10d.

THE DINOSAURS. A Short History of a Great Group of Extinct Reptiles. By W. E. Swinton, Ph.D., F.G.S., F.R.S.E. of the department of Geology, British Museum (Natural History), Fully illustrated. **15s** net. Postage : inland 6d., foreign 8d.

Mineralogy

● **RUTLEY'S MINERALOGY.** 23rd edition. Revised and enlarged. By H. H. Read, A.R.C.S., D.Sc., Herdman Professor of Geology in the University of Liverpool. Many illustrations have been redrawn and a large number added. The value of the book as an introduction to Mineralogy for the student of Geology or Mining is greatly increased. **8s.** net, postage 6d.

A HISTORY OF THE THEORY OF ORE DEPOSITS, with a Chapter on the Rise of Petrology. By Thomas Crook, Principal of the Mineral Resources Department, Imperial Institute, London. **10s. 6d.** net, postage 6d.

ORE DEPOSITS OF MAGMATIC ORIGIN : Their Genesis and Natural Classification. By Prof. Paul Niggli. Translated by Dr. H. C. Boydell, M.I.M.M. Revised and supplemented by Dr. Niggli and Dr. R. L. Parker. **9s. 6d.** net, postage 6d.

MINERALS AND THE MICROSCOPE. An introduction to the study of Petrology. By H. G. Smith, A.R.C.S., B.Sc., F.G.S., Third Edition with the section on Petrology re-written and enlarged. **5s.** net, postage 4d.

THE DETERMINATION OF MINERALS UNDER THE MICROSCOPE. By John W. Evans, C.B.E., D.Sc., F.R.S., F.G.S. Coloured plate and many line drawings. **7s. 6d.** net. postage 4d.

THE DETERMINATION OF THE FELDSPARS IN THIN SECTION. By Dr. K. Chudoba. Translated by Dr. W. Q. Kennedy. Cloth **6s. 6d.** net. ; paper **4s. 6d.** net, postage 4d.

DIAMOND : A DESCRIPTIVE TREATISE. By J. R. Sutton, M.A., Sc.D. Gives results of observations made during 35 years or so on South African diamond. 111 illustrations. **15s.** net, postage 5d.

OPAL : The Gem of the Never Never. By T. C. Wollaston. 14 plates 3 (beautiful reproductions in colour). Part I., Australia's National Gem ; Part II., On the Trail of the Opal ; Part III., Sketches of Opal Field Characters. **10s. 6d.** net, postage 5d.

Thomas Murby & Co., 1, Fleet Lane, Ludgate Circus, London, E.C.4

THE NOMENCLATURE OF PETROLOGY. By Arthur Holmes, D.Sc., A.R.C.S., D.I C., F.G.S., Professor of Geology, Durham, *2nd and cheaper Edition*. **7**s. **6**d. net, postage 5d.

PETROGRAPHIC METHODS AND CALCULATIONS. By Prof. Arthur Holmes, D.Sc., A.R.C.S., D.I.C., F.G.S. Second impression. **15**s net. Postage : inland 6d., foreign 10d.

DR. HOLMES' FORM FOR THE CALCULATION OF THE NORM OR STANDARD MINERAL COMPOSITION. 12 Forms. **1**s. **9**d. net, postage 2d.

METHODS IN PRACTICAL PETROLOGY. By H. B. Milner, B.A., F.G.S., and G. M. Part, B.A., F.G.S. Hints on the Preparation and Examination of Rock Slices. Illustrated. **3**s. **6**d. net, post. 3d.

THE STUDY OF ROCKS. By Prof. S. J. Shand. An account of the Petrology of Eruptive, Sedimentary and Metamorphic rocks for students who have already made a beginning with elementary geology. **6**s. net, postage 5d.

ERUPTIVE ROCKS. Their Genesis, Composition, Classification and their Relation to Ore Deposits. By S. J. Shand. University of Stellenbosch. 44 illustrations. **20**s. net. Postage : inland 6d., foreign 9d.

INSTRUCTIONS FOR USING THE QUANTITATIVE MINERALOGICAL CLASSIFICATION OF ERUPTIVE ROCKS. By Prof. S. J. Shand. **1**s. **3**d. net, postage 1d. Explains the application of the classification proposed in *Eruptive Rocks*.

‡ASSIMILATION AND PETROGENESIS. Separation of Ores from Magmas. By Prof. J. Stansfield. (Valley Publishing Co., Urbana.) **$4.50** net. Present price **18**s. **6**d., postage 6d.

LIMESTONES. Their Origins, Distribution and Uses. By F. J. North, D.Sc., F.G.S., Keeper in the Department of Geology, National Museum of Wales. **16**s. net. Postage : inland 6d., foreign 10d.

ON THE MINERALOGY OF SEDIMENTARY ROCKS. A Series of Essays and a Bibliography. By Professor P. G. H. Boswell, O.B.E., D.Sc., F.R.S., M.Inst.M.M A.R.C.S., D.I.C. **21**s. net. Postage : inland 6d. foreign 9d.

Reprinted from the above.

CARD INDEX OF ABSTRACTS. The abstracts (over 1,000) are available printed on one side of the paper, suitable for preparation of a card index. **10**s. **6**d. net, postage 4d.

SEDIMENTARY PETROGRAPHY. By Henry B. Milner, M.A., D.I.C., F.G.S., M.Inst.P.T *Third edition in preparation*.

●‡REGIONAL PETROLOGY OF THE SOUTHERN NORTH SEA. By J. A. Baak. Gives the results of the mineralogical examinations of more than 1,000 samples from the floor of the North Sea. **8**s. **6**d. net, postage 4d.

● SILICATE ANALYSIS. A manual for Geologists and Chemists. By A. W. Groves, D.Sc., Ph.D., D.I.C., F.G.S. *In the press*. Probable price, **12**s. **6**d.

Thomas Murby & Co., 1, Fleet Lane, Ludgate Circus, London, E.C.4

ELEMENTARY CRYSTALLOGRAPHY. By J. W. Evans, D.Sc., F.R.S., F.G.S., and G. Macdonald Davies, M.Sc., F.G.S. **7s. 6d.** postage 4d.

PATTERNS FOR THE CONSTRUCTION OF 36 CRYSTAL MODELS REPRESENTING ACTUAL MINERALS. Designed by F. Smithson, Ph.D., F.G.S. **4s.** net, postage 2d. ; cards for mounting **1s.**, mounted **7s. 6d.**, postage 3d. Models made up **32s.**

CRYSTALLOGRAPHIC NETS for constructing 41 models representing simple forms. With instructions **3s.** net ; postage 1d.; on card ready for making into models, **7s. 6d.** net ; made-up, price **23s.**

GRAPHICAL AND TABULAR METHODS IN CRYSTALLOG-RAPHY. By T. V. Barker, **14s.** net, postage 5d.

THE STUDY OF CRYSTALS. A general Introduction. By T. V. Barker. **8s. 6d.** net, postage 6d.

SYSTEMATIC CRYSTALLOGRAPHY. An Essay on Crystal Description, Classification and Identification. By T. V. Barker, **7s. 6d.** net, postage 6d. **Stereographic Nets.** 24 sheets. **3s.**

Seismology

● **GREAT EARTHQUAKES.** By C. Davison, Sc.D., F.G.S., Author of *A History of British Earthquakes, Founders of Seismology, Manual of Seismology*, etc. Describes and records scientific data of the world's great earthquakes : the Lisbon Earthquake of 1755 to the Hawkes Bay (New Zealand) Earthquake of 1931. With 97 text figures and 25 half tone illustrations. **17s. 6d.** *Oct., 1936.* Postage : inland 6d., foreign 7d.

N.B.—The Great Japanese Earthquake (1923) is not described in the above work, having been described in an earlier volume.

THE JAPANESE EARTHQUAKE OF 1923. By C. Davison, Sc.D., F.G.S. Describes the great Japanese disaster and deals with this earthquake as an event in the history of the earth. 40 diagrams, **7s. 6d.** net, postage 6d.

Geological Terminology

GERMAN-ENGLISH GEOLOGICAL TERMINOLOGY. By W. R. Jones, D.Sc., F.G.S., M.I.M.M., and Dr. A. Cissarz. An intro-duction to German and English terms used in Geology. **12s. 6d.** net. Postage : inland 6d., foreign 7d.

The Nomenclature of Petrology. By Prof. A. Holmes. See p. 5.

A FRENCH-ENGLISH VOCABULARY IN GEOLOGY AND PHYSICAL GEOGRAPHY. By G. MacDonald Davies, M.Sc., F.G.S. **6s.** net, postage 3d.

LOCAL GEOGRAPHY. By C. G. Beasley, B.A. **1s.** net, postage 1d. The ideal guide for Schools undertaking Regional Surveys.

GEOLOGICAL MODELS. By Frank Smithson, Ph.D., F.G.S. *Particulars of made up Models, etc., on application.*

> **BLOCK MODELS.** Patterns for Construction and Descriptive Notes.
> > 1st Series (Faulting, Folding, etc.); 12 models. **1s. 6d.** net, postage 1d.
> > 2nd Series (Igneous Phenomena, etc.); 14 models. **1s. 6d.** net, postage 1d.
> **PATTERNS FOR SIMPLE RELIEF MODELS.** **5s. 6d.** net. postage 5d.

Brochures for Teachers of Geography by Dr. L. Dudley Stamp. Descriptive of two collections of 30 specimens in each.

> **NOTES ON COMMON ROCKS.** 6d. net, postage ½d.
> **NOTES ON SOME ECONOMIC MINERALS AND ROCKS.** 6d. net, postage ½d.

MEMO-MAPS. Small blank maps for use with geological and other collections for recording geographical distribution, and for other uses in teaching. 25 of one kind, **6d.** net, postage 1d., 1,000 **15s.**

World, Western Europe, British Isles, England and Wales (with county boundaries,) Scotland (with county boundaries), Asia, India, Africa, North America, South America, Australia.

A GEOLOGICAL CHART. By Col. F. G. Talbot. Suitable for hanging in the Class Room. Gives in clear and simple form the main outlines of geological history. **1s. 4d.** net, postage 2d.

‡**OUTLINES OF GLACIAL GEOLOGY.** By F. T. Thwaites, University of Wisconsin. (Photo-Lithoprint of Typewritten Manuscript, 1934.) 115 pp., with 89 Figures. **12s. 6d.** net. *Out of print. New edition in preparation.*

Geology for the General Reader

EARTH-LORE : Geology without Jargon. By Professor S. J. Shand, D.Sc., F.G.S. A broad survey of geology for the general reader. **5s.** net, postage 4d.

THE STONES OF LONDON. By J. Vincent Elsden, D.Sc., F.G.S., and J. Allen Howe, O.B.E., B.Sc., F.G.S., M.I.M.M. A Guide to the stones used in London. **1s. 3d.** paper, postage 3d.

THE POETRY OF GEOLOGY. By Kenneth Knight Hallowes, M.A. Consists of an essay on the Poetry of Geological Science and a collection of thirty poems by the author. **6s.** net, postage 3d.

OTHER BOOKS of interest to the general reader.
> **Useful Aspects of Geology.** By Professor Shand. See p. 8.
> **The Dinosaurs.** By Dr. W. E. Swinton. See p. 4.
> **Limestones.** By Dr. F. J. North. See p. 5.
> **Opal.** By T. C. Wollaston. See p. 4.

Thomas Murby & Co., 1, Fleet Lane, Ludgate Circus, London, E.C.4

USEFUL ASPECTS OF GEOLOGY, By S. J. SHAND, D.Sc., Ph.,
F.G.S., Professor of Geology in Stellenbosch University, South
Africa, *2nd Edition, revised and extended.* **6s.** net, postage 4d.

ALLUVIAL PROSPECTING. The Technical Investigation of Econo-
mic Alluvial Minerals. By C. RAEBURN, D.Sc., F.G.S., Geological
Survey of Nigeria, and HENRY B. MILNER, M.A. (Cantab.),
D.I.C., F.G.S., M.Inst.P.T. Foreword by J. D. FALCONER, M.A.,
D.Sc., F.G.S., F.R.G.S , late Director of the Geological Survey
of Nigeria. **36s.** net. Postage : inland 6d., foreign 1s.

‡**STRUCTURE OF TYPICAL AMERICAN OILFIELDS.** A symposium on the relation of the accumulation of petroleum to
geological structure. Vol. I., **$7.00.** Postage : inland 9d.
foreign 1s. Vol. II. **$7.00.** Present price **30s.** per volume.
Postage : inland 7d., foreign 1s. 4d.

Previously announced as Vol. III of the above work.

‡**PROBLEMS OF PETROLEUM GEOLOGY.** Contains approximately 1,000 pages, and 200 illustrations. It is a symposium by
47 authors on origin, evolution, migration and accumulation of
petroleum. Edited by W. E. WRATHER and F. H. LAHEE.
$6.00. Present price **25s. 6d.** Postage: inland 7d., foreign 1s. 4d.

GEOLOGY OF NATURAL GAS : A Symposium. Edited by
HENRY A. LEY. xii. + 1227 pp Numerous illustrations. **$6.00.**
Present price **25s. 6d.** net. Postage, inland, 8d. Consists of
thirty-eight papers prepared by forty-seven authors.

A PRACTICAL HANDBOOK OF WATER SUPPLY. By F. DIXEY.
D.Sc., F.G.S., Director of the Geological Survey, Nyasaland. A
handbook describing the geological and other aspects of water
supply. **21s.** net. Postage : inland 6d., foreign 1s.

Periodicals

‡**ANNOTATED BIBLIOGRAPHY OF ECONOMIC GEOLOGY.** For
all subjects bearing on Economic Geology. **$5.00** per year.

‡**ECONOMIC GEOLOGY.** Annual Subscription **$5.75.**

‡**BULLETIN OF THE AMERICAN ASSOCIATION OF PETROLEUM
GEOLOGISTS.** Monthly. Subscription **$15.40** per annum.

‡**THE OIL WEEKLY.** Published in Texas. **$2.00** per aunum.
Special rate of **$3.00** for two years for old subscribers.

‡**THE REFINER AND NATURAL GASOLINE MANUFACTURER.**
Published monthly in Texas, U.S.A. Annual Subscription **$2.00.**
Special rate of **$3.00** for two years for old subscribers.

SOIL SCIENCE

● **SOILS. Their Origin, Constitution and Classification.** An Introduction to Pedology. By G. W. ROBINSON, M.A., Professor of Agricultural Chemistry in the University College of N. Wales, Bangor. *Second edition revised*, 1936. **20s**. net. Postage : inland 6d., foreign 9d.

SOIL ANALYSIS : A Handbook of Physical and Chemical Methods. By C. H. WRIGHT, M.A., F.I.C., former Senior Agricultural Chemist, Nigeria. **12s. 6d.** net. Postage : inland 6d., foreign 7d.

†**THE GREAT SOIL GROUPS OF THE WORLD, AND THEIR DEVELOPMENT.** By Prof. Dr. K. D. GLINKA, Director of the Agricultural Institute, Leningrad. Translation by C. F. MARBUT, 235 pp., Mimeographed 1928. **$3.25.** Present price **15s.** Postage : inland 6d., foreign 8d.

● **THE CYCLE OF WEATHERING.** By Prof. B. B. POLYNOV, of the Dokuchaiev Soil Institute, Moscow, corresponding member of the Academy of Sciences, U.S.S.R. Translated by Dr. ALEXANDER MUIR, of the Macaulay Institute for Soil Research, Aberdeen. *In the press.*

THE KATAMORPHISM OF IGNEOUS ROCKS UNDER HUMID TROPICAL CONDITIONS. By the late Prof. SIR J. B. HARRISON (late Director of Science and Agriculture, Government Analyst and Geologist, British Guiana). Foreword by SIR J. E. RUSSELL. Preface by Prof. F. HARDY. **5s**. net. An important work on rock weathering and soil formation.

TECHNICAL COMMUNICATIONS OF THE IMPERIAL BUREAU OF SOIL SCIENCE : No. 24—33, **2s.**, post free ; No. 34, **2s. 6d.**, post free.

No. 24, Laterite and Laterite Soils ;
No. 25, The Mitscherlich, Wiessman and Neubauer Methods of Determining the Nutrient Content of Soils (By R Stewart) ;
No. 26, The Dispersion of Soils in Mechanical Analysis ;
No. 27, Land Amelioration in Germany ;
No. 28, Soil Erosion (By T. Eden) ;
No. 29, Soil, Vegetation and Climate ;
No. 30, The Determination of Exchangeable Bases in Soils ;
No. 31, Soil Deficiencies and Plant Diseases ;
No. 32, Tea Soils (By H. H. Mann).
No. 33, Organic Manures (By S. H. Jenkins, Ph.D., F.I.C.) ;
No. 34, Tropical Soils in Relation to Tropical Crops.
Particulars of Nos. 7 to 23 on application.

●**BIBLIOGRAPHY OF SOIL SCIENCE, FERTILIZERS AND GENERAL AGRONOMY 1931-1934.** Over 6,000 references to papers, bulletins and reports published throughout the world. Entries carefully classified according to Universal Decimal System of Classification. Compiled by the IMPERIAL BUREAU OF SOIL SCIENCE. 504 pp. Cloth, **25s.** net.

Thomas Murby & Co., 1, Fleet Lane, Ludgate Circus, London, E.C.4

● **TRANSACTIONS OF THE THIRD INTERNATIONAL CONGRESS OF SOIL SCIENCE** (1935), held at Oxford, July 30th to August 7th. Subjects dealt with : Soil Physics ; Soil Chemistry ; Soil Microbiology ; Soil Fertility ; Soil Genesis ; Morphology and Cartography ; Soil Technology.

    Vol. I—COMMISSION PAPERS. 440 pp. In paper covers.
        This volume contains upwards of 156 papers—27 of which are in German and 9 in French.
        To members of the International Society of Soil Science, **23s.** net. To non-members, **28s.** net.

    Vol. II—PLENARY SESSION PAPERS AND PRESIDENTIAL ADDRESS. 200 pp. In paper covers.
        This volume contains the Presidential Address and **15** papers —four in German and two in French—in which recent advances in that branch of soil science covered by the work of the Commission concerned is reviewed in relation to soil science as a whole.
        To members, **11s.** net. To non-members, **13s.** net.

    Vol. III—PLENARY AND COMMISSION PAPERS, DISCUSSIONS, COMMISSION AND OTHER REPORTS. 290 pp. In paper covers.
        To members, **16s.** net. To non-members, **19s.** net.

● **GUIDE-BOOK FOR THE EXCURSION ROUND BRITAIN OF THE THIRD INTERNATIONAL CONGRESS OF SOIL SCIENCE.** The most up-to-date account of British Soils. iv. + 74 pp. **2s. 6d.** net.

†**PROCEEDINGS OF THE SECOND INTERNATIONAL CONGRESS OF SOIL SCIENCE**, Leningrad (Moscow, U.S.S.R., 1930).

VOL.		
I.—Soil Physics. (1932). Pp. xxxi + 304		**13s.**
„ II.—Soil Chemistry. (1933). Pp. xxiv + 225		**8s. 6d.**
„ III.—Soil Biology. (1932). Pp. xix + 303		**13s.**
„ IV.—Soil Fertility. (1932). Pp. xviii + 264		**13s.**
„ V.—Classification, Geography and Cartography of Soils. (1932). Pp. xxiii. + 424		**17s.**
„ VI.—Application of Soil Science to Agricultural Technology. (1932). Pp. xxii + 320		**13s.**
„ VII.—General Plenary Sessions, Excursions (in print)		**8s. 6d.**

Fuller particulars of the above and of other publications of the Soviet Section of the International Society of Soil Science will be sent on application.

ADDITIONAL PUBLICATIONS OF THE SOVIET SECTION OF THE INTERNATIONAL SOCIETY OF SOIL SCIENCE. Pedology in USSR., 1935. Soil Microbiology in the USSR., 1933, **7s.** Bodenfruchtbarkeit und Anwendung der Dunger in der UdSSR., 1933, **8s.** Bodenchemie in der UdSSR., 1934, **4s. 6d.** The Problem of Soil Structure, 1933, **4s. 6d.** Problemes de la Physique du Sol, 1934, **8s.** Classification Geography and Cartography of Soil in USSR. (awaiting price).

Thomas Murby & Co., 1, Fleet Lane, Ludgate Circus, London, E.C.4

- **INTERNATIONAL SOIL MAP OF EUROPE, 1 : 250.000.** Will be ready Spring 1937. Orders can be booked at 160 Rm. less 25% (except in Switzerland and Palestine), 120 Rm.

This map, produced by the International Society of Soil Science, is a development of the smaller scale map published in 1927. The new map will be more accurate in all respects and will have a more detailed nomenclature and classification, and will be based entirely on actual field surveys.

LAND UTILISATION
and Regional Survey

MAPS OF THE LAND UTILISATION SURVEY OF BRITAIN. Prepared by the Land Utilisation Survey under the Directorship of Dr. L. DUDLEY STAMP. B.A., F G.S.. from a field survey, Prices ; Flat and unmounted, **4s.** net (post free, **4s. 3d.**). Mounted on linen and folded in covers, **5s.** net (post free, **5s. 2d.**). Set of first 12 sheets, unmounted, **36s** net. (post free, **36s. 6d.**); mounted, **45s.** net.

ONE-INCH SHEETS.

ENGLAND AND WALES.—No. 11 Durham and Sunderland, 12 Keswick and Ambleside, 35 Liverpool and Birkenhead, 36 Bolton and Manchester, 44 Northwich and Macclesfield, 54 Nottingham, 55 Grantham, 57 Fakenham, 58 Cromer, 63 Leicester, 66 Swaffham, 67 Norwich and Great Yarmouth, 72 Birmingham, 76 Thetford. 87 Ipswich, 95 Luton, 99 Pembroke and Tenby, 103 Stroud and Chepstow, 106 Watford and N.W. London, 107 N.E. London and Epping Forest, 112 Marlborough, 114 Windsor, 115 S.E. London and Sevenoaks, 134 Brighton and Eastbourne, 141 Bournemouth and Swanage, 142 Isle of Wigh', 146 Land's End and Lizard.
LATEST ADDITIONS. No. 7, Newcastle-upon-Tyne; 88, St. David's and Cardigan; 101, Swansea and Aberdare ; 102, Newport; 109, Pontypridd aud Barry; 117 East Kent; 123, Winchester; 133, Chichester.

SCOTLAND.—No. 4 South Mainland—Shetland Isles, 12 Wick, 45 Aberdeen, 53 Sound of Mull, 59 Iona and Colonsay, 60 North Jura and Firth of Lorne, 68 Firth of Forth, 74 Edinburgh.

An Outline Description of the First Twelve Sheets. By L. D. STAMP and E. C. WILLATTS. With illustrations and coloured specimen map. **1s.**, postage 1d.

Wall Maps on Linen :—London (4 sheets) **25s.** with rollers **28s.** ; **Norfolk** (4 sheets) **25s.**, with rollers **28s.** ; **Mull** (3 sheets) **18s.**, with rollers **21s.**

THE LAND OF BRITAIN. Final Report of the Survey. Part 78, **Berkshire.** By J. STEPHENSON. Edited by L. DUDLEY STAMP. **2s. 6d.** post free. Other volumes to follow, about 87 parts.

ATLAS OF CROYDON AND DISTRICT. Prepared by the Croydon Natural History and Scientific Society. Edited by C. C. Fagg, F.G.S.
First Issue (loose leaf binder and several maps), **12s. 6d.** net.

BIOLOGY

- **GERMAN-ENGLISH ZOOLOGICAL TERMINOLOGY.** By T. L. GREEN, B.Sc , A.R.C.S,, and J. M. WATSON, A.R.C.S., and Dr. HEINZ GRAUPNER. *In preparation.*

- **GERMAN - ENGLISH BOTANICAL TERMINOLOGY.** By Drs. E. & H. ASHBY and Dr. H. R CHTER. *In preparation.*

THE WOAD PLANT AND ITS DYE. By J. B. HURRY, M.A., M D. 360 pages, 2 coloured plate and numerous other plates and text figures, **21s.** net. Postage · inland 6d., foreign 9d.

Thomas Murby & Co., 1, Fleet Lane, Ludgate Circus, London, E.C.4

CHEMISTRY AND PHYSICS

CHEMICAL CALCULATIONS : THEIR THEORY AND PRACTICE. By A. King, M.Sc., and Dr. J. S. Anderson. Both of the Chemistry Department of the Imperial College of Science and Technology, South Kensington. For first year students in the Universities and for the higher classes in Schools. **4s. 6d.** net, postage 4d.

A New Course in Practical Chemistry.

● **INORGANIC PREPARATIONS.** By A. King, M.Sc., A.R.C.S. D.I.C. A logical arrangement of experiments with sufficient theoretical matter for the student to correlate theory with practice. Detailed directions for about 190 preparations, and about an equal number briefly sketched. *Now Ready.* **5s. 6d.** net. postage 4d.

● **SILICATE ANALYSIS : A Manual for Geologists and Chemists, with Chapters on Check Calculations and Geo-Chemical Data.** By A. W. Groves, D.Sc., Ph.D., D.I.C., F.G.S. *In the press.* Probable price, **12s. 6d.**

GERMAN-ENGLISH CHEMICAL TERMINOLOGY. By A. King, M.Sc., and Dr. H. Fromherz. An introduction to Chemistry in English and German. In Murby's German-English Terminologies. General Editor : Dr. W. R. Jones, of the Imperial College of Science and Technology. **12s. 6d.** net. Postage : inland 6d., foreign 7d.

The sale of this book in U.S.A. and Canada is in the hands of D. Van Nostrand Company (Inc.), New York.

● **GERMAN-ENGLISH PHYSICS TERMINOLOGY.** By E. R. Franz, B.Sc., Hons. (London) A.L.A., and Dr. Von Auwers. *In preparation.*

TRILINEAR COÖRDINATE PAPER. For use in plotting three variables, in petrology, chemistry, physics, etc. Each side 20 cms., divided into 100 parts. every fifth line heavy. Price, 10 sheets for **1s. 3d.**, 20 **2s. 6d.**. 50 **4s. 6d.**

HOBBS' ARITHMETIC OF ELECTRICAL MEASUREMENTS. Revised and Edited by A. Risdon Palmer, B.Sc., B.A., Head of the Matriculation Department, the Polytechnic, W. 9th Reprint of the 16th Edition. With answers. **2s.** net, postage 2d.

In each chapter a brief explanation is followed by fully worked examples, and numerous well selected examples for the student to work.

MAGNETIC MEASUREMENTS AND EXPERIMENTS. By A. Risdon Palmer, B.Sc., B.A. With answers. **2s.** net, postage 2d.

Each chapter contains a set of experiments, *arranged to reduce a duplication of apparatus as far as possible* (or graphical questions), a short account of the theory to supplement the class lesson, some fully worked examples, and a set of carefully graduated exercises for the student to work.

ELECTRICAL EXPERIMENTS. By A. Risdon Palmer, B.Sc., B.A. **2s.** net, postage 2d.

A course of Experimental Electricity for one or two years. Details are given as to apparatus and the method of procedure, and the setting out of results.

Thomas Murby & Co., 1, Fleet Lane, Ludgate Circus, London, E.C.4

551.22
D265g

Due